Electronic Spectra
and
Quantum Chemistry

PRENTICE-HALL CHEMISTRY SERIES

PRENTICE-HALL INTERNATIONAL, INC., *London*
PRENTICE-HALL OF AUSTRALIA, PTY., LTD., *Sydney*
PRENTICE-HALL OF CANADA, LTD., *Toronto*
PRENTICE-HALL FRANCE, S.A.R.L., *Paris*
PRENTICE-HALL OF INDIA, (PRIVATE) LTD., *Bombay*
PRENTICE-HALL OF JAPAN, INC., *Tokyo*
PRENTICE-HALL DE MEXICO, S.A., *Mexico City*

Electronic Spectra
and
Quantum Chemistry

C. Sandorfy

Professor of Chemistry
Université de Montréal

Prentice-Hall, Inc.
Englewood Cliffs, New Jersey

Originally published in French as *Les Spectres Electroniques en Chimie Theorique,* Revue D'Optique, 3&5 Boulevard Pasteur, 165 Rue de Sevres, Paris 15, France. Copyright 1959.

© 1964 by PRENTICE-HALL, INC., Englewood Cliffs, N. J.

Library of Congress Catalog Card No.: 64–12549

PRINTED IN THE UNITED STATES OF AMERICA
25208—C

To the Memory of my Father

Preface

This book is a greatly augmented version of a work by the author published in French in the early part of 1959 (*Les spectres électroniques en chimie théorique*. Les Editions de la Revue d'Optique Théorique et Instrumentale, Paris) which contained a preface by the founder of wave mechanics, Professor Louis de Broglie.

Scientific literature consists almost exclusively of textbooks or scholarly works on advanced subjects. The former take care of the needs of the undergraduate student; the latter are highly profitable for those who already possess a thorough training in the respective field. Neither the former nor the latter, however, enable the beginner who has only a general scientific background or is a specialist of a different field, to introduce himself into actual research work in a given area. This book is an attempt to do this in the particular field of quantum chemistry as applied to electronic spectra. It is written for chemistry graduate students or others who are engaged in research in a different field.

No complete coverage was meant in any sense; neither in quantum chemistry nor in spectroscopy. Rather an attempt is made to give what scientific books do not generally give: working knowledge. Typical calculations are carried out in full detail to the last multiplication.

The introductory chapters treat standard subjects. Their only purpose is to spare the reader the trouble of looking for elementary facts in many different places.

The writer would gladly face the criticism of his colleagues for being too elementary at times, or for sacrificing depth for understanding. He would, however, consider his work a failure if graduate students did not find it helpful in penetrating into the practice of quantum chemistry and spectroscopy.

I wish to thank my own graduate students for their patience during the time this book was written. In particular, I wish to thank Mr. Paul Sauvageau whose devotion enabled me to save much time for this work and to Mr. Gilles Durocher who contributed many useful comments and many of the drawings.

Professor M. A. Whitehead read the manuscript and made many helpful comments. I should like to express my sincere thanks to him.

I am indebted to Mrs. Patricia Hollingdale for her excellent secretarial work. My thanks are due to Miss Denise Laberge for supplementary work on the manuscript.

C. Sandorfy

Table of Contents

ix

7 Selection Rules and the Symmetry
of Molecules 140

8 The Calculation of Spectral Quantities
by the Molecular Orbital Method 182

9 The Calculation of Spectral Quantities
by the Valence Bond Method 223

15 A Brief Review of Chemical Spectroscopy   337

1

Preliminaries

1-1 RADIATION AND MATTER

According to our present knowledge radiation is a Janus-faced dual phenomenon. It is an electromagnetic wave, but it also has corpuscular character and we must assume the existence of photons. Certain well-known optical phenomena, including the propagation of light in a straight line, reflection, refraction, and Rayleigh scattering, can be explained with either waves or photons. Diffraction, interference, and polarization require the waves; the explanation of the distribution of spectral intensity in black-body radiation, the photoelectric effect, and the Compton effect impose the photon. Planck's famous formula expresses the dual nature of light in a most elegant fashion:

$$E = h\nu \tag{1-1}$$

Here the energy of a photon is given as the product of the Planck constant and a typical wave quantity: the frequency.

According to classical electromagnetic theory, radiation or electromagnetic waves are produced whenever a particle possessing an electric or/and magnetic field, i.e., a particle with a net charge such as an electron or ion, or a dipole, quadrupole, higher multipole, or magnetic dipole is in accelerated periodic motion. The field then undergoes a perturbation which travels in vacuum with the speed of light and in all other media with a somewhat lesser speed.

Quantum mechanics added to this picture the important condition that radiation can be produced only when a system goes from a state of higher energy to a state of lower energy, the energy difference becoming the energy of an emitted photon. In bound systems only certain energy values are permitted. Absorption is the reverse of emission, the energy of the absorbed photon being used to take the system from a state of lower energy to a state of higher energy. In both cases the frequency of the photon is related to the energy difference by the Bohr formula

$$h\nu = E' - E'' \qquad (1\text{-}2)$$

which remains valid in wave mechanics. E' and E'' are, respectively, the energies of the higher and lower energy states. This expression appears without being postulated in wave mechanics when transition probabilities are computed (see p. 95), and it interprets the primary fact of spectroscopy: the existence of discrete line or band spectra of atoms and molecules.

Matter, too, has dual character, showing both corpuscular and wave aspects. With the motion of a material particle we have to associate a wave whose wavelength is given by the de Broglie relation:

$$\lambda = \frac{h}{mv} \qquad (1\text{-}3)$$

where m and v are the mass and velocity of the particle, respectively. Particles like electrons or protons may exhibit interference phenomena as do ordinary waves.

When atoms or molecules interact with radiation two things may happen. Radiation may be *absorbed* (or emitted) or it may be *scattered*. If the frequency of light is of the right value to give the system the energy needed to go over to one of its states of higher energy the photon may be absorbed, its energy becoming a part of the internal energy of the atom or molecule. This is the phenomenon of *induced absorption* or simply absorption. If by any chance the atom or molecule is already in an excited state the inverse phenomenon may take place. As a result of the interaction, a photon may be emitted, its energy being added to the energy of the electromagnetic field of the incident radiation. This is the phenomenon of *induced emission*. An excited atom or molecule may also emit a photon in the absence of an external electromagnetic field. This is *spontaneous emission*. It is shown in Dirac's radiation theory that the two cases are related [1, 2].

If the radiation has not the right frequency to be absorbed, it will be scattered. It induces a dipole moment in the atom or molecule that oscillates in phase with the incident radiation. This in turn produces radiation of the same frequency. This is the scattering of classical theory.

The quantum mechanical description of scattering is even simpler. If a photon does not have the right frequency to be absorbed, it will be scattered on collision with a molecule.

The scattered waves will interfere with each other in such a way that in a homogeneous medium they are only propagated in the forward direction, but at the limit of two different media with a smooth interface they give rise to reflection and refraction and, when passing through narrow slits, to diffraction. The angle of refraction or diffraction is frequency dependent. If the incident light is not monochromatic it will undergo dispersion. Thanks to this fact spectrographs and spectrometers can be constructed with either prisms (refraction) or gratings (diffraction). In the general case scattering will take place in every direction.

Electromagnetic waves may have wavelengths (λ) from small fractions of an angstrom to hundreds of kilometers. They are inversely related to wave numbers ($\omega = 1/\lambda$), which in turn give the frequencies (ν) when multiplied by the speed of light (c).

$$\nu = \frac{c}{\lambda} \qquad (1\text{-}4)$$

The exact value of λ depends on the medium—as does c—and should be corrected to vacuum, but ν is independent of the medium, since it represents the number of waves emitted by the source per second.

The various parts of the electromagnetic spectrum were given various names.

The *visible* spectrum extends from about $7000\,\text{Å}$ (red) to about $4000\,\text{Å}$ (violet). Next to the visible at shorter wavelengths is the *ultraviolet*. The part lying closest to the visible is called the *near ultraviolet*. From $2000\,\text{Å}$ we speak of the *far ultraviolet*. It is followed by the *X-rays* from $10\,\text{Å}$ to about $0.1\,\text{Å}$. *Gamma rays* have even shorter wavelengths. At the long-wavelength side of the visible is the *infrared*. The *near infrared* lies between 7000 and $20{,}000\,\text{Å}$ (i.e., from 0.7 to 2 microns). From 20 microns down to, say, 500 microns (half of a millimeter) we can speak of the *far infrared*. This spectral region is followed by *microwaves*, where λ is of the order of millimeters, and then by the radio-frequency region, from short waves (centimeters and meters) to long waves with λ values in the kilometer range and longer. Needless to say, there exist no natural limits between these regions. The reader may find the data in Table 1-1 useful. (The speed of light is taken as $3 \times 10^{10}\,\text{cm}\,\text{sec}^{-1}$.)

Gamma rays are emitted by the nucleus as a result of transitions between *nuclear* energy levels. Also pairs formed by an electron and a positron may transform into γ-ray photons (dematerialization). X-rays appear as a result of transitions between electronic energy levels

TABLE 1-1

λ	ω	ν
$1\,km = 10^3\,m = 10^5\,cm$	$10^{-5}\,cm^{-1}$	$3 \times 10^5\,sec^{-1} = 300\,kc$
$1\,m = 100\,cm$	$10^{-2}\,cm^{-1}$	$3 \times 10^8\,sec^{-1} = 300\,mc$
$1\,cm$	$1\,cm^{-1}$	$3 \times 10^{10}\,sec^{-1} = 30\,kmc$
$1\,mm = 10^{-1}\,cm$	$10\,cm^{-1}$	$3 \times 10^{11}\,sec^{-1}$
$10\,\mu$	$1{,}000\,cm^{-1}$	$3 \times 10^{13}\,sec^{-1}$
$1\,\mu = 10^{-3}\,mm = 10^{-4}\,cm$	$10^4\,cm^{-1}$	$3 \times 10^{14}\,sec^{-1}$
$\quad = 1{,}000\,m\mu = 10{,}000\,\text{Å}$		
$7{,}000\,\text{Å} = 700\,m\mu = 0.7\,\mu$	$14{,}200\,cm^{-1}$	$4.26 \times 10^{14}\,sec^{-1}$
$4{,}000\,\text{Å} = 400\,m\mu = 0.4\,\mu$	$25{,}000\,cm^{-1}$	$7.5 \times 10^{14}\,sec^{-1}$
$2{,}000\,\text{Å} = 200\,m\mu = 0.2\,\mu$	$50{,}000\,cm^{-1}$	$1.5 \times 10^{15}\,sec^{-1}$
$1{,}000\,\text{Å} = 100\,m\mu = 0.1\,\mu$	$100{,}000\,cm^{-1}$	$3 \times 10^{15}\,sec^{-1}$
$100\,\text{Å} = 10\,m\mu$	$10^6\,cm^{-1}$	$3 \times 10^{16}\,sec^{-1}$
$10\,\text{Å} = 10^{-7}\,cm$	$10^7\,cm^{-1}$	$3 \times 10^{17}\,sec^{-1}$
$1\,\text{Å} = 10^{-8}\,cm = 10^{-1}\,m\mu$	$10^8\,cm^{-1}$	$3 \times 10^{18}\,sec^{-1}$
$\quad = 10^{-4}\,\mu$		
$0.01\,\text{Å} = 10^{-10}\,cm$	$10^{10}\,cm^{-1}$	$3 \times 10^{20}\,sec^{-1}$

$8{,}066\,cm^{-1} = 23.06$ kcal/mole $= 1\,ev.$

kc = kilocycle, mc = megacycle, kmc = kilomegacycle.

close to the nucleus and relatively far apart from each other. The bands in the ultraviolet and in the visible correspond to transitions of electrons occupying the outer shells. This book will be devoted exclusively to this latter part of the electromagnetic spectrum. In the infrared we find transitions between energy levels linked to the motions of the atomic nuclei. In vibrations the mutual distances between nuclei and the valence angles vary; in rotations the whole molecule undergoes a circular motion in space without change in interatomic distances or angles. Rotational spectra are usually found in the far infrared. These two phenomena are purely molecular, as they imply at least two nuclei linked together.

At even longer wavelengths we find transitions between levels resulting from the splitting of the electronic levels in a magnetic field (electron paramagnetic resonance) and between levels resulting from the splitting of nuclear spin energy levels in a magnetic field (nuclear magnetic resonance). The spectral location of the corresponding bands depends on the strength of the magnetic field applied, that is, on external circumstances.

Radio waves are due to the periodic motion of charged particles between the two poles of a spark-gap. This phenomenon is not directly related to atomic or molecular structure.

Raman spectra are neither absorption nor emission spectra. When a photon is scattered by a *molecule* it may give to it or take from it an amount of energy corresponding to its vibrational or rotational levels. This, too, is a purely molecular phenomenon and is a case of inelastic scattering with some change in the internal energy of the molecule.

Next, some aspects of electronic spectra will be considered in more detail.

1-2 SOME ASPECTS OF ELECTRONIC SPECTRA

Any electron in any atom or molecule can undergo electronic transitions. The question is only in what part of the spectrum the corresponding bands are to be found.

Chemical spectroscopy is mainly concerned with visible (from 7000 to 4000 Å) and ultraviolet spectra (from 4000 to 2000 Å). Among organic compounds, aromatic and other conjugated molecules and their substituted derivatives absorb in this part of the spectrum. Some heteroatomic compounds, even with only one double bond, such as ketones and aldehydes, also have bands in this area. These spectra usually continue into the far ultraviolet. Up till the present this part of the spectrum has been less thoroughly explored owing to experimental difficulties. Mono-olefins and saturated hydrocarbons absorb only in the far ultraviolet.

Among inorganic compounds most of the transition metal complexes absorb in the visible and in the ultraviolet. Most other inorganic compounds absorb only in the ultraviolet or in the far ultraviolet.

This subject will be taken up in more detail in Chapter 15.

Our main interest in this book is in the visible and ultraviolet spectra, which are due to the interaction of light and the so-called optical (or chemical) electrons which occupy the external shells of the atoms and, in the molecules, establish bonds between the atoms or are present as lone pairs of electrons. We shall usually refer to absorption spectra, which, for experimental reasons, are more generally obtainable than emission spectra.

In chemical spectroscopy absorption spectra of dissolved molecules are generally presented in the form of extinction curves. As an example, in Fig. 1-1 is shown the extinction curve of β-naphthylamine in ethanol solution. On the horizontal axis we have the wavelength, λ, in angstrom units and on the vertical axis the logarithm of the molecular extinction coefficient (ϵ) defined by the Beer-Lambert-Bouguer law:

$$\log \frac{I_0}{I} = \epsilon c l \tag{1-5}$$

where I_0 and I are the intensities of the incident and transmitted

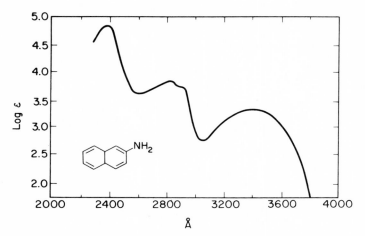

Fig. 1-1 The Ultraviolet absorption spectrum of β-naphthyl-amine in ethanol solution (Y. Hirshberg and R. N. Jones. *Can. J. Res.* B27: 437, 1949).

light, respectively, c is the concentration in moles/liter, and l is the width of the cell in centimeters (cf. p. 100).

It is immediately seen that this spectrum does not consist of sharp lines but of large areas of selective absorption. There are two principal reasons for this.

1. According to Bohr's formula the wave number, ω, is given by

$$\omega = \frac{1}{\lambda} = \frac{E' - E''}{hc} \tag{1-6}$$

where E' and E'' are the energies of the excited state and the ground state, respectively, h is the Planck constant, and c is the speed of light. In the case of free atoms the energies are purely electronic except, possibly, for a very small contribution of nuclear spin but molecules also have vibrational and rotational energies. These latter are quantized as well and Bohr's formula applies to them. Pure vibrational spectra are to be found in the infrared and pure rotational spectra in the far infrared; they do not concern us here. These motions, however, have a decisive influence on the electronic spectra as well.

As a first approximation the energy of a molecule can be considered as the sum of the electronic energy, the vibrational energy, and the rotational energy.

$$E = E_{el} + E_{vib} + E_{rot} \tag{1-7}$$

The main contributor to the total energy is generally the electronic energy. Vibrational energies are about ten times less, and rotational energies are again 10 or 100 times less than vibrational energies. (In polyatomic molecules, however, which have several vibrations—$3n - 6$, if n is the number of atoms, or $3n - 5$ for linear molecules—the contribution of the vibrational energy may be quite important.)

With every electronic term there are associated a series of vibrational terms and with every vibrational term a series of rotational terms. Figure 1-2 is a schematic representation of this situation with two electronic levels. In reality the vibrational levels are slowly convergent and the rotational terms are divergent. To this triple structure of the energies corresponds the triple structure of molecular spectra. A given electronic transition may depart from several vibrational and rotational levels of the initial state and it may arrive at a number of vibrational and rotational levels of the final state; therefore, the transition energy varies in a more or less broad region. The results are "band systems" which replace the lines of the atomic spectra.

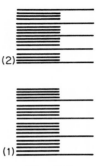

Fig. 1-2

It is not always possible to distinguish the individual rotation lines. Generally they appear only for low-pressure gases. In most cases in condensed phases the strong forces acting between the molecules prevent them from rotating, and the remaining incomplete rotation becomes a vibration ("libration").

Even the vibrational fine structure is often lost, the individual bands themselves being broad and melting together to give broad regions of absorption as in Fig. 1-1.

In Fig. 1-3 we see the spectrum of benzene, with its well-pronounced vibrational fine structure.

2. The width of the individual bands or lines depends on several factors [3]. We shall mention only the one that is by far the most important in the circumstances under which the chemical spectroscopist measures his spectra.

In reality we never measure the spectrum of one molecule isolated in space. Even in low-pressure gases there are collisions between molecules, during which they might exert forces on each other. In gases under high pressure and in solutions, pure liquids, and crystals the molecules are constantly in a force field due to the surrounding molecules. Because of the motions of the molecules the energy levels are modified to varying degrees, causing a spread in the sharp energy levels. (See references on p. 363).

We must make an observation about units. In most publications extinction curves are presented as λ against $\log \varepsilon$ as in Fig. 1-1. This has many advantages, the most important being that we can

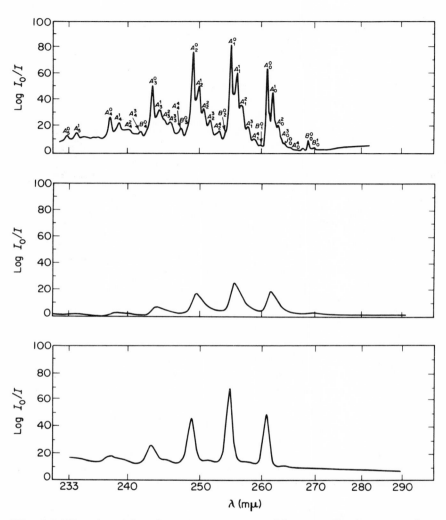

Fig. 1-3 The ultraviolet absorption spectrum of benzene. In the vapor phase (top) and in a paraffinic hydrocarbon solution at 21°C and at −190°C.

represent a complete curve on a drawing of moderate size, as the extinction coefficients in the same spectrum might vary from zero to several hundred thousands. However, on theoretical grounds presentation of the curves as $1/\lambda$ against ϵ itself, is much more satisfactory. The wave numbers are proportional to the transition energies, the wavelengths are not. The intensities are an integral of the ϵ, not of the log ϵ (see Chapter 5), and it is hardly possible to study the fine structure of the band systems when log ϵ is used.

The Molecule as a Wave-Mechanical Problem

2-1 DE BROGLIE WAVES AND SCHRÖDINGER'S EQUATION

Every molecule is built from a certain number of charged particles: nuclei and electrons. As a result of the interactions among these particles the molecule assumes a certain shape having a specific arrangement of the nuclei and an equally characteristic distribution of the electrons in the frame constituted by the nuclei. If we want to know the properties of a molecule, we have to treat it as a problem of interaction between the given number of charged particles. The means of doing this is to solve Schrödinger's equation for the given molecule.

In order to solve the difficulties of the old quantum (Bohr) theory, Louis de Broglie in 1923 suggested that a wave should be associated with the motion of a system. He was able to predict the wavelength (λ) of this wave using the analogy of the photon and equating Planck's formula (1-1) and Einstein's formula for the energy

$$E = mc^2 \qquad (2\text{-}1)$$

where m is the mass of the particle and c the speed of light. Then, for the photon

$$E = h\nu = mc^2$$

and from $\nu = c/\lambda$

$$\lambda = \frac{h}{mc} \qquad (2\text{-}2)$$

De Broglie suggested that for a particle (such as an electron)

$$\lambda = \frac{h}{mv} \qquad (2\text{-}3)$$

v being the speed of the particle. This formula applies if the particle is in a field of constant potential, i.e., if the particle has a constant speed. This formula received experimental confirmation by electron diffraction measurements first performed by Davisson and Germer [4]. The electron microscope is based on this experiment.

The speed of the associated wave is not, in general, the same as the speed of the particle (velocity of phase and velocity of group) but we do not need to discuss this problem here. Instead we are going to consider de Broglie's formula as our experimentally based starting point. In the absence of external forces the whole energy is kinetic energy, and from Eq. (2-3)

$$T = \frac{1}{2} mv^2 = \frac{1}{2m} \frac{h^2}{\lambda^2} \qquad (2\text{-}4)$$

For stationary states the wave representing the particle can be taken as a standing wave.

The simplest wave has the form of a sinusoid, it is perfectly monochromatic and polarized, the amplitude is the same at every point, and it is reached periodically with time. Such a wave progresses without deforming itself. Standing waves are composite waves. The simplest type of standing wave is obtained by superposing two sinusoids originating from two synchronous sources and progressing in opposite directions. The resultant wave is deforming itself with time without progressing. It has the form:

$$s = A \cos 2\pi \frac{x}{\lambda} \cos 2\pi \left(\frac{t}{T} = \frac{l}{\lambda} \right) \qquad (2\text{-}5)$$

where s is the displacement (light vector), T the period of the wave motion, the two component waves are supposed to progress in the x direction, and l is a constant, half of the distance separating the two sources.

This wave is the product of two functions, the first one depending only on the space coordinates, the second one only on time. The first one represents the amplitude at a given point which now varies with x.

In wave mechanics s is usually replaced by ψ and the amplitude function is

$$\psi = A \cos 2\pi \frac{x}{\lambda} \qquad (2\text{-}6)$$

Taking the second derivative

$$\frac{d^2\psi}{dx^2} = -\frac{4\pi^2}{\lambda^2} A \cos 2\pi \frac{x}{\lambda} = -\frac{4\pi^2}{\lambda^2} \psi$$

we have

$$\frac{1}{\lambda^2} = -\frac{1}{\psi}\frac{d^2\psi}{dx^2}\frac{1}{4\pi^2}$$

and substituting this into the expression of the kinetic energy [Eq. (2-4)]

$$T = -\frac{h^2}{8\pi^2 m}\frac{1}{\psi}\frac{d^2\psi}{dx^2} \tag{2-7}$$

This equation is equivalent to de Broglie's formula (2-3). Schrödinger suggested that we might replace T by $E - V$ where V is the potential energy and E the total energy, at least when $E = $ const., i.e. if we are in one of the stationary states of the molecule. Then

$$E - V = -\frac{h^2}{8\pi^2 m}\frac{1}{\psi}\frac{d^2\psi}{dx^2}$$

or

$$\frac{d^2\psi}{dx^2} + \frac{8\pi^2 m}{h^2}(E - V)\psi = 0 \tag{2-8}$$

This is the time-independent Schrödinger equation in one dimension. In three dimensions it becomes

$$\nabla^2\psi + \frac{8\pi^2 m}{h^2}(E - V)\psi = 0 \tag{2-9}$$

with

$$\nabla^2 \equiv \frac{\partial^2}{\partial x^2} + \frac{\partial^2}{\partial y^2} + \frac{\partial^2}{\partial z^2}$$

being the Laplace operator. We may also write

$$-\frac{h^2}{8\pi^2 m}\nabla^2\psi + V\psi = E\psi$$

or

$$H\psi = E\psi \tag{2-10}$$

where

$$H \equiv -\frac{h^2}{8\pi^2 m}\nabla^2 + V$$

is the Hamilton operator, the operator of the total energy.

For the discussion of spectral intensities we shall also need the time-dependent Schrödinger equation.

If we want a solution for a stationary state, we can write

$$\Psi = \psi e^{-i\omega t} \tag{2-11}$$

where ψ is a function of the space coordinates only and $e^{-i\omega t}$ of time only. $\omega = 2\pi\nu$ is the angular frequency. Differentiation with respect to time gives

$$\frac{\partial \Psi}{\partial t} = - i\omega\psi e^{-i\omega t} = - i\omega\Psi \qquad (2\text{-}12)$$

If we suppose that

$$E = h\nu$$

is valid for the electron we can write

$$\nu = \frac{E}{h}$$

and

$$\omega = 2\pi\nu = \frac{2\pi E}{h}$$

This again implies replacing c by the speed, v, of the electron. Hence,

$$\frac{\partial \Psi}{\partial t} = - \frac{2\pi i E}{h} \Psi = - \frac{2\pi i}{h} H\Psi$$

replacing the total energy by its operator, H.

Finally, we obtain

$$H\Psi = - \frac{h}{2\pi i} \frac{\partial \Psi}{\partial t} \qquad (2\text{-}13)$$

As can be seen we have here another energy operator

$$- \frac{h}{2\pi i} \frac{\partial}{\partial t}$$

2-2. THE PROPERTIES OF THE EIGENFUNCTIONS

The reason why s was replaced by ψ in Eq. (2-5) is the particular interpretation given to this function in wave mechanics. We cannot regard it as describing the actual path of the particle with whose motion it is associated. Indeed, we have to renounce such an undertaking because of Heisenberg's uncertainty principle. A looser interpretation must be given. In optics the intensity of light in a given volume element is proportional to the square of the total amplitude of the waves in that volume or, alternatively, the number of photons encountered there at a given moment. This is equivalent to saying that the intensity depends on the probability of finding photons in the volume element. By analogy Born [5] interpreted the square of the wave function $\psi^*\psi d\tau$ or $\psi^2 d\tau$, if the function is real as a measure of the probability of finding particles in volume element $d\tau$.[1]

----

[1] ψ^* is the complex conjugate of ψ.

This interpretation can be extended to the case when we have only one particle.

It follows from the probabilistic interpretation that ψ must be finite, single-valued, and continuous, although the latter condition is less stringent than the former two. These conditions impose a severe restriction on the physically acceptable solutions of the Schrödinger equation, the acceptable solutions being characterized by quantum numbers which are integers (just like the possible wavelengths in a restricted space).

If

$$\psi_0, \psi_1, \psi_2, \psi_3, \cdots$$

are the acceptable solutions, or eigenfunctions, of the system, the corresponding energies

$$E_0, E_1, E_2, E_3, \cdots$$

also obtained from the Schrödinger equation are called the eigenvalues of the system.

It also follows from the probabilistic interpretation of ψ that the wave function must be normalized, that is to say

$$\int \psi^2 \, d\tau = 1 \quad \text{or} \quad \int \psi^* \psi \, d\tau = 1 \tag{2-14}$$

where integration is extended over the whole space. The probability of finding the particle somewhere in space is indeed certainty.

It can be shown too that the integral

$$\int \psi_k \psi_l \, d\tau = 0 \quad \text{or} \quad \int \psi_k^* \psi_l \, d\tau = 0 \tag{2-15}$$

if $k \neq l$. This is the orthogonality relation.

To see this we suppose that ψ_k and ψ_l are two different eigenfunctions related to the same problem. Since both are solutions of the same Schrödinger equation we may write:

$$\nabla^2 \psi_k + \frac{8\pi^2 m}{h^2} (E_k - V)\psi_k = 0 \tag{2-16}$$

and

$$\nabla^2 \psi_l + \frac{8\pi^2 m}{h^2} (E_l - V)\psi_l = 0 \tag{2-17}$$

If we multiply (2-16) by ψ_l and (2-17) by ψ_k, subtract the first from the second, and then integrate over the whole space we obtain (with real wave functions):

$$\int (\psi_k \nabla^2 \psi_l - \psi_l \nabla^2 \psi_k) \, d\tau = \frac{8\pi^2 m}{h^2} (E_k - E_l) \int \psi_k \psi_l \, d\tau \tag{2-18}$$

To the left-hand side we may apply Green's theorem [6]. Then we have

$$\int (\psi_k \nabla^2 \psi_l - \psi_l \nabla^2 \psi_k)\, d\tau = \int \left(\psi_k \frac{\partial \psi_l}{\partial n} - \psi_l \frac{\partial \psi_k}{\partial n} \right) df \qquad (2\text{-}19)$$

where the volume integral at the left is equated to an integral taken over the surface of the volume. ∂n indicates differentiation according to the normal of the surface. Since the volume integral is taken over the whole space, ψ_k and ψ_l as eigenfunctions vanish at infinite distance and thus the right-hand side of (2-19) is zero. Hence the left-hand side is also zero and from (2-18):

$$\frac{8\pi^2 m}{h^2} (E_k - E_l) \int \psi_k \psi_l\, d\tau = 0 \qquad (2\text{-}20)$$

Since, however, $E_k - E_l \neq 0$, except for $k = l$ we must have

$$\int \psi_k \psi_l\, d\tau = 0$$

which is identical to (2-15).

The wave functions related to a given system are said to form an orthonormal set.

The Schrödinger equation and, more generally, wave mechanics avoid the arbitrariness of the older quantum theory. Experimental confirmation is still needed, however.

This was achieved in the case of the hydrogen atom and nearly so in the case of the helium atom and the hydrogen molecule. In all other cases only approximate solutions are known because of the complexity of the problems. However, the contemporary approach to molecular problems is based on the confidence that a rigorous solution of the Schrödinger equation would give definite and accurate information on them in every case and that the validity of our results depends only on the degree of approximation used.

The way we introduced the Schrödinger equation is not the most rigorous or the most modern one. It is generally considered at present as taken directly from observation, like Newton's laws; wave mechanics are then based on a certain number of postulates (see, for example, [7] or [8]). It is believed, however, that the historical approach is satisfactory for the purposes of the chemical spectroscopist.

2-3. THE HYDROGEN ATOM

The wave functions obtained for the H atom are well known. They are characterized by three quantum numbers: the principal quantum number n, the azimuthal quantum number l, and the magnetic quantum number m_l, with the permitted values

$$n = 1, 2, 3, \ldots$$
$$l = 0, 1, 2, \ldots, (n - 1)$$
$$m_l = 0, \pm 1, \ldots, \pm l$$

The energy depends only on n.

$$E_n = -\frac{2\pi^2 m e^4}{n^2 h^2} \tag{2-21}$$

This, however, is only so in the case of the hydrogen atom; generally the energy depends on n and l. In an external field it also depends on m_l.

l is a measure of the orbital angular momentum of the electron whose magnitude is $\sqrt{l(l+1)}\, h/2\pi$, and to its value is linked a very important classification of electron orbitals. If $l = 0, 1, 2, 3, 4, \ldots$, we say that the orbital is an $s, p, d, f, g, \ldots$ orbital, respectively. Table 2-1 shows the hydrogenlike wave functions for the K and L shells [9, p. 138]. (r, θ, and ψ are the spherical polar coordinates.)

Table 2-1 Hydrogenlike wave functions

$$\sigma = \frac{Z}{a_0} r$$

K shell

$n = 1, l = 0, m_l = 0$

$$\psi_{1s} = \frac{1}{\sqrt{\pi}} \left(\frac{Z}{a_0}\right)^{3/2} e^{-\sigma}$$

L shell

$n = 2, l = 0, m_l = 0$

$$\psi_{2s} = \frac{1}{4\sqrt{2\pi}} \left(\frac{Z}{a_0}\right)^{3/2} (2 - \sigma) e^{-\sigma/2}$$

$n = 2, l = 1, m_l = 0$

$$\psi_{2p_z} = \frac{1}{4\sqrt{2\pi}} \left(\frac{Z}{a_0}\right)^{3/2} \sigma e^{-\sigma/2} \cos\theta$$

$n = 2, l = 1, m_l = \pm 1$

$$\psi_{2p_x} = \frac{1}{4\sqrt{2\pi}} \left(\frac{Z}{a_0}\right)^{3/2} \sigma e^{-\sigma/2} \sin\theta \cos\phi$$

$$\psi_{2p_y} = \frac{1}{4\sqrt{2\pi}} \left(\frac{Z}{a_0}\right)^{3/2} \sigma e^{-\sigma/2} \sin\theta \sin\phi$$

Spin does not appear in the Schrödinger equation; it is usually introduced by multiplying the electronic (space) wave function by an adequate spin function. Spin appears automatically in the relativistic wave mechanics due to Dirac [10].

The hydrogenlike wave functions given in the table may be used for constructing the electronic wave functions of higher atoms, although in order to be exact solutions for the particular atom they should be modified to take into account the interactions between the electrons. This can be done only approximately.

Atomic wave functions are also often used for building molecular wave functions. This procedure also is an approximate one. Very often combinations of pure $s, p, d, \ldots$ wave functions, so-called hybridized orbitals, are used to build molecular wave functions instead of the pure atomic orbitals themselves.

In the next chapter we shall deal with the need for, and the nature of, such approximate methods.

2-4 ON APPROXIMATE WAVE-MECHANICAL METHODS

The simplicity of the problem made it possible to solve the Schrödinger equation rigorously in the case of the hydrogen atom. With only one nucleus and only one electron one can put the center of the coordinate system in the center of the nucleus and use spherical coordinates r, θ, and ϕ. In this way the Schrödinger equation is separable into three parts, each containing only one of the variables. These are of known mathematical form and can be solved exactly. Then, the usual wave-mechanical conditions permit us to select the physically adequate solutions among the mathematically possible ones. The potential function entering the Hamiltonian is simply

$$- \frac{e^2}{r}$$

the coulombic attraction between a positive nucleus and the negative electron.

In more complicated cases we have more particles and more coordinates. The potential function will be a sum of all attractions between particles of opposite charge and all repulsions between particles of like charge. Some of the terms will depend on the coordinates of two particles, and the Schrödinger equation will no longer be separable, nor will it be of a known mathematical type.

It is an old academic joke that only those differential equations are soluble that have been solved before. In complicated cases we cannot simply obtain the exact wave function by solving the Schrödinger equation. We might try various suitable functions and see if they can be taken as approximate solutions.

The variation method. Let us take the time-independent Schrödinger equation in its most concise form.

$$H\psi = E\psi \tag{2-22}$$

We might multiply both sides by ψ (or its complex conjugate ψ^* if the wave function is complex) and integrate for the whole space for all the coordinates $(d\tau)$.

$$\int \psi^* H \psi \, d\tau = \int \psi^* E \psi \, d\tau \qquad (2\text{-}23)$$

Since E is a constant of the system it can be brought before the sign of integration, and

$$\int \psi^* H \psi \, d\tau = E \int \psi^* \psi \, d\tau$$

or

$$E = \frac{\int \psi^* H \psi \, d\tau}{\int \psi^* \psi \, d\tau} \qquad (2\text{-}24)$$

where the denominator is equal to one if the wave functions are normalized.

Now the variation principle states that if ψ is not an exact solution of the Schrödinger equation, the energy (of the ground state) will always be higher than the one we would obtain with the exact wave function (E_0).

In other words, if ϕ is a function satisfying the usual conditions in wave mechanics, then

$$\int \phi^* H \phi \, d\tau \geq E_0 \qquad (2\text{-}25)$$

where the sign of equality holds if ϕ happens to be the exact wave-function. This theorem can be proved in the following way:

We expand ϕ in a complete series of some normalized, orthogonal functions. These may be the (unknown) exact wave functions ψ_i of the same problem satisfying

$$H\psi_i = E_i \psi_i \qquad (2\text{-}26)$$

Then

$$\phi = \sum_i c_i \psi_i \qquad (2\text{-}27)$$

and

$$\int \phi^* H \phi \, d\tau = \int \sum_i c_i^* \psi_i^* H \sum_i c_i \psi_i \, d\tau \qquad (2\text{-}28)$$

or, using (2-26),

$$\int \phi^* H \phi \, d\tau = \int \sum_i c_i^* \psi_i^* \sum_i E_i c_i \psi_i \, d\tau \qquad (2\text{-}29)$$

When we carry out the summation all terms will be zero, because of the orthogonality of the ψ_i, unless we have the same index i at both places. Hence

$$\int \phi^* H\phi \, d\tau = \sum_i c_i^2 E_i \int \psi^* \psi \, d\tau = \sum_i c_i^2 E_i \qquad (2\text{-}30)$$

Furthermore,

$$\int \phi^* H\phi \, d\tau - E_0 = \int \phi^* H\phi \, d\tau - \int \phi^* E_0 \phi \, d\tau$$

$$= \sum_i c_i^* c_i E_i - \sum_i c_i^* c_i E_0 = \sum_i c_i^* c_i (E_i - E_0) \qquad (2\text{-}31)$$

Now c_i^2 as a square is either positive or zero, and since E_0 is the lowest of the E_i, then necessarily

$$E_i \geq E_0$$

hence

$$\int \phi^* H\phi \, d\tau \geq E_0 \qquad (2\text{-}32)$$

where the equality holds if all the c_i except c_0 are equal to zero; i.e. ϕ turned out to be the exact wave function giving the exact energy.

Thus Eq. (2-25) is proved. This fact is extremely important, because it means that if we take any two functions and compute the energy from (2-24) for each one, then the function giving the lower energy is a better approximation to the real wave function than the other. There is no danger of getting to the other side of the real energy.

In practice we usually take a function which seems to be a reasonable one for the given problem. There usually are certain adjustable parameters in the function. We choose them so as to have the lowest possible energy with the given type of function. We "minimize the energy" with respect to these parameters.

This is the basis of the variational method.

We cannot simply minimize the quantity

$$E = \frac{H\phi}{\phi}$$

corresponding to $H\phi = E\phi$, because unless ϕ is the exact wave function, $H\phi/\phi$ will be a function of the coordinates of the system and it would be necessary to compute it to a very great number of places to take an average—not to speak of the difficulties of minimization [11, p. 58].

The expression

$$E = \int \phi^* H\phi \, d\tau \qquad (2\text{-}33)$$

is important not only because the variation theorem applies to it. It is the so-called *expectation value* of the energy.

Let us suppose that we want to measure the x coordinate of an electron. Since we cannot speak of the trajectory of the electron but only the probability of finding it in a given volume element $d\tau$, all we can say is that, if we carry out a very great number of measurements, after each one letting the electron revert into its original situation, the probability of finding the electron with a given value of x will be proportional to the square of the wave function in the given volume element $d\tau$, or, in one dimension, dx:

$$\phi^* \phi \, dx$$

Hence the mean value obtained from a very great number of measurements, or the expectation value is

$$\bar{x} = \int x\phi^* \phi \, dx = \int \phi^* x\phi \, dx \tag{2-34}$$

if ϕ is normalized, otherwise

$$\bar{x} = \frac{\int \phi^* x\phi \, dx}{\int \phi^* \phi \, dx} \tag{2-35}$$

For the energy the expectation value is

$$\bar{E} = \int \phi^* H\phi \, d\tau \tag{2-36}$$

H being the energy operator. The true expectation value would be obtained, however, with the exact wavefunction only.

The perturbation method.[1] Another way of finding approximate solutions is to omit from the potential function one or more terms that make the solution of the equation difficult. If in this way the equation becomes soluble, then we may use the obtained wave functions with the complete Hamiltonian for computing approximate values of the energies and wave functions of the system. This method is called the *perturbation method*, the perturbing terms being the ones first omitted and then reintroduced.

Let us suppose that we have a given problem whose Schrödinger equation is

$$H\psi_n = E_n \psi_n \tag{2-37}$$

and that we do not know the form of the eigenfunctions. We know, however, the solutions (eigenfunctions) of a similar problem, which can be taken as an approximation to the real one. [One might, for example, think of toluene and benzene respectively, or to an atom first in a field-free space and then in an electric field (Stark effect).]

If the solutions of the latter are the functions ψ_n^0, these necessarily form a complete set of orthonormal functions and thus we might expand the ψ_n in terms of the ψ_n^0

$$\psi_n = \sum_m S_{mn} \psi_m^0 \tag{2-38}$$

[1] The treatment given here follows the same general lines as the one given by Slater and Frank [6].

where the S_{mn} are numerical coefficients and the complete set of ψ_n^0 has to be taken, including those belonging to continuous levels.

The problem is then to determine the energies and wave functions of the perturbed system. For the latter the S_{mn} are needed. In order to obtain them we substitute (2–38) into the Schrödinger equation of the problem (2–37), and multiply by ψ_k^{0*} and integrate. On the right-hand side only one term will remain, since the E_n are constants which may be brought before the integration sign and all the ψ_n^0 are mutually orthogonal. On the left-hand side there will be a linear combination of terms like

$$H_{km} = \int \psi_k^{0*} H \psi_m^0 \, d\tau$$

giving

$$\sum_m (H_{km} - E_n \delta_{km}) S_{mn} = 0$$

where

$$\delta_{km} = \begin{cases} 1, & \text{if } k = m \\ 0, & \text{if } k \neq m \end{cases} \tag{2–39}$$

This is an infinite set of linear, homogeneous equations. For a state n and $k = 1, 2, \ldots$ for the different rows:

$$(H_{11} - E_n)S_{1n} + H_{12}S_{2n} + H_{13}S_{3n} + \cdots = 0$$
$$H_{21}S_{1n} + (H_{22} - E_n)S_{2n} + H_{23}S_{3n} + \cdots = 0 \tag{2–40}$$
$$\cdots\cdots\cdots\cdots\cdots\cdots\cdots\cdots\cdots\cdots\cdots\cdots$$

These can have (non-all zero) solutions for the S_{mn} only if their determinant vanishes:

$$\begin{vmatrix} H_{11} - E_n & H_{12} & H_{13} \cdots \\ H_{21} & H_{22} - E_n & H_{23} \cdots \\ \cdots & \cdots & \cdots\cdots\cdots \end{vmatrix} = 0 \tag{2–41}$$

(This secular equation resembles those encountered in the molecular orbital or valence-bond methods, but the wave functions in the H_{km} here are molecular wave functions while in the molecular orbital and valence-bond treatments they are only wave functions from which the molecular wave functions are built.) (See Chapters 3 and 4.)

If the ψ_n^0 were solutions of the problem, the nondiagonal terms in the matrix of H (2–41) would be equal to zero. This can be understood on the following way:

In $H\psi_n = E_n\psi_n$ the eigenvalue of H is constant, E_n, thus the Hamiltonian itself is constant for any stationary state. Now the matrix for a constant C will consist of components like

$$C_{nm} = \int \psi_n^* C \psi_n = C \tag{2-42}$$

if $n = m$ and 0 if $n \neq m$.

(If $C = 1$ this gives

$$\int \psi_n^* \psi_m \, d\tau = \begin{cases} 0, & \text{if } n \neq m \\ 1, & \text{if } n = m \end{cases}$$

giving simply the normalization and orthogonality conditions.)

Thus we see that if the ψ_n^0 were solutions belonging to H, the Hamiltonian of the real problem, the matrix would be diagonal and H_{11}, H_{22}, . . . would be the energy levels. Actually, looking for solutions of the Schrödinger equation is the same as looking for wave functions that diagonalize the H matrix.

In the perturbation method the ψ_n^0 are not exact eigenfunctions of H and, therefore, do not diagonalize the H matrix (see also the discussion of configurational interaction on p. 281).

However, if we suppose that the perturbation is a slight one, the ψ_n^0 will not be far from the real solutions. Also the nondiagonal terms will be small and the diagonal ones will not be far from the exact energies, E_n. Thus the H_{nn} will be approximate values of the E_n.

The rest of the argument depends on whether or not some of the states are degenerate.

1. *Nondegenerate states only.* With the above suppositions, if we expand the determinant into the $N!$ permutations of N elements, obviously the permutation containing only the elements in the main diagonal will be by far the greatest. In a *first approximation* we may neglect all the other permutations and write

$$(H_{11} - E_n)(H_{22} - E_n) \cdots = 0 \tag{2-43}$$

One of the factors must then be zero, and only one can be zero, since all levels are nondegenerate. For state n, it will be $(H_{nn} - E_n)$, hence

$$H_{nn} = E_n \tag{2-44}$$

On the other hand

$$H_{nn} = \int \psi_n^{0*} H \psi_n^0 \, d\tau \tag{2-45}$$

and thus, in first approximation, the energy of the nth state of the perturbed problem is the average of the *perturbed* Hamiltonian with the *unperturbed* wave functions.

The Hamiltonian of the perturbed system may be written as

$$H = H^0 + H'$$

where H' is the perturbation. Substituting this into (2-45) we obtain

$$E_n = H_{nn} = \int \psi_n^{0*}(H^0 + H')\psi_n^0 \, d\tau$$

$$= \int \psi_n^{0*} H^0 \psi_n^0 \, d\tau + \int \psi_n^{0*} H' \psi_n^0 \, d\tau = E_n^0 + E_n' \qquad (2\text{-}46)$$

where the last term is the average of the perturbing Hamiltonian with the *unperturbed* wave function.

We now have to derive the S_{mn} and the new, perturbed wave functions. If the ψ_n^0 were eigenfunctions of the perturbed problem, then in a stationary state n we should have

$$S_{nn} = 1$$

and all the other S_{mn} would be zero. Though this is not the case, we can assume to this approximation that $S_{nn} = 1$ and that the others are negligible. Then we have from (2-40), with $E_n = H_{nn}$ and observing that the multiplier of S_{nn} is H_{1n} in the first equation, H_{2n} in the second equation, and so forth,

$$(H_{11} - H_{nn})S_{1n} + H_{1n} = 0$$
$$(H_{22} - H_{nn})S_{2n} + H_{2n} = 0 \qquad (2\text{-}47)$$
$$\dots\dots\dots\dots\dots\dots\dots\dots$$

From these equations, for the nth level,

$$S_{1n} = -\frac{H_{1n}}{H_{11} - H_{nn}}$$

$$S_{2n} = -\frac{H_{2n}}{H_{22} - H_{nn}}$$

$$\dots\dots\dots\dots\dots\dots$$

$$S_{nn} = 1$$

so that the wave function is [from (2-38)]:

$$\psi_n = \psi_n^0 - \sum_{k \neq n} \frac{H_{kn}}{H_{kk} - H_{nn}} \psi_k^0 \qquad (2\text{-}48)$$

Again we introduce $H = H^0 + H'$. Then

$$H_{kn} = H_{kn}^0 + H_{kn}'$$

but

$$H_{kn}^0 = \int \psi_k^0 H^0 \psi_n^0 \, d\tau = 0$$

if $k \neq n$ since the ψ^0 are exact solutions for H^0. In the denominator

$$H_{kk} = H_{kk}^0 + H_{kk}' \quad \text{and} \quad H_{nn} = H_{nn}^0 + H_{nn}'$$

but, since the perturbation is slight, we may neglect the primed quantities before the much larger difference $(H_{kk}^0 - H_{nn}^0)$. With these approximations we obtain

$$\psi_n = \psi_n^0 - \sum_{k \neq n} \frac{H'_{kn}}{E_k^0 - E_n^0} \psi_k^0 \qquad (2\text{-}49)$$

This together with

$$E_n = E_n^0 + E_n' = E_n^0 + H_n' \qquad (2\text{-}50)$$

is the fundamental formula of first-order perturbation theory for non-degenerate levels. It is valid not only for the ground state but for any state, since the numbering of the states is arbitrary.

To obtain the laws of second-order perturbation theory we must retain more terms of the secular determinant.

If we had only two energy levels the secular determinant would be

$$\begin{vmatrix} H_{11} - E_n & H_{12} \\ H_{21} & H_{22} - E_n \end{vmatrix} = (H_{11} - E_n)(H_{22} - E_n) - H_{12}H_{21} = 0 \quad (2\text{-}51)$$

This, of course, is easy to solve. If we look for E_1 we can divide by $(H_{22} - E_1)$ and obtain

$$H_{11} - E_1 = \frac{H_{12}H_{21}}{H_{22} - E_1}$$

where $H_{12} = H_{21}$ for real functions. This is due to the Hermitian character of the Hamiltonian operator [8, p. 112]. Now $H_{11} = E_1$ to the first order and we introduce this in the denominator. Then

$$E_1 = H_{11} - \frac{H_{12}H_{21}}{H_{22} - H_{11}}$$

and similarly

$$E_2 = H_{22} - \frac{H_{12}H_{21}}{H_{11} - H_{22}} \qquad (2\text{-}52)$$

In the general case we retain those terms in the secular equation that are in the row and column that cross each other at the diagonal term corresponding to the state we are looking for.

$$E_n = H_{nn} - \sum_{k \neq n} \frac{H_{kn}H_{nk}}{H_{kk} - H_{nn}} \qquad (2\text{-}53)$$

Introducing again $H = H^0 + H'$ it follows that

$$E_n = E_n^0 + H_n' - \sum_{k \neq n} \frac{H'_{kn}H'_{nk}}{E_k^0 - E_n^0} \qquad (2\text{-}54)$$

where H_n' is the first-order perturbation and the sum on the right-hand side is the second-order perturbation.

The S_{mn} and the perturbed eigenfunctions can be obtained by consideration of (2-40), yielding:

$$S_{mn} = \sum_{k \neq n} \frac{H'_{mk}H'_{kn}}{(E_n^0 - E_k^0)(E_n^0 - E_m^0)} - \frac{H'_{nn}H'_{mn}}{(E_n^0 - E_m^0)^2} \qquad (2\text{-}55)$$

and

$$\psi_n = \psi_n^0 + \sum_{k \neq n} \frac{H'_{kn}}{E_n^0 - E_k^0} \psi_k^0$$

$$+ \sum_{m \neq n} \left[\sum_{k \neq n} \frac{H'_{mk}H'_{kn}}{(E_n^0 - E_m^0)(E_n^0 - E_k^0)} - \frac{H'_{nn}H'_{nm}}{(E_n^0 - E_m^0)^2} \right] \psi_m^0 \qquad (2\text{-}56)$$

Third- and higher-order approximations are seldom used. To obtain them we have to retain further terms of secular determinant.

2. *The degenerate case.* The formulas (2-49), (2-54) and (2-56) cannot be used when there are degenerate states among the E_n since the denominators would be zero. Then we have to go back to the secular determinant whose solution will give the perturbed energies and the S_{mn}. In many cases sufficient accuracy is achieved by retaining the terms between states belonging to the same degenerate set but neglecting those between one of them and states not forming part of that set. Degenerate states may or may not split upon perturbation. We shall not go into further detail; more information may be found in works of Slater and Franck [6, p. 388], Margenau and Murphy [89, p. 371], Eyring, Walter, and Kimball [40, p. 92], Pauling and Wilson [9, p. 156], and others.

Only the following remarks will be made. Any complete set of orthonormal functions can serve as a starting point for a perturbation calculation. They need not be the exact eigenfunctions of the unperturbed problem, which are seldom known anyway.

To have a complete set we need all the solutions of the exact Schrödinger equation including those belonging to the continuous energy levels, i.e., an infinite number of functions. It can be shown, however, that approximate solutions obtained from a finite set of functions may also form a complete, orthonormal set and, therefore, can serve as a starting point for perturbation calculations (see Daudel, Lefebvre, and Moser [19, p. 318]).

[A set of orthogonal functions is complete if there is no other function orthogonal to all the functions forming the set. Then a function $f(x)$, which satisfies the same boundary conditions as the functions of the set, can be expressed without approximation as a weighted linear sum of the functions forming the set, such as (2-38).]

The most stringent requirement on perturbation calculations is that the successive first-, second-, and higher-order perturbations should converge to zero. In many cases this condition is not satisfied and the method cannot be used.

Actual approximate wave-mechanical methods are often mixtures of the variation and perturbation method.

2-5 MOLECULAR ORBITAL AND VALENCE-BOND APPROXIMATION

Speaking of molecular problems, the most popular approximate method is undoubtedly the molecular orbital method. Another method which was used much in past years is the valence-bond method. In both these methods the molecular wave functions (orbitals) are built from atomic wave functions (orbitals). This is, of course, an approximation in itself.

Let us take the example of the hydrogen molecule. If ψ_A and ψ_B are the atomic orbitals that an electron would have if it were restricted to the field of nucleus A and nucleus B, respectively, the molecular orbital extending over the whole molecule is taken for electron 1 as

$$\phi(1) = c_A \psi_A + c_B \psi_B \qquad (2\text{-}57)$$

where (1) stands for the three coordinates of electron 1 and c_A and c_B are numerical coefficients with respect to which the energy has to be minimized in order to make the energy of the ground state the lowest possible. It will be shown in the next chapter by means of a detailed example how this is done.

In the simple case of the hydrogen molecule we obtain for the ground state, omitting normalization factors,

$$\phi_1 = \psi_A + \psi_B \qquad (c_A = c_B) \qquad (2\text{-}58)$$

and for the excited state

$$\phi_2 = \psi_A - \psi_B \qquad (c_A = -c_B) \qquad (2\text{-}59)$$

This is natural, as there is no reason why atom A should make a different contribution to $\int \phi_i^2 \, d\tau$ than atom B, the two being the same from every point of view.

In the ground state both electrons can have ϕ_1 as their wave function if only they have opposite spins satisfying the Pauli principle (see, however, discussion on pp. 48 and 262). Such a molecular orbital is called an LCAO molecular orbital (MO), where LCAO stands for linear combination of atomic orbitals. It depends only on the coordinates of one electron.

The total wave function depending on the coordinates of both electrons is then essentially the product of the two molecular orbitals

$$\Psi = \phi_1(1)\phi_1(2) \qquad (2\text{-}60)$$

(For an exact account see Chapter 3.)

We may substitute $\psi_A + \psi_B$ for ϕ_1 and obtain

$$\Psi = (\psi_A + \psi_B)(1)(\psi_A + \psi_B)(2)$$

or

$$\Psi = \psi_A(1)\psi_A(2) + \psi_A(1)\psi_B(2) + \psi_B(1)\psi_A(2) + \psi_B(1)\psi_B(2) \quad (2\text{-}61)$$

The first and last term represent a situation where both electrons are at atom A and atom B, respectively.

$$\overset{-}{A}\ \overset{+}{B} \qquad \overset{+}{A}\ \overset{-}{B}$$

The second and third term correspond to a situation where there is one electron in the field of both atom A and atom B.

$$\overset{\cdot}{A}—\overset{\cdot}{B}$$

We see how the wave function leads to an image resembling chemical structures. The former are ionic or heteropolar terms, the latter are homopolar terms.

It is natural to try to use (2-61) as our starting wave function. Then we have no molecular orbitals, the total wave function being a sum of terms which in turn are products of the atomic orbitals themselves. This function is the basic approximate wave function of the valence-bond method, also called the method of atomic orbitals.

The two methods are clearly equivalent technically. In practice, however, because of subsequent approximations made in both methods, they usually cease to be equivalent. They also represent two rather different languages to describe molecular phenomena. We will go into more detail in the next chapters.

The wave functions are ultimately built from atomic orbitals in both the molecular orbital and valence-bond methods. The development of quantum chemistry has shown, however, in recent years that better results are achieved when this approach is discarded. Molecular wave functions not based on atomic orbitals have been known for a long time. One is that of James and Coolidge [12] which enabled these authors to compute the dissociation energy of the H_2 molecule with high accuracy. Another wave function not based on atomic orbitals is the Hylleraas type function [13]. Many more have been devised recently. This subject will be treated in Chapter 13.

2-6 HYBRIDIZATION

As most of our examples in this book will be taken from among the organic molecules, we must have a look at the orbital arrangement which carbon atoms assume in molecules.

Each carbon atom has six electrons around its nucleus. They are distributed among the electronic shells in the following manner:

$$1s^2 2s^2 2p^2$$

that is to say, two electrons have orbitals with $n = 1$ and $l = 0$, two have orbitals with $n = 2$ and $l = 0$, and two have orbitals with $n = 2$ and $l = 1$. According to the Pauli exclusion principle no two electrons can have their four quantum numbers identical. (n, l, m_l and $m_s = \pm\frac{1}{2}$, the latter representing the projection of spin in a given field direction.) Therefore, the electrons in the $1s$ and $2s$ orbitals must have opposed spins. Those in the $2p$ orbital, however, may not be coupled, i.e. may have parallel spins because the magnetic quantum number may now have the values 1, −1, or 0. So we may put them

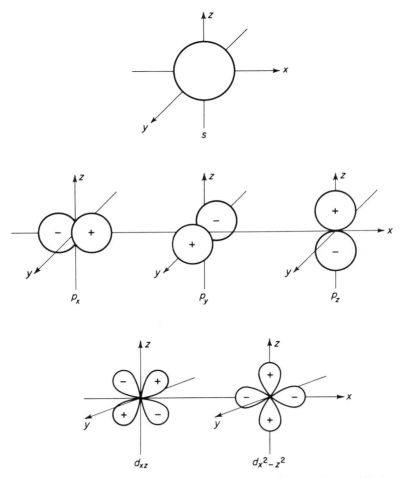

Fig. 2-1 Orbitals s, p, and d (approximate boundary surfaces. (C. A. Coulson, *Quarterly Reviews*. 1947. **1** : 144.) (Only two of the five d orbitals are shown.)

into either $2p_x$, $2p_y$, or $2p_z$ orbitals (Fig. 2-1). Only two covalent bonds could be formed in this way. However, the quadrivalence of carbon could be explained only by a configuration with four non-coupled electrons. We can "promote" an electron from $2s$ to $2p$ to obtain

$$C \quad 1s^2 2s 2p_x 2p_y 2p_z$$

Even so the four bonds would not be equivalent, $2s$ having a different shape and a different binding power than the $2p$'s. Pauling [14] proposed to form from the "pure" atomic orbitals "hybrid" atomic orbitals, which are linear combinations of the former.

Mathematically any such linear combination is a solution of the Schrödinger equation, although the corresponding energy would vary. There is, however, only one linear combination to give four hybrid orbitals that are equivalent except for their orientation in space. This is tetrahedral or sp^3 hybridization (Fig. 2-2). The carbon is in the center of a tetrahedron, the axes of the hybrids being at mutual angles of 109°28'. The typical example is methane, but all saturated hydrocarbons have this hybridization.

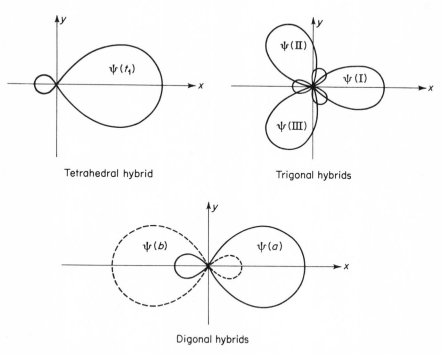

Tetrahedral hybrid

Trigonal hybrids

Digonal hybrids

Fig. 2-2 Tetrahedral, trigonal, and digonal hybrids. (Approximate boundary surfaces.) (C. A. Coulson, *Quarterly Reviews*. 1947. **1** : 144.)

There is one way of obtaining three equivalent hybrids plus one unhybridized $2p$ orbital. This is trigonal or sp^2 hybridization. In this case the three hybrid orbitals have their greatest amplitudes in a plane and their axes form angles of 120° between themselves. The fourth orbital has its axis perpendicular to the plane of the others, which is a nodal plane with respect to it. (See the $2p_z$ orbital on Fig. 2-1.) This is the hybridization of the doubly bonded carbon atoms in non-saturated and, in particular, conjugated and aromatic molecules. The three electrons that have their orbitals in the same plane are called σ electrons. The fourth one having the unhybridized orbital is the π electron (also called $2p_z$ or $2p_x$ electron according to the choice of axes). Naturally it would be more correct to say σ orbitals and π orbitals instead of σ or π "electrons," since all the electrons are alike and indistinguishable. In the abovementioned molecules the π electrons have a nodal plane where the others have their greatest amplitude; therefore, in first approximation, we might regard the π electrons as living a more or less independent life in the field constituted by the nuclei and the other electrons. (See, however, discussion in Chapter 13.) These π electrons are responsible for most of the specific properties of unsaturated compounds. We shall be dealing with π electrons in most of the examples considered in this book.

There is, as we have seen, one π electron per carbon atom, typical examples being ethylene and benzene.

As there is only one way of forming four or three equivalent hybrid orbitals from the atomic orbitals of carbon, there is only one way, too, of forming two equivalent hybrids leaving two orbitals unhybridized. This is the case of triple-bonded molecules like acetylene or cumulative double-bonded molecules like allene.[2] In digonal or sp hybridization only two orbitals are mixed, $2s$ and $2p_x$ (Fig. 2-2). There are now two π electrons for each carbon atom, $\pi_y = 2p_y$ and $\pi_z = 2p_z$, having their axes in planes perpendicular to each other and to the direction of the σ bond. The mutual angle between the two sp hybrids is now 180°, giving a linear arrangement.

In the case of carbon, the three kinds of hybridization can be symbolized as follows, the upper index representing the number of electrons:

$$sp^3: \quad C\ 1s^2 2s^2 2p_x^1 2p_y^1 2p_z^0 \rightarrow C\ 1s^2 te_1^1 te_2^1 te_3^1 te_4^1$$

$$sp^2: \quad C\ 1s^2 2s^2 2p_x^1 2p_y^1 2p_z^0 \rightarrow C\ 1s^2 tri_1^1 tri_2^1 tri_3^1 2p_z^1$$

$$sp: \quad C\ 1s^2 2s^2 2p_x^1 2p_y^1 2p_z^0 \rightarrow C\ 1s^2 di_1^1 di_2^1 2p_y^1 2p_z^1$$

In each case we used all the $2p$ orbitals although one of them

[2] More exactly the central carbon atom has digonal hybridization in allene, the two other carbons have trigonal hybridization.

was empty in the atom. This $2s \rightarrow 2p$ "promotion" (which of course is not a spectral transition) would require energy, but we recover this abundantly in the molecule where the pronounced directional properties of the hybrid orbitals lead to increased overlapping in the bonds.

In other cases this "promotion" is not necessary. In the case of nitrogen with one more electron we would have

sp^3: $N\ 1s^2 2s^2 2p_x^1 2p_y^1 2p_z^1 \rightarrow N\ 1s^2\ te_1^1 te_2^1 te_3^1 te_4^2$

sp^2: $N\ 1s^2 2s^2 2p_x^1 2p_y^1 2p_z^1 \rightarrow N\ 1s^2\ tri_1^1 tri_2^1 tri_3^2 2p_z^2$

    or $\rightarrow N\ 1s^2\ tri_1^1 tri_2^1 tri_3^2 2p_z^1$

sp: $N\ 1s^2 2s^2 2p_x^1 2p_y^1 2p_z^1 \rightarrow N\ 1s^2\ di_1^1 di_2^2 2p_y^1 2p_z^2$

    or $\rightarrow N\ 1s^2\ di_1^1 di_2^2 2p_y^1 2p_z^1$

The right procedure is to hybridize the orbitals and then place the available electrons into them, instead of first distributing the electrons into unhybridized orbitals and then hybridizing them.

In the case of nitrogen there will be a "lone pair" of electrons in a tetrahedral orbital (as in ammonia) in sp^3 hybridization. In the case of sp^2 hybridization the lone pair either is in a $2p_z$ orbital (as in aniline) or in a trigonal hybrid (as in pyridine).

In the case of oxygen we have eight electrons. The main possibilities would be the following:

sp^3: $O\ 1s^2 2s^2 2p_x^1 2p_y^1 2p_z^2 \rightarrow O\ 1s^2\ te_1^1 te_2^1 te_3^2 te_4^2$

sp^2: $O\ 1s^2 2s^2 2p_x^1 2p_y^1 2p_z^2 \rightarrow O\ 1s^2\ tri_1^1 tri_2^1 tri_3^2 2p_z^2$

sp: $O\ 1s^2 2s^2 2p_x^1 2p_y^1 2p_z^2 \rightarrow O\ 1s^2\ di_1^1 di_2^2 2p_y^2 2p_z^2$

Examples are the water molecule in ice and phenol for sp^3 and sp^2, respectively.

Two points deserve to be mentioned: First, hybridization always increases the angle ($180°$, $120°$, and $109°28'$ against $90°$ in the unhybridized carbon atom). This is the main reason why the HOH angle is not $90°$ in the water molecule but $104°30'$. Second, hybridization increases the number of valences only in the case of carbon, not in those of nitrogen and oxygen. This is due to the involvement of an originally empty orbital in the case of carbon.

The mathematical expressions for the hybrid orbitals are as follows ($s = \psi_{2s}$, etc.):

$$sp^3: \begin{cases} \psi_1 = \dfrac{1}{2}(s + p_x + p_y + p_z) \\[2mm] \psi_2 = \dfrac{1}{2}(s + p_x - p_y - p_z) \\[2mm] \psi_3 = \dfrac{1}{2}(s - p_x + p_y - p_z) \\[2mm] \psi_4 = \dfrac{1}{2}(s - p_x - p_y + p_z) \end{cases} \tag{2-62}$$

$$sp^2: \begin{cases} \psi_1 = \dfrac{1}{\sqrt{3}}(s + \sqrt{2}\, p_x) \\[2mm] \psi_2 = \dfrac{1}{\sqrt{3}}\left(s + \dfrac{\sqrt{2}}{2}p_x + \dfrac{\sqrt{6}}{2}p_y\right) \\[2mm] \psi_3 = \dfrac{1}{\sqrt{3}}\left(s - \dfrac{\sqrt{2}}{2}p_x - \dfrac{\sqrt{6}}{2}p_y\right) \end{cases} \tag{2-63}$$

$$sp: \begin{cases} \psi_1 = \dfrac{1}{\sqrt{2}}(s + p_x) \\[2mm] \psi_2 = \dfrac{1}{\sqrt{2}}(s - p_x) \end{cases} \tag{2-64}$$

with suitably chosen axes.

In all three sets the hybrid orbitals are normalized, mutually orthogonal, and equivalent but for their orientation in space. They are calculated by imposing these conditions. A particularly clear description of this subject is given in Kauzmann's *Quantum Chemistry* [8, pp. 410–415].

Hybridization is not really a fundamental concept in wave mechanics. It is only one way of modifying atomic orbitals to be used in molecular problems [11, Chap. 8].

3

The Method of Molecular Orbitals

In approximate wave-mechanical methods like the molecular orbital or valence-bond methods the molecular wave function may be built of pure or hybridized atomic orbitals.

A molecular orbital is a wave function depending on the coordinates of only one electron. In its LCAO form we associate with the motion of each electron a molecular orbital ϕ_j, expressed as a linear combination of atomic orbitals ψ_r which the electron would have if it were restricted to the field of atom r only.

$$\phi_j = c_{j1}\psi_1 + c_{j2}\psi_2 + c_{j3}\psi_3 + \cdots = \sum_r c_{jr}\psi_r \tag{3-1}$$

The index j stands for the MO; the second index $1, 2, \ldots, r$, for the AO belonging to the respective atom of the molecule.

With this wave function the Schrödinger equation becomes

$$H\phi_j = \sum_r c_{jr}H\psi_r{}' = E_j \sum_r c_{jr}\psi_r \tag{3-2}$$

We suppose that the AO are normalized; that is

$$\int \psi_r^* \psi_r d\tau = 1$$

The variational method gives the energy in the form of

$$E = \frac{\int \phi_j^* H \phi_j \, d\tau}{\int \phi_j^* \phi_j \, d\tau} \tag{3-3}$$

where the asterisk can be omitted if the ϕ_j are real. This energy will be certainly higher than the one corresponding to the unknown accurate wave function (see Chapter 2).

From (3-1) we obtain

$$E = \frac{\int \sum_r c_{jr}\psi_r H \sum_r c_{jr}\psi_r \, d\tau}{\int (\sum_r c_{jr}\psi_r)^2 \, d\tau} \tag{3-4}$$

We shall now minimize the energy with respect to the c_{jr}, i.e., choose the latter in such a way that the energy is the lowest possible with the given type of wave function.

For doing this we consider the energy as a function of the coefficients c_{jr}. This function will have a maximum or minimum if for all the coefficients simultaneously

$$\frac{\partial E}{\partial c_{jr}} = 0 \tag{3-5}$$

For the sake of simplicity let us first examine the case where there are only two (identical) atoms. Then

$$\phi = c_1\psi_1 + c_2\psi_2 \tag{3-6}$$

omitting the index j. The energy becomes

$$E = \frac{\int (c_1\psi_1 + c_2\psi_2) H(c_1\psi_1 + c_2\psi_2) \, d\tau}{\int (c_1\psi_1 + c_2\psi_2)^2 \, d\tau} \tag{3-7}$$

or

$$E = \frac{c_1^2 \int \psi_1 H\psi_1 \, d\tau + 2c_1c_2 \int \psi_1 H\psi_2 \, d\tau + c_2^2 \int \psi_2 H\psi_2 \, d\tau}{c_1^2 \int \psi_1^2 \, d\tau + 2c_1c_2 \int \psi_1\psi_2 \, d\tau + c_2^2 \int \psi_2^2 \, d\tau} \tag{3-8}$$

The integral $\int \psi_1 H\psi_1 \, d\tau$ is called a *Coulomb integral* because it represents the energy originating from the electrostatic forces between an electron and the core formed by the nuclei and the other electrons in their spheres that we do not want to consider explicitly since their orbitals are largely localized and they are not significantly affected by the formation of the bonds or the spectral transitions we are interested in. Since ψ_1 has large values in the neighborhood of atom 1 only it would be approximately the total energy of atom 1 if the two atoms were at infinite distance from each other. The integral $\int \psi_1 H\psi_2 \, d\tau$ is called *resonance integral;* it contains the wave functions of the electron on two atoms, and has no classical analogue. It would vanish if the two atoms were at infinite distance and may be considered as an approximate measure of the strength of the bond. $\int \psi_1\psi_2 \, d\tau$ is an overlap integral. The contribution to this integral of a given volume element is different from zero only if both ψ_1 and ψ_2 are different from zero in that volume element, that is, where the two wave functions overlap. The overlap integral is usually roughly proportional to the resonance integral. It can be expected, therefore, that the bond strength will be proportional to the overlap integral (criterion of maximum overlapping) [15, 16, 17].

The following standard notations will be adopted.

$$\alpha_r \equiv H_{rr} \equiv \int \psi_r^* H \psi_r \, d\tau, \qquad \text{Coulomb integral}$$

$$\beta_{rs} \equiv H_{rs} \equiv \int \psi_r^* H \psi_s \, d\tau, \qquad \text{resonance integral}$$

$$S_{rs} \equiv \int \psi_r^* \psi_s \, d\tau, \qquad \text{overlap integral}$$

$$S_{rr} \equiv \int \psi_r^* \psi_r \, d\tau = 1$$

since the atomic orbitals are normalized.

We then have

$$E = \frac{c_1^2 H_{11} + 2c_1 c_2 H_{12} + c_2^2 H_{22}}{c_1^2 S_{11} + 2c_1 c_2 S_{12} + c_2^2 S_{22}} \tag{3-9}$$

This expression has to be partially differentiated with respect to c_1 and c_2 and the two equations obtained equated simultaneously to 0. As both the numerator and the denominator depend on the coefficients,

$$\frac{\partial E}{\partial c_1} = [(c_1 H_{11} + c_2 H_{12})(c_1^2 S_{11} + 2c_1 c_2 S_{12} + c_2^2 S_{22})$$

$$- (c_1^2 H_{11} + 2c_1 c_2 H_{12} + c_2^2 H_{22})(c_1 S_{11} + c_2 S_{12})]$$

$$\times \frac{1}{(c_1^2 S_{11} + 2c_1 c_2 S_{12} + c_2^2 S_{22})^2} \tag{3-10}$$

where we have divided by 2 everywhere. Omitting the denominator and dividing both members by $(c_1^2 S_{11} + 2c_1 c_2 S_{12} + c_2^2 S_{22})$ we obtain

$$(c_1 H_{11} + c_2 H_{12}) - E(c_1 S_{11} + c_2 S_{12}) = 0 \tag{3-11}$$

taking account of the expression (3-9) of E. After rearrangement this gives

$$c_1(H_{11} - ES_{11}) + c_2(H_{12} - ES_{12}) = 0 \tag{3-12}$$

By a similar procedure applied to $\dfrac{\partial E}{\partial c_2}$ we obtain

$$c_1(H_{12} - ES_{12}) + c_2(H_{22} - ES_{22}) = 0 \tag{3-13}$$

In general there will be as many equations as coefficients. In the case of conjugated hydrocarbons and their derivatives where we consider the π electrons as a separate system, there is one π orbital on each carbon (also, in some cases, for nitrogen or oxygen atoms, etc.), hence, there are as many equations as atoms having a π orbital. In general, then, we can write

$$c_r(H_{rr} - ES_{rr}) + \sum_s{}'(H_{rs} - ES_{rs})c_s = 0 \qquad (3\text{-}14)$$

Here the j index is omitted and the prime on the summation sign means that the term for which $r = s$ is not included in the sum. (It is in the first parenthesis, naturally.)

3-2. THE HÜCKEL APPROXIMATION. THE EXAMPLE OF BUTADIENE

In the most simple approximation, first used by Hückel [18] and used widely thereafter, we suppose that all the resonance integrals, β, between adjacent atoms are equal and that the others are zero. We also suppose that all the overlap integrals, S_{rs}, are zero, even those between adjacent atoms. This is obviously not true, and it will be shown later how the overlap integrals are reintroduced (p. 186). However, the S_{rs} are usually much smaller than the β_{rs}.[1]

In this approximation, taking the Coulomb integrals the same for identical atoms (irrespective of their environment in the molecule) we can write

$$(\alpha - E)c_r + \sum_s{}' \beta c_s = 0 \qquad (3\text{-}15)$$

This is a system of linear, homogeneous equations. In order to obtain the coefficients we have to set their determinant equal to zero:

$$|(\alpha - E) + \sum_s{}' \beta| = 0 \qquad (3\text{-}16)$$

This is possible only for certain E values, which are the roots of the determinant, and at the same time the energies of an electron in the respective molecular orbitals. Once we have obtained the E values we can put them back one by one into the system of the above linear and homogeneous equations (called the "secular" equation because of the occurrence of a similar equation in an astronomic problem, that of the secular motion) and compute the c_r corresponding to each one.

We are going to work out completely the example of 1, 3 butadiene with four π electrons.

$$\begin{array}{cccc} 1 & 2 & 3 & 4 \\ \text{C} & \text{C} & \text{C} & \text{C} \end{array}$$

C—C—C—C

---

[1] Hückel's name became closely associated with these approximations; however, his contribution to molecular orbital theory has been much greater. [See his review, *Z. Elektrochem.* **43**, 775 (1937) or, for his appraisal of newer developments, *Z. Elektrochem.*, **61**, 866 (1957).]

In the Hückel approximation the secular determinant (3–16) has the following form:

$$\begin{vmatrix} \alpha - E & \beta & 0 & 0 \\ \beta & \alpha - E & \beta & 0 \\ 0 & \beta & \alpha - E & \beta \\ 0 & 0 & \beta & \alpha - E \end{vmatrix} = 0$$

There are as many rows and columns as carbon atoms. Let us divide everywhere by β and introduce

$$\frac{\alpha - E}{\beta} = y \qquad (3\text{--}18)$$

Then

$$\begin{vmatrix} y & 1 & 0 & 0 \\ 1 & y & 1 & 0 \\ 0 & 1 & y & 1 \\ 0 & 0 & 1 & y \end{vmatrix} = 0 \qquad (3\text{--}19)$$

We have to compute the four roots of the determinant. This can be done in various ways; one of the simplest is to take the corresponding set of equations and eliminate the coefficients successively.

$$0 = c_1 y + c_2$$
$$0 = c_2 y + c_1 + c_3$$
$$0 = c_3 y + c_2 + c_4 \qquad (3\text{--}20)$$
$$0 = c_4 y + c_3$$

First we divide everywhere by one of the coefficients, say c_1. (But it may turn out to be zero, in which case another coefficient has to be chosen.)

$$0 = y + \frac{c_2}{c_1}$$

$$0 = \frac{c_2}{c_1} y + 1 + \frac{c_3}{c_1}$$

$$0 = \frac{c_3}{c_1} y + \frac{c_2}{c_1} + \frac{c_4}{c_1} \qquad (3\text{--}21)$$

$$0 = \frac{c_4}{c_1} y + \frac{c_3}{c_1}$$

From the first equation

$$\frac{c_2}{c_1} = -y \qquad (3\text{--}22)$$

If we substitute this into the second equation we obtain

$$0 = -y^2 + 1 + \frac{c_3}{c_1}$$

hence

$$\frac{c_3}{c_1} = y^2 - 1 \tag{3-23}$$

Substituting both (3-22) and (3-23) into the third equation gives

$$0 = y^3 - y - y + \frac{c_4}{c_1}$$

and

$$\frac{c_4}{c_1} = -y^3 + 2y \tag{3-24}$$

From the last equation we then have

$$0 = -y^4 + 2y^2 + y^2 - 1$$

or

$$0 = y^4 - 3y^2 + 1 \tag{3-25}$$

The roots of this equation are ± 1.618 and ± 0.618. In the general case we can obtain them, for example, by Horner's method (given at the end of this chapter), but often much simpler ways can be found [19]. The roots are all real because of the hermiticity of the matrix corresponding to the determinant.

From $\frac{(\alpha - E)}{\beta} = y$, the energies of the molecular orbitals are

   ——————————— $-1.618\beta + \alpha$
   ——————————— $-0.618\beta + \alpha$
   ——×——×—— $+0.618\beta + \alpha$
   ——×——×—— $+1.618\beta + \alpha$

In the ground state there will be two electrons in each of the orbitals of lowest energy but they must have opposite spin projections according to the Pauli principle.

It is important to remember that β (and α) are negative quantities. Therefore, the most negative roots (y) of the secular equation belong to the orbitals of lowest energy. These correspond to the most positive E values but in terms of the negative quantities α and β.

The total energy of the π electrons in the ground state is the sum of the energies of the individual electrons.

$$E = 2(1.618 + 0.618)\beta + 4\alpha = 4.472\beta + 4\alpha$$

The corresponding total wave function is

$$\Psi = \phi_1(1)\,\phi_1(2)\,\phi_2(3)\,\phi_2(4)$$

if we disregard the fact that any other permutation of the electrons is acceptable.

At this point we can see clearly the nature of the most important approximation involved with this form of the molecular orbital method. The energies of the individual π electrons are computed as being in the field of the nuclei and the other electrons of the cores (see p. 263) and then simply added together as if the π electrons would not influence each other. In this way we neglect mutual Coulomb repulsion between the π electrons. This is the price for writing the total energy as a sum of the energies of the individual electrons with no "cross terms," that is, terms depending on the mutual interaction of the electrons, and for writing the total wave function as a product of the individual molecular orbitals. One may think of the π-electronic interaction energy as being, in first approximation, included in the core energy, which does not directly enter the calculation, and one may then try to compensate for the error by a suitable choice of parameters α and β. This is why α and β are not usually computed but are based on experimental data, usually thermochemical or spectral data (see Sec. 9-2). The method, therefore, is "empirical."

We can proceed now to calculate the coefficients c_r. To do so we have to put back the values of y one by one into the secular equation (3-21). Let us take, for example, the root corresponding to the lowest energy, $y_1 = -1.618$. The secular equation then becomes

$$0 = -1.618 + \frac{c_2}{c_1}$$

$$0 = -1.618\frac{c_2}{c_1} + 1 + \frac{c_3}{c_1}$$

$$0 = -1.618\frac{c_3}{c_1} + \frac{c_2}{c_1} + \frac{c_4}{c_1}$$

$$0 = -1.618\frac{c_4}{c_1} + \frac{c_3}{c_1}$$

where we again divided all the terms by c_1.

The first equation gives

$$\frac{c_2}{c_1} = 1.618$$

Substituting this into the second equation we obtain

$$0 = -2.618 + 1 + \frac{c_3}{c_1} \quad \text{and} \quad \frac{c_3}{c_1} = 1.618$$

The third equation gives

$$0 = -2.618 + 1.618 + \frac{c_4}{c_1} \quad \text{and} \quad \frac{c_4}{c_1} = 1$$

The last equation gives only

$$0 = -1.618 + 1.618 = 0$$

and can serve as a check to the whole calculation, as it has to give an equality.

Thus we have obtained the ratios of the coefficients but not the coefficients themselves. This was expected, as the secular equation was homogeneous.

We are, however, able to obtain the coefficients themselves, thanks to the condition of normalization, which we now have to apply.

$$\int \phi_j^2 \, d\tau = \int (c_1\psi_1 + c_2\psi_2 + c_3\psi_3 + c_4\psi_4)^2 \, d\tau$$

$$= c_1^2 \int \psi_1^2 \, d\tau + c_2^2 \int \psi_2^2 \, d\tau + c_3^2 \int \psi_3^2 \, d\tau + c_4^2 \int \psi_4^2 \, d\tau$$

$$+ 2c_1c_2 \int \psi_1\psi_2 \, d\tau + 2c_1c_3 \int \psi_1\psi_3 \, d\tau + 2c_1c_4 \int \psi_1\psi_4 \, d\tau$$

$$+ 2c_2c_3 \int \psi_2\psi_3 \, d\tau + 2c_2c_4 \int \psi_2\psi_4 \, d\tau + 2c_3c_4 \int \psi_3\psi_4 \, d\tau = 1$$

$$(3\text{-}26)$$

Since we neglected all overlap integrals, all but the four first terms are zero. Since, furthermore, the atomic orbitals are supposed to be normalized we have simply

$$c_1^2 + c_2^2 + c_3^2 + c_4^2 = 1 \qquad (3\text{-}27)$$

or, dividing by c_1^2,

$$1 + \left(\frac{c_2}{c_1}\right)^2 + \left(\frac{c_3}{c_1}\right)^2 + \left(\frac{c_4}{c_1}\right)^2 = \frac{1}{c_1^2}$$

In our example:

$$1 + (1.618)^2 + (1.618)^2 + 1 = 7.236 = \frac{1}{c_1^2}$$

Hence $\qquad c_1^2 = 0.1382$

$$c_2^2 = \left(\frac{c_2}{c_1}\right)^2 c_1^2 = 2.618\cdot0.1382 = 0.3618$$

$$c_3^2 = 0.3618$$

$$c_4^2 = 0.1382 \quad \text{and} \quad 2(0.1382 + 0.3618) = 1$$

as required. Computing the square roots we obtain that

$$c_1 = c_4 = 0.3717, \qquad c_2 = c_3 = 0.6015$$

Only for the orbital of lowest energy do we obtain all coefficients positive [20]. For the rest, we have to choose the sign of one of them arbitrarily, and then the signs of the others are determined by those of the ratios.

For $y_2 = -0.618$ we obtain similarly:

$$c_1^2 = c_4^2 = 0.3618; \quad c_1 = 0.6015, \quad c_2 = 0.3717$$

$$c_2^2 = c_3^2 = 0.1382; \quad c_3 = -0.3717, \quad c_4 = -0.6015 \qquad (3\text{-}28)$$

The related wave functions (molecular orbitals) are

$$\phi_1 = 0.3717\psi_1 + 0.6015\psi_2 + 0.6015\psi_3 + 0.3717\psi_4$$

$$\phi_2 = 0.6015\psi_1 + 0.3717\psi_2 - 0.3717\psi_3 - 0.6015\psi_4$$

The two other MO's ϕ_3 and ϕ_4 which belong to $y_3 = 0.618$ and $y_4 = 1.618$ contain electrons in the excited states only. These will be discussed in Sec. 8-1.

3-3. ELECTRONIC CHARGE DENSITIES AND BOND ORDERS

Coulson and Coulson and Longuet-Higgins [21] have shown how the distribution of the π electrons in a molecule can be characterized with the help of the coefficients c_r. We are going to discuss briefly those of their definitions which we shall need later. (See already Wheland and Pauling [123].)

The π-electronic charge density around atom r is defined as

$$q_r = \sum c_r^2 \qquad (3\text{-}29)$$

where the summation is over all molecular orbitals occupied by electrons, and the orbitals which contain two electrons (as in the ground state of butadiene) have to be counted twice. We might also say that the summation is extended over all molecular spin orbitals containing electrons, the molecular spin orbital being a molecular orbital with a given spin projection.

It can be seen immediately that in the case of butadiene all charge densities are equal to unity.

$$\begin{array}{cccc} 1 & 1 & 1 & 1 \\ C & - C & - C & - C \end{array}$$

This is the case of all conjugated hydrocarbons unless they contain and odd-numbered ring [20]. In the latter case or if the molecule contains hetroatoms the charges will be different from unity.

The electronic charge density may, to a certain extent, characterize the behavior of the different atoms of a molecule toward electrophilic or nucleophilic reagents. (See remark at the end of the chapter.) It is logical to think that an electrophilic reagent will by preference attack sites where the probability of finding an electron is greater, that is to say where the net charge is relatively the most negative, and a nucleophilic reagent sites where it is relatively the most positive.

The bond order of a bond between atoms r and s was defined by Coulson as

$$p_{rs} = \sum c_r c_s \qquad (3\text{-}30)$$

where the summation is again extended to all occupied spin orbitals.

q_r and p_{rs} have well-defined energetical meanings in the frame of the Hückel approximation. The energy of an electron in orbital ϕ_1 is equal to

$$E_1 = \int \phi_1 H \phi_1 \, d\tau$$

Introducing the expression of ϕ_1 with the normalized coefficients

$$E_1 = \int (c_1\psi_1 + c_2\psi_2 + c_3\psi_3 + c_4\psi_4)H(c_1\psi_1 + c_2\psi_2 + c_3\psi_3 + c_4\psi_4)d\tau$$

$$= c_1^2 \int \psi_1 H \psi_1 \, d\tau + c_2^2 \int \psi_2 H \psi_2 \, d\tau + c_3^2 \int \psi_3 H \psi_3 \, d\tau$$

$$+ c_4^2 \int \psi_4 H \psi_4 \, d\tau + 2c_1 c_2 \int \psi_1 H \psi_2 \, d\tau + 2c_2 c_3 \int \psi_2 H \psi_3 \, d\tau$$

$$+ 2c_3 c_4 \int \psi_3 H \psi_4 \, d\tau$$

neglecting interactions between nonneighbors. With our previous notation the energy becomes, for one π electron,

$$E_1 = (c_1^2 + c_2^2 + c_3^2 + c_4^2)\alpha + (2c_1 c_2 + 2c_2 c_3 + 2c_3 c_4)\beta \quad (3\text{-}31)$$

Thus we see that, for example, c_1^2 is a measure of the contribution to the total Coulomb energy of the molecule of atom 1 from an electron in orbital ϕ_1. Hence, q_1 is a measure of the total contribution to the total Coulomb energy of atom 1 because c_1^2 then was summed over all occupied molecular spin orbitals. On the other hand p_{rs} is a measure of the contribution of bond r-s to the total bonding energy of the molecule. There are good semiempirical relations between bond orders, bond lengths, and bond energies [22].

Let us now, for a given atom, find the sum of the bond orders of all the bonds having one end at this atom. It can be shown that the highest value this sum can reach in conjugated hydrocarbons is $\sqrt{3} = 1.732$ [23].

Coulson [21] defined as the free valence number of atom r the quantity

$$F_r = 1.732 - \sum p_{rs} \quad (3\text{-}32)$$

which varies like the fraction of noncoupled electrons around an atom. (For a long time 1.68 was used instead of 1.732. The reader should take this fact into account when examining free valences to be found in the literature.) The free valence number should be particularly important for radical reactions, but it has a certain role to play in other types of reactions as well.

Here is the diagram of the bond orders and free valence numbers of butadiene, which was first published by Coulson and Longuet-Higgins [24].

$$0.84 \quad 0.39 \quad 0.39 \quad 0.84$$
$$C - C - C - C$$
$$0.894 \quad 0.447 \quad 0.894$$

The π bond order would be zero in a saturated compound and unity for an insulated double bond as in ethylene.

The above defined quantities are often useful in interpreting (or even predicting) the course of a chemical reaction. They have to be used, however, with great caution. According to present-day reaction-rate theories,[2] rate constants are essentially determined by free energies of activation or, in other words, entropies of activation and enthalpies of activation,

$$k = \frac{\bar{k}T}{h} e^{-\Delta F/RT} = \frac{\bar{k}T}{h} e^{(\Delta S/R)-(\Delta H/RT)} \tag{3-33}$$

the latter being practically the same as the activation energy in the Arrhenius theory. In (3-33) $\bar{k}$ is the Boltzmann constant, R the gas constant, h the Planck constant, and T is the absolute temperature. For determining these quantities we need knowledge not only of the reactants but also of the activated complex. Now charges and bond orders refer to the initial products of a reaction. The evolution of charges during a reaction may be approximately characterized by Coulson and Longuet-Higgins' self-polarizabilities [21, 25], and Wheland [26] gave an approximate method to compute activation energies in the case of substitution reactions on conjugated compounds. Yvan has shown [27] that in the frame of the Hückel method there is an analytical relationship between free valences and Wheland's activation energies. These concepts are useful when we study relations between spectra and chemical reactivity.

3-4. A SIMPLE USE OF SYMMETRY

Let us return to the case of butadiene. In order to give a general example of how energies and wave functions can be obtained in the LCAO MO method we did not exploit all the possibilities of simplification in this particular case.

The Hamiltonian (and in particular the potential function contained in it) must have the symmetry of the molecule. There is no reason, for example, why the forces between atoms 1 and 2 should be different from those between 3 and 4. The square of a molecular wave function must have the same symmetry, since it represents the distribution of the electronic charge density, which is conditioned

[2] See, for example, K. J. Laidler, *Chemical Kinetics* (New York: McGraw-Hill Book Company, Inc., 1950).

by the potential function. The wave functions themselves may still have the same sign or opposite sign in volume elements having equivalent location from the point of view of symmetry.[3] We can say, more generally, that every molecular wave function has to belong to one of the irreducible representations of the group of symmetry to which a given molecule belongs. This introduces group theory into the study of molecular structure and of molecular spectra. We will deal with this problem later in some detail (Chapters 7, 8, and 9). At present we shall follow a somewhat more intuitive argument.

In the simple case of cis-butadiene it is sufficient to take into account the fact that the molecule possesses a plane of symmetry vertical to the plane of the molecule (which is also a plane of symmetry) bisecting the bond between atoms 2 and 3 (Fig. 3-1).

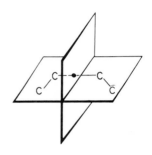

Fig. 3-1

The molecular orbitals have to be symmetrical or antisymmetrical (i.e., they have to keep or change their sign) with respect to a reflection in this plane, which exchanges atoms 1 and 4 and 2 and 3. Thus

$$c_1 = c_4 \quad \text{and} \quad c_2 = c_3$$

or

$$c_1 = -c_4 \quad \text{and} \quad c_2 = -c_3$$

If we introduce these conditions into the secular equation (3-20) we immediately obtain two systems of only two equations.

Symmetrical	*Antisymmetrical*
$0 = c_1 y + c_2$	$0 = c_1 y + c_2$
$0 = c_2 y + c_1 + c_2$	$0 = c_2 y + c_1 - c_2$
$y_1 = -1.618$	$y_2 = -0.168$
$y_3 = 0.618$	$y_4 = 1.618$

For the ground state we take the two negative roots and compute the coefficients from the system to which the root belongs. The condition of normalization becomes:

$$2c_1^2 + 2c_2^2 = 1$$

Naturally, the results are the same as obtained before.

A great number of molecules were treated by means of the LCAO MO method. A good reference is Pullman's book [28]. A dictionary of molecular diagrams (charges, bond orders, etc.) was published

---

[3] For degenerate wave functions see chapter 7.

under the joint direction of Coulson and Daudel [29].

Naturally, all approximations made in the Hückel method are not inherent to the molecular orbital method. For example, the resonance integrals β vary from one bond to the other according to the bond length, and we might well use several different β in the secular equation. We might also take into account the β between nonadjacent atoms. All this increases the complexity of the calculations.

The overlap integrals have a value of about 0.26 between adjacent π electron orbitals and are far from being negligible. However, Wheland [30] and Coulson and Chirgwin [31] have shown that in the case of nonsubstituted hydrocarbons the ratios of the coefficients do not change because of their omission and that the energies can be modified by means of a simple formula to give the values which would have been obtained if the overlap integrals had been taken into account.

We shall return to these refinements and others as we shall need them in discussing spectra of individual molecules.

We have to remember too in treating π-electron problems that the carbon atoms have trigonal hybridization and that the coplanarity of the molecule (or near-coplanarity) is a prerequisite for the treatment described above.

3-5. COMPLEMENTS

Electrophilic, nucleophilic, and radical reagents. Electrophilic reagents are positive ions or dipoles whose reacting part is positive. Such reagents would by preference attack negatively charged parts of the molecules. Example: nitration ($\overset{+}{N}O_2$).

Nucleophilic reagents are negative ions or dipoles whose reacting part is negative. Such reactants would by preference attack positively charged parts of the molecules. Example: amination by NH_2Na.

Radical reagents have no net charges but they have an electron with an uncoupled spin. Such reagents will look for other uncoupled electrons. Example: $C_6H_5 - N = N - Cl$ in diazotation.

Electronegativity. This is a quantity measuring the electron-attracting power of an atom in a molecule. Pauling [32] established a scale of electronegativities for the whole periodic system. Improved values were given by Haïssinsky [33] and by Daudel and Bellugue [34].

According to Mulliken the arithmetical mean of the first ionization potential and of the electroaffinity is a measure of electronegativity.

For a thorough discussion of this quantity the reader may consult one of Mulliken's papers [35].

Resonance energy. Resonance energies or conjugation energies can be easily determined in the semiempirical molecular orbital method. All we have to do is to put $\beta = 0$ for the bonds that are single in the classical chemical structure. This cuts interaction between the different π bonds.

In the case of butadiene, putting $\beta_{23} = 0$ simply yields two ethylenes from the π-electronic point of view. Then the resonance energy of butadiene is the difference in total energy of butadiene and of two ethylenes.

$$E_{res} = (4.472\beta + 4\alpha) - 2(2\beta + 2\alpha)$$
$$= 0.472\beta$$

(see p. 80 for the determination of this quantity in the valence-bond method).

Horner's method for computing the roots of a secular equation (example of butadiene).

We write the coefficients of y^n, y^{n-1}, ... in this order on the upper horizontal line of the following table. We have to write zero for the missing powers.

	1	0	-3	0	1
-1	1	-1	-2	2	-1
-2	1	-2	1	-2	5
-1.5	1	-1.5	-0.75	1.125	-0.6875
-1.6	1	-1.6	-0.44	0.704	-0.1264
-1.7	1	-1.7	-0.11	0.187	0.6821
-1.62	1	-1.62	-0.3756	0.608472	0.0143
...	...	...	...	...	...

The value of the function $f(y) = y^4 - 3y^2 + 1$ (3-25) is obtained for a given value of y, for example $y = -1$ (first column), by multiplying it by the coefficient of y^4, adding the product to the coefficient of y^3, then multiplying the result by -1, adding it to the coefficient of y^2, and so forth. The value of $f(y)$ is in the last column under the coefficient of y^0. Then we try $y = -2$. We see that $f(y)$ changes sign between $y = -1$ and $y = -2$. So we try intermediate values, in order to find the y for which $f(y) = 0$. At the last stage we interpolate between two close lying values of y to obtain the root with the desired precision. We proceed similarly for the other roots.

3-6. REFERENCES TO SOME FUNDAMENTAL WORKS ON THE MOLECULAR ORBITAL METHOD

The molecular orbital method has received important contributions from several authors: Bloch, Lennard-Jones, Mulliken, Hückel, Hund, Coulson, and others. The greatest contributor, Mulliken, has been improving and developing this method for three decades. Here are a few references to their early publications:

F. Bloch, *Z. Physik*, **52**, 555 (1928).

F. Hund, *Z. Physik*, **51**, 759 (1928).

J. E. Lennard-Jones, *Trans. Faraday Soc.* **25**, 668 (1929).

E. Hückel, *Z. Physik*, **60**, 423 (1930); **70**, 204 (1931).

R. S. Mulliken, *Phys. Rev.*, **32**, 186 (1928); **41**, 49 (1932); **43**, 279 (1933); *J. Chem. Phys.*, **3**, 375 (1935).

C. A. Coulson, *Trans. Faraday Soc.*, **33**, 1479 (1937); *Proc. Cambridge Phil. Soc.*, **34**, 204 (1938).

A rather more complete list of references is found in Streitwieser's *Molecular Orbital Theory for Organic Chemists* (New York: John Wiley & Sons, Inc., 1961), pp. 22 and 36.

For an excellent early review comparing the molecular orbital and valence-bond methods see J. H. Van Vleck and A. Sherman, *Rev. Mod. Phys.*, **7**, 168–228 (1935).

4

The Valence-Bond Method

4-1. INTRODUCTORY REMARKS

Another way of building approximate molecular wave functions is used in the valence-bond method. This method, which is also called the method of atomic orbitals, or of electron pairs, or of mesomerism (mainly in the literature of French language), was initiated by Heitler and London, who were the first to treat the problem of the hydrogen molecule by a quantum-mechanical method. The year in which their paper appeared, 1927, is often considered as the date of birth of quantum chemistry [36].

The popularity of the valence-bond method is, at present, at a low ebb as a consequence of some justified criticism against its usual form. Therefore, the length at which it is dealt with in this book may appear excessive. It is the author's opinion, however, that

1. this method is useful as an introduction to general quantum chemical thinking;
2. the valence-bond method is bound to have a new upsurge when certain refinements have been introduced into it. This is very desirable, as resonance theory which is widely used by chemists is really a qualitative extension of the valence-bond method. However, naturally, the reader, if he wishes, may skip this chapter altogether.

As we have already seen (Chapter 2) the wave function in this method is built from atomic orbitals just as in the molecular orbital method, but with the important difference that the total wave function belonging to the various individual energy levels of the molecule is now constructed directly as a product of the atomic wave functions which an electron would have in the field of one nucleus and its core only, while in the molecular orbital method the atomic orbitals were first used to form a linear combination to give a molecular orbital for each electron and then the total wave function was taken as a product of these molecular orbitals.

The following treatment applies either to the hydrogen molecule or to the ethylene molecule in the π-electron approximation. Only the actual form of the atomic orbitals would be different.

Let us take $\psi_a(1)$ and $\psi_b(2)$ as the atomic orbitals presumed to be at infinite distance from, and thus unperturbed by, each other. The numbers 1 and 2 in parentheses represent, as before, the three space coordinates of electrons 1 and 2, respectively.

Until now we have not taken into account the spin of the electrons. In the empirical form of the molecular orbital method which we presented in the preceding chapter this was done rather unsatisfactorily, by placing the electrons into orbitals two by two after all the calculation was done. This situation will be corrected in the method of antisymmetrized molecular orbitals (Chapter 10). In the valence-bond method spin has to be introduced right from the beginning.

An electron may have two spin projections

$$+\frac{1}{2}\frac{h}{2\pi}(\text{spin } \alpha) \quad \text{or} \quad -\frac{1}{2}\frac{h}{2\pi}(\text{spin } \beta)$$

The corresponding spin functions are given in matrix form as

$$\left|\begin{matrix}1\\0\end{matrix}\right| \quad \text{and} \quad \left|\begin{matrix}0\\1\end{matrix}\right|$$

respectively, and are normalized and orthogonal to each other (see for example [37, p. 138].) They are sometimes called *spin coordinates*.

Every wave function should be multiplied by a spin function and any atomic or molecular system must satisfy the Pauli principle, which in wave-mechanical language postulates that [38] the total spin-orbital wave function of a system must be antisymmetric (change sign) with respect to the exchange of the coordinates (space and spin) of two of its electrons. This is related to the tendency of electrons of like spin to avoid each other. The probability of finding two electrons having the same spin projection in the same volume

element is zero (see p. 263). Pauli's principle seems to be a fundamental law of nature and it has a profound influence on electronic
distribution in atoms and molecules.

4-2. EXAMPLE OF A TWO-ELECTRON SYSTEM

Our first example is a system of two electrons. The wave function
in the valence-bond approximation would have, for the ith state of
energy and excluding spin, the form

$$\Psi_i = \psi_a(1)\,\psi_b(2)$$

where the atomic wave functions are taken as normalized.

Since, however, the electrons cannot be distinguished,

$$\Psi_i = \psi_a(2)\,\psi_b(1)$$

is an equally good wave function, and we have to choose the more
general function

$$\Psi_i = N[\psi_a(1)\,\psi_b(2) \pm \psi_a(2)\,\psi_b(1)] \tag{4-1}$$

where N is a normalizing factor. If the $(+)$ sign holds, this latter
function is symmetrical (does not change sign) if we exchange the
coordinates of the electrons—here symbolized by (1) and (2)—while
it is antisymmetric (it does change sign) if the $(-)$ sign holds. In
fact, we would obtain in the latter case

$$N[\psi_a(1)\psi_b(2) - \psi_a(2)\psi_b(1)] \rightarrow N[\psi_a(2)\psi_b(1) - \psi_a(1)\psi_b(2)]$$
$$= -N[\psi_a(1)\psi_b(2) - \psi_a(2)\psi_b(1)]$$

Pauli's principle, however, does not apply to *this* wave function
but to the complete, spin-orbital wave function.

The following spin functions can be written for the case of two
electrons:

$$\alpha(1)\alpha(2), \qquad \beta(1)\beta(2)$$
$$N'[\alpha(1)\beta(2) + \alpha(2)\beta(1)]$$
$$N'[\alpha(1)\beta(2) - \alpha(2)\beta(1)]$$

$\alpha(1)$ means that the electron having space coordinates x_1, y_1, z_1,
has spin projection α, and so on.

The first three spin functions are obviously symmetrical with
respect to the exchange of the coordinates of the two electrons, while
the fourth one is antisymmetrical. If we want the complete, spin-
orbital wave function to be antisymmetrical we have to multiply the
space function that has the $(+)$ sign between the two members by
the spin function having the $(-)$ sign, or the space function having

the $(-)$ sign by one of the three other spin functions. In the former case the wave function will describe a singlet state, in the latter case a triplet state. The energy difference between the three components of the triplet is very small, at least for light atoms. Writing the spin-orbital wave function as a simple product of a space and a spin function amounts to neglecting the interaction between the magnetic moments due to the orbital motion and spin or to giving all three components of the triplet the same energy. The total spin projection is, of course, $S = 0$ for singlet states, and $S = 1$ for triplet states.

We are now going to compute the energy corresponding to the singlet state in our example.

First we compute the normalization factor for the wave function depending only on the space coordinates.

$$\begin{aligned}
\int \Psi_i^2 d\tau &= N^2 \int [\psi_a(1)\psi_b(2) + \psi_a(2)\psi_b(1)]^2 \, d\tau \\
&= N^2 \Big[\int \psi_a^2(1)\psi_b^2(2)\,d\tau + \int \psi_a^2(2)\psi_b^2(1)\,d\tau \\
&\quad + 2\int \psi_a(1)\psi_b(2)\psi_a(2)\psi_b(1)\,d\tau \Big] \\
&= N^2[2 + 2S^2] = 1
\end{aligned} \tag{4-2}$$

Here $d\tau$ is really $d\tau = d\tau_1 d\tau_2$ and we have to integrate over all three coordinates of electron 1 $(d\tau_1)$ and electron $2(d\tau_2)$. This gives unity in each case since the atomic wave functions are normalized. The last integral is the square of the overlap integral.

Therefore,

$$N = \frac{1}{\sqrt{2 + 2S^2}}$$

or simply $1/\sqrt{2}$, if the overlap integral is neglected as it often is in this method. The normalization factor of the appropriate spin function is

$$\begin{aligned}
N'^2 &\int [\alpha(1)\beta(2) - \alpha(2)\beta(1)]^2 ds_1 ds_2 \\
&= N'^2 \Big[\int \alpha^2(1)\beta^2(2)\,ds_1 ds_2 + \int \alpha^2(2)\beta^2(1)\,ds_1 ds_2 \\
&\quad - 2\int \alpha(1)\beta(2)\alpha(2)\beta(1)\,ds_1 ds_2 \Big] \\
&= 2N'^2 = 1
\end{aligned} \tag{4-3}$$

hence
$$N' = \frac{1}{\sqrt{2}}$$

Here the two first integrals are equal to unity because the spin functions are normalized, and the third one is zero because they are mutually orthogonal.

Finally the wave function takes the following form (neglecting overlap):

$$X_S = \tfrac{1}{2}[\psi_a(1)\psi_b(2) + \psi_a(2)\psi_b(1))(\alpha(1)\beta(2) - \alpha(2)\beta(1)]$$

$$= \tfrac{1}{2}[\psi_a(1)\alpha(1)\psi_b(2)\beta(2) + \psi_a(2)\beta(2)\psi_b(1)\alpha(1)$$

$$- \psi_a(1)\beta(1)\psi_b(2)\alpha(2) - \psi_a(2)\alpha(2)\psi_b(1)\beta(1)] \quad (4\text{-}4)$$

$$= \tfrac{1}{2}[\psi_a(1)\overline{\psi_b(2)} + \overline{\psi_a(2)}\psi_b(1)$$

$$- \overline{\psi_a(1)}\psi_b(2) - \psi_a(2)\overline{\psi_b(1)}]$$

The last notation is very useful. The bar over the function means spin β, no bar means spin α.

The energy can now be calculated from

$$E_S = \frac{\int X_S H X_S d\tau}{\int X_S^2 d\tau} \quad (4\text{-}5)$$

where the denominator is equal to unity since the functions are normalized. Then,

$$E_S = \tfrac{1}{4}\Big[\int \psi_a(1)\overline{\psi_b(2)}\, H\psi_a(1)\overline{\psi_b(2)}\, dv$$

$$+ \int \overline{\psi_a(2)}\psi_b(1)\, H\overline{\psi_a(2)}\psi_b(1)\, dv$$

$$+ \int \overline{\psi_a(1)}\psi_b(2)\, H\overline{\psi_a(1)}\psi_b(2)\, dv$$

$$+ \int \psi_a(2)\overline{\psi_b(1)}\, H\psi_a(2)\overline{\psi_b(1)}\, dv$$

$$+ \int \psi_a(1)\overline{\psi_b(2)}\, H\overline{\psi_a(2)}\psi_b(1)\, dv$$

$$- \int \psi_a(1)\overline{\psi_b(2)}\, H\overline{\psi_a(1)}\psi_b(2)\, dv$$

$$- \int \psi_a(1)\overline{\psi_b(2)}\, H\psi_a(2)\overline{\psi_b(1)}\, dv$$

$$+ \int \overline{\psi_a(2)}\psi_b(1)\, H\psi_a(1)\overline{\psi_b(2)}\, dv$$

$$- \int \overline{\psi_a(2)}\psi_b(1)\, H\overline{\psi_a(1)}\psi_b(2)\, dv \quad (4\text{-}6)$$

$$- \int \overline{\psi_a(2)}\psi_b(1)\, H\psi_a(2)\overline{\psi_b(1)}\, dv$$

$$- \int \overline{\psi_a(1)}\psi_b(2)\, H\psi_a(1)\overline{\psi_b(2)}\, dv$$

$$- \int \overline{\psi_a(1)}\psi_b(2)\, H\overline{\psi_a(2)}\psi_b(1)\, dv$$

$$+ \int \overline{\psi_a(1)}\psi_b(2)\, H\psi_a(2)\overline{\psi_b(1)}\, dv$$

$$- \int \psi_a(2)\overline{\psi_b(1)}\, H\psi_a(1)\overline{\psi_b(2)}\, dv$$

$$- \int \psi_a(2)\overline{\psi_b(1)}\, H\overline{\psi_a(2)}\psi_b(1)\, dv$$

$$+ \int \psi_a(2)\overline{\psi_b(1)}\, H\overline{\psi_a(1)}\psi_b(2)\, dv\Big]$$

The Hamilton operator has no effect on the spin functions since magnetic interaction terms were excluded from it. On the other hand, the integration has to be carried out according to both space and spin coordinates.

$$(dv = dv_1 dv_2 = d\tau_1 d\tau_2 ds_1 ds_2)^1$$

When we integrate according to the spin coordinate, the orthogonality of the spin functions renders the integral zero unless the same electrons have the same spin preceding and following the operator. For example, the sixth term in (4-6)

$$\int \psi_a(1)\alpha(1)\psi_b(2)\beta(2) H \psi_a(1)\beta(1)\psi_b(2)\alpha(2) \, d\tau \, ds$$

$$= \int \alpha(1)\beta(2)\alpha(2)\beta(1) \, ds \int \psi_a(1)\psi_b(2) H \psi_a(1)\psi_b(2) \, d\tau$$

$$= \int \alpha(1)\beta(1) \, ds_1 \int \alpha(2)\beta(2) \, ds_2 \int \psi_a(1)\psi_b(2) H \psi_a(1)\psi_b(2) \, d\tau$$

$$= 0 \tag{4-7}$$

For this reason all the negative terms are zero in (4-6). Since electrons 1 and 2 play the same role and atoms a and b are indentical atoms, the first four terms are equal among each other. They all have the same electrons in the same orbital before and after the operator. These integrals are called *Coulomb integrals*.

$$Q = \int \psi_a(v)\psi_b(u) H \psi_a(v)\psi_b(u) \, dv$$
$$= \int \psi_a(u)\psi_b(v) H \psi_a(u)\psi_b(v) \, dv \tag{4-8}$$

with v and u being general indices for the three space coordinates of the electrons. It is not the same as the Coulomb integral defined in the simple, empirical molecular orbital method, which contains two wave functions only, not four. The spin can be omitted from here on, since it does not contribute to the energy. It did, however, impose a selection upon the terms in (4-6), thus influencing the energy indirectly, but profoundly.

The four remaining positive terms in (4-6) are called *exchange integrals* as they contain (1) and (2) in different order before and after the Hamiltonian. In general

$$A = \int \psi_a(v)\psi_b(u) H \psi_a(u)\psi_b(v) \, dv \tag{4-9}$$

Finally we have for the energy of the singlet state

$$E_s = Q + A$$

There would be only one singlet state in this approximation.

---

[1] Except for this chapter only $d\tau$ is used in this book, meaning integration according to all coordinates including spin coordinates.

The complete wave function X_S can also be written in the following determinantal form:

$$X_S = \frac{1}{2}\left\{ \begin{vmatrix} \psi_a(1)\alpha(1) & \psi_b(1)\beta(1) \\ \psi_a(2)\alpha(2) & \psi_b(2)\beta(2) \end{vmatrix} - \begin{vmatrix} \psi_a(1)\beta(1) & \psi_b(1)\alpha(1) \\ \psi_a(2)\beta(2) & \psi_b(2)\alpha(2) \end{vmatrix} \right\} \quad (4\text{-}10)$$

One such determinant is called a Slater determinant or Slater function [39].[2] Each one corresponds to a fixed assignment of spins to the atoms, here

$$\frac{\alpha \qquad\qquad\qquad \beta}{a \qquad\qquad\qquad b}$$

for the first determinant and

$$\frac{\beta \qquad\qquad\qquad \alpha}{a \qquad\qquad\qquad b}$$

for the second determinant.

The rule for developing a determinant assures the antisymmetry of the wave function. This is extremely useful in problems with more than two electrons.

The determinantal form also helps us understand somewhat better the meaning of the Pauli principle.

If we were to use the same spin orbital twice, in other words, if we put two electrons having the same spin projection in, say, ψ_a, then there would be two indentical columns in the determinant; therefore the determinant would vanish, indicating that the probability of such a situation is zero.

The energy of the triplet state can be obtained by using any of the three symmetrical spin functions with the antisymmetrical space function. If we choose $\alpha(1)\alpha(2)$ (or $\beta(1)\beta(2)$) the spin can be omitted, since $\alpha(1)\alpha(2) = \alpha(2)\alpha(1)$. Then

$$E_T = \tfrac{1}{2}\int [\psi_a(1)\psi_b(2) - \psi_a(2)\psi_b(1)]H[\psi_a(1)\psi_b(2) - \psi_a(2)\psi_b(1)]\,dv$$

$$= \tfrac{1}{2}\Big[\int \psi_a(1)\psi_b(2)H\psi_a(1)\psi_b(2)\,dv$$

$$+ \int \psi_a(2)\psi_b(1)H\psi_a(2)\psi_b(1)\,dv$$

$$- \int \psi_a(1)\psi_b(2)H\psi_a(2)\psi_b(1)\,dv \qquad\qquad (4\text{-}11)$$

$$- \int \psi_a(2)\psi_b(1)H\psi_a(1)\psi_b(2)\,dv\Big]$$

$$= Q - A$$

[2] In order to avoid confusion, wave functions expressed in such determinantal form will be called *Slater functions* and the atomic wave functions introduced by the same author will be called *Slater orbitals* throughout.

The normalization factor would be $1/(2 - 2S^2)$, not neglecting overlap integrals. We might also use the spin function

$$\tfrac{1}{2}[\alpha(1)\beta(2) + \alpha(2)\beta(1)]$$

which would lead to the same result. Had we not neglected overlap integrals the results would be

$$E_S = \frac{Q + A}{1 + S^2} \quad \text{and} \quad E_T = \frac{Q - A}{1 - S^2}$$

The singlet state has the lower energy and it corresponds to the ground state of the molecule. The triplet state is an excited state. It has no minimum in its potential curve and it is, therefore, highly unstable [11, p. 113]. Q and A are not usually computed in this approximation but are taken from experiment. We shall come back to this problem in Chapter 9, Sec. 9-2 and 9-4. Polar structures will be included in Sec. 9-4.

4-3. THE EXAMPLE OF BUTADIENE: THE WAVE FUNCTIONS

We are now going to treat in detail a polyatomic molecule. This is necessary because some important features of the method do not appear in the diatomic case. We again choose 1,3 butadiene in the π electron approximation. First we shall be concerned only with singlet states (Eyring, Walter, and Kimball [40, p. 233] have treated this problem in some detail).

In this case two of the π electrons must have spin projection α, the two others β. Furthermore, as a consequence of the Pauli principle,

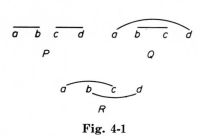

P

Q

R

Fig. 4-1

if there is a bond between two atoms, the two AO electrons forming the bond must overlap and, therefore, the two electrons must have opposite spin projections. Taking only the π electrons, the schemes of coupling shown in Fig. 4-1 would satisfy these conditions. In this figure a, b, c, and d represent the cores of the four carbon atoms. By "coupling" we mean here simply having opposite spins and forming a bond. This latter is often called "effective" if it is between two neighbors, and "ineffective" otherwise.

It was required only that electrons forming a bond should have opposite spins, but the spins are free otherwise, as if there was no overlap between non-bonded orbitals. The following arrangements of spin are compatible with bonding schemes P, Q, and R.

	P				Q				R			
	a	b	c	d		a	b	c	d	a	b	c	d
I	α	β	α	β	V	α	α	β	β	α	α	β	β
II	α	β	β	α		β	α	β	α	α	β	β	α
III	β	α	α	β		α	β	α	β	β	α	α	β
IV	β	α	β	α	VI	β	β	α	α	β	β	α	α

"Structures" P, Q, and R resemble chemical formulas, and this may appear to give them some descriptive value. It is not correct, however, to think of them as if they were introduced by chemical evidence. We shall discuss this point further below.

The total wave function of the molecule will be constructed as a linear combination of wave functions, which the molecule would possess if it could be represented by the respective structures alone.

$$X = s_p \Psi_p + s_Q \Psi_Q + s_R \Psi_R \qquad (4\text{-}12)$$

where the coefficients will be chosen so that the energy of the ground state is the lowest possible. The eigenfunctions related to the individual structures are sometimes called "structure" or "bond" eigenfunctions.

Each structure eigenfunction will be a product of a wave function depending on the space coordinates only and a spin function. The Pauli exclusion principle requires for a singlet state that the spin function should be antisymmetrical, i.e., change its sign if the spin projections of two electrons are exchanged. This is, indeed, the only way of having only one spin function associated with the space function as in the diatomic case (see p. 49). More exactly this is required only for electrons forming a bond, that is, electrons whose wave functions share the same part of space.

The spin function for Ψ_P will be

$$\frac{1}{\sqrt{4}} [\alpha\beta\alpha\beta - \alpha\beta\beta\alpha - \beta\alpha\alpha\beta + \beta\alpha\beta\alpha] \qquad (4\text{-}13)$$

where the spins are in the order of the atomic cores a, b, c, and d. It is easily seen that if we exchange the spins of a and b or c and d, which are bound together, this function changes its sign. For the exchange between a and b, for example,

$$\frac{1}{\sqrt{4}} [\alpha\beta\alpha\beta - \alpha\beta\beta\alpha - \beta\alpha\alpha\beta + \beta\alpha\beta\alpha]$$

$$\rightarrow \frac{1}{\sqrt{4}} [\beta\alpha\alpha\beta - \beta\alpha\beta\alpha - \alpha\beta\alpha\beta + \alpha\beta\beta\alpha]$$

$$= -\frac{1}{\sqrt{4}} [\alpha\beta\alpha\beta - \alpha\beta\beta\alpha - \beta\alpha\alpha\beta + \beta\alpha\beta\alpha]$$

An exchange between a and d or b and c leads to a spin function not compatible with the binding scheme of structure P and is not to be considered. It is important to realize that the sign of the whole spin function is free. If, however, we have chosen a sign for one of the terms, the others are fixed. Here we gave the positive sign to the fully alternant term, $\alpha\beta\alpha\beta$.

For Ψ_Q we have

$$\frac{1}{\sqrt{4}}[-\alpha\alpha\beta\beta + \beta\alpha\beta\alpha + \alpha\beta\alpha\beta - \beta\beta\alpha\alpha] \tag{4-14}$$

b and c and a and d being bound together. The signs in this function and the former are independent from one another. We have chosen it so that $\alpha\beta\alpha\beta$ is positive in the spin functions of both Ψ_P and Ψ_Q, but this is not necessary. The choice of this sign has no influence on the calculation of the energy and it only influences the signs of the coefficients in the secular equation, as we shall see below (p. 68).

For Ψ_R we have

$$\frac{1}{\sqrt{4}}[\alpha\alpha\beta\beta - \alpha\beta\beta\alpha - \beta\alpha\alpha\beta + \beta\beta\alpha\alpha] \tag{4-15}$$

For each structure eigenfunction we have to choose the sign of one of the terms as positive; then those which differ from it by an odd number of permutations between atoms that are bound together in the respective structure will be negative, and those differing by an even number of such permutations, positive.

The factor of normalization due to spin is always $1/\sqrt{2^m}$ if m is the number of *bonds*, since in each bond we can have $\alpha\beta$ or $\beta\alpha$ and thus every bond multiplies by two the number of possible spin-arrays. (We designate by spin-array the spin function corresponding to *one* Slater function.) In our example

$$\frac{1}{\sqrt{2^2}} = \frac{1}{2}$$

Basically the space function for all the structure eigenfunctions is of the form

$$\psi_a(1)\,\psi_b(2)\,\psi_c(3)\,\psi_d(4)$$

but, naturally, any possible permutation of the electrons is equally admissible. Their number is $n!$ if there are n electrons. In our example this is $4! = 24$. A term of the complete, spin-orbital wave function will be of the form

$$\psi_a(1)\,\alpha(1)\,\psi_b(2)\,\beta(2)\,\psi_c(3)\,\alpha(3)\,\psi_d(4)\,\beta(4)$$

There will be 24 terms like this with every spin-array where one term has to be chosen positive (usually the one placing the electrons into the space functions in the natural order) and all permutations differing from it by an odd number of exchanges will have to be given the negative sign because of the requirement of antisymmetry of the wave function.

It is very convenient to write a function corresponding to a given spin-array in the form of a determinant. Then the rule of developing the determinant insures antisymmetry. The one with spin-array I for Ψ_P will be

$$\psi_I = \frac{1}{\sqrt{4!}} \begin{vmatrix} \psi_a(1)\alpha(1) & \psi_b(1)\beta(1) & \psi_c(1)\alpha(1) & \psi_d(1)\beta(1) \\ \psi_a(2)\alpha(2) & \psi_b(2)\beta(2) & \psi_c(2)\alpha(2) & \psi_d(2)\beta(2) \\ \psi_a(3)\alpha(3) & \psi_b(3)\beta(3) & \psi_c(3)\alpha(3) & \psi_d(3)\beta(3) \\ \psi_a(4)\alpha(4) & \psi_b(4)\beta(4) & \psi_c(4)\alpha(4) & \psi_d(4)\beta(4) \end{vmatrix} \quad (4\text{-}16)$$

This is again a Slater function or Slater determinant. (It was also called a "spin-state" [41], although it is not a state in the sense of a state of energy.)

The Slater function corresponding to spin-array II is

$$\psi_{II} = \frac{1}{\sqrt{4!}} \begin{vmatrix} \psi_a(1)\alpha(1) & \psi_b(1)\beta(1) & \psi_c(1)\beta(1) & \psi_d(1)\alpha(1) \\ \psi_a(2)\alpha(2) & \psi_b(2)\beta(2) & \psi_c(2)\beta(2) & \psi_d(2)\alpha(2) \\ \psi_a(3)\alpha(3) & \psi_b(3)\beta(3) & \psi_c(3)\beta(3) & \psi_d(3)\alpha(3) \\ \psi_a(4)\alpha(4) & \psi_b(4)\beta(4) & \psi_c(4)\beta(4) & \psi_d(4)\alpha(4) \end{vmatrix} \quad (4\text{-}17)$$

and so forth.

It follows that

$$\Psi_P = \frac{1}{\sqrt{4}} [\psi_I - \psi_{II} - \psi_{III} + \psi_{IV}]$$

$$\Psi_Q = \frac{1}{\sqrt{4}} [\psi_I + \psi_{IV} - \psi_V - \alpha_{VI}]$$

and $$\Psi_R = \frac{1}{\sqrt{4}} [-\psi_{II} - \psi_{III} + \psi_V + \psi_{VI}] \quad (4\text{-}18)$$

Thus the eigenfunctions of the individual structures are expressed as a linear combination of Slater functions.

It can be seen immediately that not all three structures are mutually independent. In fact

$$\Psi_R = \Psi_P - \Psi_Q$$

and should be eliminated. Therefore the total wave function becomes

$$X = s_P\Psi_P + s_Q\Psi_Q \quad (4\text{-}19)$$

A word should be said about the normalizing factor of the individual Slater functions (here $\sqrt{4!}$). It is clear from the previous treatment of the diatomic case that this simple factor is obtained only at the price of neglecting the overlap integrals between atomic orbitals. This means supposing them orthogonal, although being solutions of the Schrödinger equations for two separate atoms they of course are not. Including the overlap integrals would complicate the calculations very much. Normalizing a Slater function means developing the determinant, which in our example would yield a polynomial of 24 terms, and then integrating its square and equating the result to unity.

It is instructive (although tedious) to study an example in full detail. We choose the Slater function Ψ_I. Developing the determinant, we obtain the following 24 terms:

$$
\begin{array}{l|l}
\psi_a(1)\alpha(1)\psi_b(2)\beta(2)\psi_c(3)\alpha(3)\psi_d(4)\beta(4) & +\ 1234 \\
-\ \psi_a(1)\alpha(1)\psi_b(2)\beta(2)\psi_c(4)\alpha(4)\psi_d(3)\beta(3) & -\ 1243 \\
-\ \psi_a(1)\alpha(1)\psi_b(3)\beta(3)\psi_c(2)\alpha(2)\psi_d(4)\beta(4) & -\ 1324 \\
+\ \psi_a(1)\alpha(1)\psi_b(3)\beta(3)\psi_c(4)\alpha(4)\psi_d(2)\beta(2) & +\ 1342 \\
+\ \psi_a(1)\alpha(1)\psi_b(4)\beta(4)\psi_c(2)\alpha(2)\psi_d(3)\beta(3) & +\ 1423 \\
-\ \psi_a(1)\alpha(1)\psi_b(4)\beta(4)\psi_c(3)\alpha(3)\psi_d(2)\beta(2) & -\ 1432 \\
-\ \psi_a(2)\alpha(2)\psi_b(1)\beta(1)\psi_c(3)\alpha(3)\psi_d(4)\beta(4) & -\ 2134 \\
+\ \psi_a(2)\alpha(2)\psi_b(1)\beta(1)\psi_c(4)\alpha(4)\psi_d(3)\beta(3) & +\ 2143 \\
+\ \psi_a(2)\alpha(2)\psi_b(3)\beta(3)\psi_c(1)\alpha(1)\psi_d(4)\beta(4) & +\ 2314 \\
-\ \psi_a(2)\alpha(2)\psi_b(3)\beta(3)\psi_c(4)\alpha(4)\psi_d(1)\beta(1) & -\ 2341 \\
-\ \psi_a(2)\alpha(2)\psi_b(4)\beta(4)\psi_c(1)\alpha(1)\psi_d(3)\beta(3) & -\ 2413 \\
+\ \psi_a(2)\alpha(2)\psi_b(4)\beta(4)\psi_c(3)\alpha(3)\psi_d(1)\beta(1) & +\ 2431 \\
+\ \psi_a(3)\alpha(3)\psi_b(1)\beta(1)\psi_c(2)\alpha(2)\psi_d(4)\beta(4) & +\ 3124 \\
-\ \psi_a(3)\alpha(3)\psi_b(1)\beta(1)\psi_c(4)\alpha(4)\psi_d(2)\beta(2) & -\ 3142 \\
-\ \psi_a(3)\alpha(3)\psi_b(2)\beta(2)\psi_c(1)\alpha(1)\psi_d(4)\beta(4) & -\ 3214 \\
+\ \psi_a(3)\alpha(3)\psi_b(2)\beta(2)\psi_c(4)\alpha(4)\psi_d(1)\beta(1) & +\ 3241 \\
+\ \psi_a(3)\alpha(3)\psi_b(4)\beta(4)\psi_c(1)\alpha(1)\psi_d(2)\beta(2) & +\ 3412 \\
-\ \psi_a(3)\alpha(3)\psi_b(4)\beta(4)\psi_c(2)\alpha(2)\psi_d(1)\beta(1) & -\ 3421 \\
-\ \psi_a(4)\alpha(4)\psi_b(1)\beta(1)\psi_c(2)\alpha(2)\psi_d(3)\beta(3) & -\ 4123 \\
+\ \psi_a(4)\alpha(4)\psi_b(1)\beta(1)\psi_c(3)\alpha(3)\psi_d(2)\beta(2) & +\ 4132 \\
+\ \psi_a(4)\alpha(4)\psi_b(2)\beta(2)\psi_c(1)\alpha(1)\psi_d(3)\beta(3) & +\ 4213 \\
-\ \psi_a(4)\alpha(4)\psi_b(2)\beta(2)\psi_c(3)\alpha(3)\psi_d(1)\beta(1) & -\ 4231 \\
-\ \psi_a(4)\alpha(4)\psi_b(3)\beta(3)\psi_c(1)\alpha(1)\psi_d(2)\beta(2) & -\ 4312 \\
+\ \psi_a(4)\alpha(4)\psi_b(3)\beta(3)\psi_c(2)\alpha(2)\psi_d(1)\beta(1) & +\ 4321
\end{array}
\tag{4-20}
$$

On the right, an obvious, short notation is given.

It is sufficient to take one term, say the first one, and combine it with all the others. Since all other terms play the same role they cannot introduce new features. The first term with itself gives

$$
\int \psi_a(1)\overline{\psi_b(2)}\psi_c(3)\overline{\psi_d(4)}\,1\,\psi_a(1)\overline{\psi_b(2)}\psi_c(3)\overline{\psi_d(4)}\,dv_1\,dv_2\,dv_3\,dv_4
\tag{4-21}
$$

where again the bars mean spin β and where we put the unity operator between the two expressions for more clarity. Since all the electrons have the same spin preceding and following the operator integrating over the spin functions gives unity, and integrating according to the space coordinates of each electron yields again

$$S_{aa} = S_{bb} = 1$$

since the atomic orbitals are normalized. Thus this integral is equal to 1.

The first term with the second term gives zero, because electrons 3 and 4 do not have the same spin in the two terms and the orthogonality of the spin functions makes the integral vanish. Actually, it can be seen immediately that only exchanges of electrons having the same spin can lead to nonzero values for integrals of type (4-21). Therefore, the first term combined with the second, third, fourth, and fifth terms gives zero. With the sixth it gives

$$-\int \psi_a(1)\overline{\psi_b(2)}\psi_c(3)\overline{\psi_d(4)}\,1\,\psi_a(1)\overline{\psi_b(4)}\psi_c(3)\overline{\psi_d(2)}\,dv_1\ldots dv_4 \quad (4\text{-}22)$$

Integrating over the spins gives unity, as does integrating over the space coordinates of electrons (1) and (3). There remains

$$-\int \psi_b(2)\psi_d(2)\,dv_2 \int \psi_d(4)\psi_b(4)\,dv_4 = -S_{bd}^2 \qquad (4\text{-}23)$$

This corresponds to an exchange between atoms which are not close neighbors. Therefore, this integral will have a small value. (For example, the π electron overlap integrals in benzene have approximately the following values: ortho 0.26, meta 0.04, para 0.02.)

The spin β assigned to electron (2) is enough to render zero the next six integrals. Among the following six there will be two having values different from zero. These are the fifteenth

$$-\int \psi_a(1)\overline{\psi_b(2)}\psi_c(3)\overline{\psi_d(4)}\,1\,\psi_a(3)\overline{\psi_b(2)}\psi_c(1)\psi_d(4)\,dv_1\ldots dv_4$$

yielding

$$-\int \psi_a(1)\psi_c(1)\,dv_1 \int \psi_c(3)\psi_a(3)\,dv_3 = -S_{ac}^2 \qquad (4\text{-}24)$$

which is of the previous type, and the seventeenth

$$+\int \psi_a(1)\overline{\psi_b(2)}\psi_c(3)\overline{\psi_d(4)}\,1\,\psi_a(3)\overline{\psi_b(4)}\psi_c(1)\overline{\psi_d(2)}\,dv_1\ldots dv_4$$

giving

$$+\int \psi_a(1)\psi_c(1)\,dv_1 \int \psi_b(2)\psi_d(2)\,dv_2 \int \psi_c(3)\psi_a(3)\,dv_3$$
$$\int \psi_d(4)\psi_b(4)\,dv_4$$
$$= +S_{ac}^2 \times S_{bd}^2 \qquad (4\text{-}25)$$

This corresponds to a double exchange and it is expected to be very small.

With the remaining six terms we obtain only zero.

Finally we have obtained

$$1 - S_{bd}^2 - S_{ac}^2 + S_{ac}^2 S_{bd}^2 = 1 - 2S_{ac}^2 + S_{ac}^4$$

since $S_{ac} = S_{bd}$. All the terms will give similar results with the other 24 and the normalization factor will be

$$\frac{1}{\sqrt{4!\,(1 - 2S_{ac}^2 + S_{ac}^4)}} \tag{4-26}$$

Neglecting overlap integrals gives simply $1/\sqrt{4!}$ as we have seen above. The approximation may not seem to be too bad. However, if we now examine a Slater function where electrons on neighbor atoms have the same spin, the situation becomes worse. Slater function V constitutes a good example.

$$\begin{pmatrix} a & b & c & d \\ \alpha & \alpha & \beta & \beta \end{pmatrix}$$

We can reason on the column where the short notation was used (p. 58). Let us consider the integrals given by term 1234 with the other 24 terms. We obtain nonzero integrals with the first, second, seventh, and eighth terms, giving

$$1 - S_{cd}^2 - S_{ab}^2 + S_{ab}^2 \cdot S_{cd}^2$$

and the normalization factor

$$\frac{1}{\sqrt{4!\,(1 - 2S_{ab}^2 + S_{ab}^4)}} \tag{4-27}$$

Neglecting overlap integrals is more grave here. S_{ab} belongs to two neighbor atoms and has a large value. Yet, if we compute the factor using $S_{ab} = 0.26$, we obtain $1/\sqrt{4!\,0.87} = 0.219$ instead of $1/\sqrt{4!} = 0.204$. The situation will be worse the bigger the molecule, as more and more terms would be added under the square root. Slater's criticism [42] of the valence-bond method as it has been generally used for larger molecules was based on this. Overlap integrals play an important role in the calculation of the matrix elements necessary to obtain the eigenvalues as well. We are now going to turn our attention to the latter.

4-4. THE EXAMPLE OF BUTADIENE: THE ENERGIES

Once more we use the variation formula

$$E_i = \frac{\int X_i H X_i \, dv}{\int X_i^2 \, dv} \tag{4-28}$$

Substituting

$$X_i = s_P \Psi_P + s_Q \Psi_Q$$

we obtain

$$E_i = \frac{\int (s_P \Psi_P + s_Q \Psi_Q) H (s_P \Psi_P + s_Q \Psi_Q) \, dv}{\int (s_P \Psi_P + s_Q \Psi_Q)^2 \, dv} \qquad (4\text{-}29)$$

In order to minimize the energy with respect to the coefficients we differentiate E_i with respect to s_P and s_Q. Omitting the index i we may write

$$E = \frac{s_P^2 \int \Psi_P H \Psi_P \, dv + 2 s_P s_Q \int \Psi_P H \Psi_Q \, dv + s_Q^2 \int \Psi_Q H \Psi_Q \, dv}{s_P^2 \int \Psi_P^2 \, dv + 2 s_P s_Q \int \Psi_P \Psi_Q \, dv + s_Q^2 \int \Psi_Q^2 \, dv} \qquad (4\text{-}30)$$

or, with simpler notations,

$$E = \frac{s_P^2 H_{PP} + 2 s_P s_Q H_{PQ} + s_Q^2 H_{QQ}}{s_P^2 d_{PP} + 2 s_P s_Q d_{PQ} + s_Q^2 d_{QQ}} \qquad (4\text{-}31)$$

Then we differentiate E according to s_P and s_Q and equate the derivatives simultaneously to zero, following exactly the procedure used in the molecular orbital method (p. 34). We obtain the set of two equations:

$$\begin{aligned} s_P(H_{PP} - E d_{PP}) + s_Q(H_{PQ} - E d_{PQ}) = 0 \\ s_P(H_{PQ} - E d_{PQ}) + s_Q(H_{QQ} - E d_{QQ}) = 0 \end{aligned} \qquad (4\text{-}32)$$

There will be, in general, as many equations as structures.

We now have to compute the integrals occurring in the secular equation. As will be seen below, $H_{PQ} = H_{QP}$. From (4-18)

$$\begin{aligned} H_{PP} &= \int \Psi_P H \Psi_P \, dv \\ &= \tfrac{1}{4} \int (\psi_{\mathrm{I}} - \psi_{\mathrm{II}} - \psi_{\mathrm{III}} + \psi_{\mathrm{IV}}) H (\psi_{\mathrm{I}} - \psi_{\mathrm{II}} - \psi_{\mathrm{III}} + \psi_{\mathrm{IV}}) \, dv \end{aligned} \qquad (4\text{-}33)$$

This expression can be broken down into the sum of 16 integrals of type

$$\int \psi_{\mathrm{I}} H \psi_{\mathrm{I}} \, dv \qquad \text{or} \qquad \int \psi_{\mathrm{I}} H \psi_{\mathrm{II}} \, dv$$

The Slater functions ψ_{I}, ψ_{II}, ... all contain $4! = 24$ permutations. Since the Hamiltonian does not operate on the spin functions, which, furthermore, are mutually orthogonal, the same electrons must have the same spin preceding and following the operator or else the term is zero. Neglecting overlap integrals in normalizing the Slater functions,

$$\int \psi_{\mathrm{I}} H \psi_{\mathrm{I}} \, dv = \frac{1}{4!} \int (\alpha\beta\alpha\beta) H (\alpha\beta\alpha\beta) \, dv \qquad (4\text{-}34)$$

where $(\alpha\beta\alpha\beta)$ stands for the Slater determinant except for the normalization factor. An important simplification can be introduced at this stage. Since there are 24 terms in $(\alpha\beta\alpha\beta)$ which are all equivalent, we might simply omit the normalization factor and replace one of the $(\alpha\beta\alpha\beta)$ by, say, the first permutation and write

$$\int \psi_I H \psi_I \, dv = \int \psi_a(1)\overline{\psi_b(2)}\psi_c(3)\overline{\psi_d(4)} H(\alpha\beta\alpha\beta) \, dv \quad (4\text{-}35)$$

This integral can be broken down into 24 parts. The one containing the same permutation of electrons left and right of the Hamiltonian is a Coulomb integral

$$Q = \int \psi_a(1)\overline{\psi_b(2)}\psi_c(3)\overline{\psi_d(4)} \, H \psi_a(1)\overline{\psi_b(2)}\psi_c(3)\overline{\psi_d(4)} \, dv$$

Outside of this, only those terms will be different from zero where electrons having the *same* spin projection are exchanged. Using again the development (4-20), we see that there are only three such permutations. They are the same as the ones we have already encountered. They yield two single exchange integrals:

$$-\int \psi_a(1)\overline{\psi_b(2)}\psi_c(3)\overline{\psi_d(4)} \, H \psi_a(1)\overline{\psi_b(4)}\psi_c(3)\overline{\psi_d(2)} \, dv = -(bd)$$

and

$$-\int \psi_a(1)\overline{\psi_b(2)}\psi_c(3)\overline{\psi_d(4)} \, H \psi_a(3)\overline{\psi_b(2)}\psi_c(1)\overline{\psi_d(4)} \, dv = -(ac)$$

and one double exchange integral

$$+\int \psi_a(1)\overline{\psi_b(2)}\psi_c(3)\overline{\psi_d(4)} \, H \psi_a(3)\overline{\psi_b(4)}\psi_c(1)\overline{\psi_d(2)} \, dv = +(ac, bd)$$

using a notation introduced by Eyring, Walter, and Kimball [40]. Thus we have obtained that

$$H_{II} = \int \psi_I H \psi_I \, dv = Q - (bd) - (ac) + (ac, bd) \quad (4\text{-}36)$$

If we neglect multiple exchange integrals we obtain the general rule [40, p. 241]: "The matrix element between a Slater function and itself is the Coulomb integral minus the sum of all exchange integrals between atomic orbitals having the same spin."

If we are looking for matrix element between two different Slater functions we can still use the above simplification and write, for example:

$$\int \psi_I H \psi_V \, dv = \int \psi_a(1)\overline{\psi_b(2)}\psi_c(3)\overline{\psi_d(4)} \, H(\alpha\alpha\beta\beta) \, dv \quad (4\text{-}37)$$

In $(\alpha\alpha\beta\beta)$ we find four permutations in which electrons (1) and (3) have α spin projections and electrons (2) and (4) β spin projections. Only these will make nonzero contributions. These permutations are:

$$-\int \psi_a(1)\overline{\psi_b(2)}\psi_c(3)\overline{\psi_d(4)}\,H\psi_a(1)\psi_b(3)\overline{\psi_c(2)}\overline{\psi_d(4)}\,dv$$
$$= -(bc)$$

$$+\int \psi_a(1)\overline{\psi_b(2)}\psi_c(3)\overline{\psi_d(4)}\,H\psi_a(1)\psi_b(3)\overline{\psi_c(4)}\psi_d(2)\,dv$$
$$= (bd, cb, dc)$$

$$+\int \psi_a(1)\overline{\psi_b(2)}\psi_c(3)\overline{\psi_d(4)}\,H\psi_a(3)\psi_b(1)\overline{\psi_c(2)}\overline{\psi_d(4)}\,dv$$
$$= (ab, bc, ca)$$

$$-\int \psi_a(1)\overline{\psi_b(2)}\psi_c(3)\overline{\psi_d(4)}\,H\psi_a(3)\psi_b(1)\overline{\psi_c(4)}\psi_d(2)\,dv$$
$$= (ab, bd, ca, dc)$$

All but the first one are multiple exchange integrals. If we neglect these we have the simple rule: "The matrix element between two different Slater functions is zero unless the functions differ only in the spins of two atomic orbitals; then it is the negative of the corresponding exchange integral."

Thus, we might write down easily all the matrix elements we need. There are six Slater functions occurring in the structure eigenfunctions Ψ_P and Ψ_Q.

$$
\begin{array}{lll}
H_{\mathrm{I\,I}} = Q - (ac) - (bd) & (\alpha\beta\alpha\beta)(\alpha\beta\alpha\beta) \\
H_{\mathrm{I\,II}} = -(cd) & (\alpha\beta\beta\alpha) \\
H_{\mathrm{I\,III}} = -(ab) & (\beta\alpha\alpha\beta) \\
H_{\mathrm{I\,IV}} = 0 & (\beta\alpha\beta\alpha) \\
H_{\mathrm{I\,V}} = -(bc) & (\alpha\beta\alpha\beta)(\alpha\alpha\beta\beta) \\
H_{\mathrm{I\,VI}} = -(ad) & (\beta\beta\alpha\alpha) \\
H_{\mathrm{II\,II}} = Q - (ad) - (bc) & (\alpha\beta\beta\alpha)(\alpha\beta\beta\alpha) \\
H_{\mathrm{II\,III}} = 0 & (\beta\alpha\alpha\beta) \\
H_{\mathrm{II\,IV}} = -(ab) & (\beta\alpha\beta\alpha) \\
H_{\mathrm{II\,V}} = -(bd) & (\alpha\alpha\beta\beta) \\
H_{\mathrm{II\,VI}} = -(ac) & (\beta\beta\alpha\alpha) \\
H_{\mathrm{III\,III}} = Q - (ad) - (bc) & (\beta\alpha\alpha\beta)(\beta\alpha\alpha\beta) \\
H_{\mathrm{III\,IV}} = -(cd) & (\beta\alpha\beta\alpha) \\
H_{\mathrm{III\,V}} = -(ac) & (\alpha\alpha\beta\beta) \\
H_{\mathrm{III\,VI}} = -(bd) & (\beta\beta\alpha\alpha) \\
H_{\mathrm{IV\,IV}} = Q - (ac) - (bd) & (\beta\alpha\beta\alpha)(\beta\alpha\beta\alpha) \\
H_{\mathrm{IV\,V}} = -(ad) & (\alpha\alpha\beta\beta) \\
H_{\mathrm{IV\,VI}} = -(bc) & (\beta\beta\alpha\alpha) \\
H_{\mathrm{V\,V}} = Q - (ab) - (cd) & (\alpha\alpha\beta\beta)(\alpha\alpha\beta\beta) \\
H_{\mathrm{V\,VI}} = 0 & (\beta\beta\alpha\alpha) \\
H_{\mathrm{VI\,VI}} = Q - (ab) - (cd) & (\beta\beta\alpha\alpha)(\beta\beta\alpha\alpha) \\
\end{array}
\tag{4-38}
$$

Here $H_{\mathrm{I\,II}} = H_{\mathrm{II\,I}}$, etc. since these integrals reduce to terms like

$$\int \psi_a(1)\psi_b(2)\,H\psi_a(2)\psi_b(1)\,d\tau_1\,d\tau_2$$
$$= \int \psi_a(1)\,H\psi_b(1)\,d\tau_1 \int \psi_b(2)\,H\psi_a(2)\,d\tau_2$$

and

$$\int \psi_a H \psi_b \, d\tau = \int \psi_b H \psi_a \, d\tau$$

since the atoms are identical. Therefore also

$$H_{PQ} = H_{QP}$$

since these integrals are linear combinations of H_{II} and H_{III} type integrals.

Now we can compute the matrix elements to be fitted into the secular equation.

$$H_{PP} \equiv \int \Psi_P H \Psi_P \, dv$$

$$= \tfrac{1}{4} \int (\psi_I - \psi_{II} - \psi_{III} + \psi_{IV}) H (\psi_I - \psi_{II} - \psi_{III} + \psi_{IV}) \, dv$$

$$= \tfrac{1}{4} [H_{II} + H_{IIII} + H_{IIIIII} + H_{IVIV} - 2H_{III}$$

$$\quad - 2H_{IIII} + 2H_{IIV} - 2H_{IIIII} - 2H_{IIIIV} - 2H_{IIIIV}]$$

$$= \tfrac{1}{4} [Q - (ac) - (bd) + Q - (ad) - (bc)$$

$$\quad + Q - (ad) - (bc) + Q - (ac) - (bd) + 2(cd)$$

$$\quad + 2(ab) + 2 \cdot 0 - 2 \cdot 0 + 2(ab) + 2(cd)]$$

$$= \tfrac{1}{4} [4Q - 2(ac) - 2(bd) - 2(ad) - 2(bc) - 4(ab) + 4(cd)]$$

Neglecting (ac), (bd), and (ad), which represent exchanges between nonneighbors, and admitting the equality of all exchange integrals between neighbors,

$$(bc) = (ab) = (cd) = A$$

this gives

$$H_{PP} = Q + \tfrac{3}{2}A \qquad (4\text{-}39)$$

For the other structure

$$H_{QQ} \equiv \int \Psi_Q H \Psi_Q \, dv$$

$$= \tfrac{1}{4} \int (\psi_I + \psi_{IV} - \psi_V - \psi_{VI}) H (\psi_I + \psi_{IV} - \psi_V - \psi_{VI}) \, dv$$

$$= \tfrac{1}{4} [H_{II} + H_{IVIV} + H_{VV} + H_{VIVI} + 2H_{IIV} - 2H_{IV}$$

$$\quad - 2H_{IVI} - 2H_{IVV} - 2H_{IVVI} + 2H_{VVI}]$$

$$= \tfrac{1}{4} [Q - (ac) - (bd) + Q - (ac) - (bd) + Q$$

$$\quad - (ab) - (cd) + Q - (ab) - (cd) + 2 \cdot 0 + 2(bc)$$

$$\quad + 2(ad) + 2(ad) + 2(bc) + 2 \cdot 0]$$

$$= \tfrac{1}{4} [4Q - 2(ac) - 2(bd) - 2(ab) - 2(cd) + 4(bc) + 4(ad)]$$

Again putting $(ac) = (bd) = (ad) = 0$ and $(ab) = (cd) = (bc) = A$ we obtain

$$H_{QQ} = Q \qquad (4\text{-}40)$$

The nondiagonal matrix component is evaluated as follows:

$$H_{PQ} \equiv \int \Psi_P H \Psi_Q \, dv$$

$$= \tfrac{1}{4} \int (\psi_I - \psi_{II} - \psi_{III} + \psi_{IV}) H (\psi_I + \psi_{IV} - \psi_V - \psi_{VI}) \, dv$$

$$= \tfrac{1}{4} [H_{I\,I} - H_{I\,II} - H_{I\,III} + H_{I\,IV} + H_{I\,V} - H_{II\,IV} - H_{III\,IV}$$
$$+ H_{IV\,IV} - H_{I\,V} + H_{II\,V} + H_{III\,V} - H_{IV\,V} - H_{I\,VI} + H_{II\,VI}$$
$$+ H_{III\,VI} - H_{IV\,VI}]$$

$$= \tfrac{1}{4} [Q - (ac) - (bd) + (cd) + (ab) + 0 + 0 + (ab) + (cd)$$
$$+ Q - (ac) - (bd) + (bc) - (bd) - (ac) + (ad) + (ad)$$
$$- (ac) - (bd) + (bc)]$$

$$= \tfrac{1}{4} [2Q - 4(ac) - 4(bd) + 2(cd) + 2(ab) + 2(bc) + 2(ad)]$$

Neglecting (ac), (bd), and (ad) and writing as before

$$(cd) = (ab) = (bc) = A$$

we obtain

$$H_{PQ} = \tfrac{1}{2} Q + \tfrac{3}{2} A \qquad (4\text{-}41)$$

We need outside of H_{PP}, H_{QQ}, and H_{PQ} the simpler integrals d_{PP}, d_{QQ}, and d_{PQ} which do not contain the Hamilton operator. We can write

$$d_{PP} \equiv \int \Psi_P^2 \, dv = \tfrac{1}{4} \int (\psi_I - \psi_{II} - \psi_{III} + \psi_{IV})^2 \, dv$$

Developing this integral we shall obtain terms like $\int \psi_I^2 \, dv$ and terms with two different Slater functions like $\int \psi_I \psi_{II} \, dv$.

$$\int \psi_I \psi_I \, dv = \frac{1}{4!} \int (\alpha\beta\alpha\beta)(\alpha\beta\alpha\beta) \, dv$$

Both $(\alpha\beta\alpha\beta)$ contain 24 terms. In multiplying we obtain $(4!)^2 = 24^2$ terms. In all the terms all electrons have to have the same spin in both factors and, furthermore, if we neglect overlap integrals between atomic orbitals, i.e. we take them as mutually orthogonal, all electrons have to be in the same orbital in both factors. Thus from the $(4!)^2$ terms only the squared ones do not vanish, giving each unity because the atomic orbitals are taken as normalized. Therefore

$$\int \psi_I \psi_I \, dv = \frac{4!}{4!} = 1$$

This is really equivalent to normalizing the Slater functions and it is not dependent on neglecting overlap integrals. If the two Slater functions are not the same, as in

$$\int \psi_I \psi_{II} \, dv = \frac{1}{4!} \int (\alpha\beta\alpha\beta)(\alpha\beta\beta\alpha) \, dv$$

we again have $(4!)^2$ terms after multiplying, but since only those terms will be different from zero which have the same permutation of the electrons in both factors, and all electrons cannot have the same spin in these or every term will vanish individually. Thus, the integrals of this type vanish.

$$\int \psi_I \psi_{II} \, dv = 0$$

(This step *is* dependent on neglecting overlap integrals. If we do not neglect them, some other permutations in which the spins are matched become possible, and some of the terms do not vanish. We will not go into detail at this point, however.)

Then we see that

$$d_{PP} = 1, \qquad d_{QQ} = 1, \qquad d_{PQ} = \tfrac{1}{2} \qquad (4\text{-}42)$$

These values are the number of Slater functions the two structure eigenfunctions contain in common, divided by the square of the normalization factor of the structure eigenfunctions (here $\tfrac{1}{4}$). They are, of course, equal to the coefficients of the coulombic terms since they are counted similarly.

Now we have all the elements needed to set up the secular equation [Eq. (4-32)].

$$\begin{aligned}
s_P(Q + \tfrac{3}{2}A - E) + s_Q(\tfrac{1}{2}Q + \tfrac{3}{2}A - \tfrac{1}{2}E) &= 0 \\
s_P(\tfrac{1}{2}Q + \tfrac{3}{2}A - \tfrac{1}{2}E) + s_Q(Q - E) &= 0
\end{aligned} \qquad (4\text{-}43)$$

For the sake of simplification we divide everywhere by A and put

$$\frac{Q - E}{A} = X \qquad (4\text{-}44)$$

Then[3]

$$\begin{aligned}
s_P(X + \tfrac{3}{2}) + s_Q(\tfrac{1}{2}X + \tfrac{3}{2}) &= 0 \\
s_P(\tfrac{1}{2}X + \tfrac{3}{2}) + s_Q X &= 0
\end{aligned} \qquad (4\text{-}45)$$

The determinant of the coefficients has to vanish so that the s_i are not all zero.

$$\begin{vmatrix} X + \tfrac{3}{2} & \tfrac{1}{2}X + \tfrac{3}{2} \\ \tfrac{1}{2}X + \tfrac{3}{2} & X \end{vmatrix} = 0$$

or

$$X^2 + \tfrac{3}{2}X - (\tfrac{1}{4}X^2 + \tfrac{3}{2}X + \tfrac{9}{4}) = 0$$
$$3X^2 - 9 = 0$$

and

$$X = \pm\sqrt{3} = \pm 1.732 \qquad (4\text{-}46)$$

Then from (4-44) the eigenvalues are

$$E_0 = Q + 1.732A \qquad E_1 = Q - 1.732A$$

The ground state (E_0) is given by the (most) negative value of X. Thus the lowest energy level is the most negative one since both Q

---

[3] X is not to be confused with the similar symbol X which is used for the total wave function.

and A, which represent energies due to attractive forces, are negative quantities, and in (4-44) X and E have opposite signs.

In this method, in general, there will be as many energy levels as structures.

Like the molecular orbital method in its simplest form, the valence-bond method as presented here is also treated as an empirical method. Q and A are not usually computed but are obtained from comparisons with experimental quantities (see Section 9-2).

We can now compute the coefficients s_P and s_Q belonging to each of the two eigenvalues. To do this we have to put back each eigenvalue into the secular equation. Let us take first $X_0 = -1.732$ which corresponds to E_0. From (4-45) we have, dividing everywhere by s_P,

$$-0.232 + \frac{s_Q}{s_P}0.634 = 0$$
$$0.634 - \frac{s_Q}{s_P}1.732 = 0 \qquad (4\text{-}47)$$

Then from the first equation

$$\frac{s_Q}{s_P} = 0.366$$

Substituting this into the second equation for a check we actually obtain equality:

$$0.634 - 0.366 \times 1.732 = 0$$

The total wave function is

$$X_0 = s_P\Psi_P + s_Q\Psi_Q \qquad (4\text{-}48)$$

which we still have to normalize. The condition of normalization is

$$\int (s_P\Psi_P + s_Q\Psi_Q)^2 \, dv = s_P^2 \int \Psi_P^2 dv + s_Q^2 \int \Psi_Q^2 dv + 2s_Ps_Q \int \Psi_P\Psi_Q dv = 1 \qquad (4\text{-}49)$$

As we have seen above,

$$d_{PP} \equiv \int \Psi_P^2 \, dv = 1$$

$$d_{QQ} \equiv \int \Psi_Q^2 \, dv = 1$$

$$d_{PQ} \equiv \int \Psi_P\Psi_Q \, dv = \tfrac{1}{2}$$

Thus

$$s_P^2 + s_Q^2 + s_Ps_Q = 1$$

Dividing everywhere by s_P^2 gives

$$1 + \left(\frac{s_Q}{s_P}\right)^2 + \frac{s_Q}{s_P} = \frac{1}{s_P^2}$$

Hence

$$\frac{1}{s_P^2} = 1 + 0.134 + 0.366 = 1.500$$

$$s_P^2 = 0.667$$

Furthermore

$$s_Q^2 = \left(\frac{s_Q}{s_P}\right)^2 s_P^2 = 0.134 \times 0.667 = 0.089$$

and $s_P s_Q = 0.244$, where $0.667 + 0.089 + 0.244 = 1$.

Giving the opposite sign to the spin function of Ψ_Q (p. 56) would have rendered negative the nondiagonal terms in the secular equation and also the ratio s_Q/s_P. This, however, would not affect either the energy or the square of the total wave function, which are the only quantities having a physical meaning.

Neglecting d_{PQ} according to a procedure employed by Pauling, Brockway, and Beach [43] we obtain an approximate measure of the weight of the different structures in the representation of the molecule.

Then the condition of normalization is simply

$$s_P^2 + s_Q^2 = 1$$

Dividing by s_P^2 gives

$$1 + \left(\frac{s_Q}{s_P}\right)^2 = \frac{1}{s_P^2}, \qquad \frac{1}{s_P^2} = 1.134$$

$$s_P^2 = 0.882 \qquad \text{and} \qquad s_Q^2 = 0.118$$

This means that the weight of structure P is 88% and the weight of structure Q 12% in the ground state.

We have a singlet excited state with energy E_1 ($X_1 = +1.732$). For this root the secular equation becomes

$$3.232 + \frac{s_Q}{s_P} 2.366 = 0$$

$$2.366 + \frac{s_Q}{s_P} 1.732 = 0$$

(4-50)

From here

$$\frac{s_Q}{s_P} = -1.366$$

After normalization

$$s_P^2 = 0.667, \qquad s_Q^2 = 1.244, \qquad s_P s_Q = -0.911$$

Neglecting the mixed term we obtain

$$s_P^2 = 0.350 \qquad \text{and} \qquad s_Q^2 = 0.650$$

In general, the weight of the structures containing long bonds increases in the excited states.

The total wave function for the ground state (taking the d_{PQ} into account) is

$$X_0 = \sqrt{0.667}\ \Psi_P + \sqrt{0.089}\ \Psi_Q \tag{4-51}$$

and for the excited state

$$X_1 = \sqrt{0.667}\ \Psi_P - \sqrt{1.244}\ \Psi_Q \tag{4-52}$$

4-5. THE EXAMPLE OF BUTADIENE; THE TRIPLET STATES[4]

Butadiene has an even number of π electrons. Thus we obtain not only singlet states but also triplet states and even quintets. In the following treatment we neglect overlap integrals throughout.

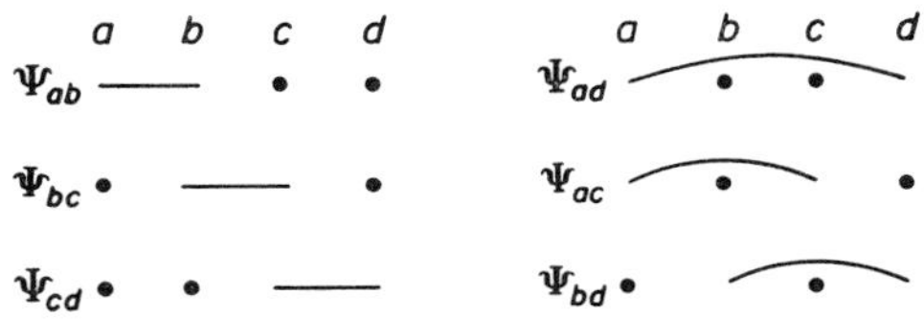

Fig. 4-2

The structures shown in Fig. 4.2 may contribute to the representation of the molecule in its triplet states. The points stand for non-bonded electrons. There are three spin functions for triplet states. We can write simply α for nonbonded electron and then we have the following spin functions for the related structure eigenfunctions.

$$\Psi_{ab}: \quad \frac{1}{\sqrt{2}}\,[\alpha\beta\alpha\alpha - \beta\alpha\alpha\alpha]$$

$$\Psi_{bc}: \quad \frac{1}{\sqrt{2}}\,[-\alpha\alpha\beta\alpha + \alpha\beta\alpha\alpha]$$

$$\Psi_{cd}: \quad \frac{1}{\sqrt{2}}\,[\alpha\alpha\alpha\beta - \alpha\alpha\beta\alpha]$$

$$\Psi_{ad}: \quad \frac{1}{\sqrt{2}}\,[\alpha\alpha\alpha\beta - \beta\alpha\alpha\alpha]$$

$$\Psi_{ac}: \quad \frac{1}{\sqrt{2}}\,[\alpha\alpha\beta\alpha - \beta\alpha\alpha\alpha]$$

$$\Psi_{bd}: \quad \frac{1}{\sqrt{2}}\,[\alpha\alpha\alpha\beta - \alpha\beta\alpha\alpha]$$

[4] The first calculatins on triplet states using the valence-bond method were made by H. Hartmann, *Z. Naturforschung.* **2a:** 684 (1947) and by F. Seel, *ibid.* **3a:** 180 (1948).

There are four spin-arrays in these spin functions ($\alpha\beta\alpha\alpha, \beta\alpha\alpha\alpha,$ $\alpha\alpha\beta\alpha,$ and $\alpha\alpha\alpha\beta$).

It is immediately clear that only three of the six structure eigenfunctions are linearly independent. If we choose the first three, then the other three (with the long bonds) can be expressed as linear sums of the first three.

$$\Psi_{ad} = \Psi_{ab} - \Psi_{bc} + \Psi_{cd}$$

$$\Psi_{ac} = \Psi_{ab} - \Psi_{bc}$$

$$\Psi_{bd} = -\Psi_{bc} + \Psi_{cd}$$

Therefore these can be omitted.

The other set of spin functions is obtained in writing β for all the non bonded electrons:

$$\Psi_{ab}: \quad \frac{1}{\sqrt{2}} [\alpha\beta\beta\beta - \beta\alpha\beta\beta]$$

$$\Psi_{bc}: \quad \frac{1}{\sqrt{2}} [-\beta\alpha\beta\beta + \beta\beta\alpha\beta]$$

$$\Psi_{cd}: \quad \frac{1}{\sqrt{2}} [\beta\beta\alpha\beta - \beta\beta\beta\alpha]$$

The third set of spin functions is analogous to $1/\sqrt{2} [\alpha\beta + \beta\alpha]$ in the dielectronic case. In order to find these spin functions we have to keep in mind that they have to be antisymmetrical with respect to exchange of the spins on atoms that are bonded together, but symmetrical with respect to exchange of the spins on nonbonded atoms. (This is, of course, satisfied with the first and second set of spin functions.) Then we have to use the same spin-arrays as on p. 55 where the spin functions of the singlet states were constructed.

For Ψ_{ab} we can use the spin-arrays having a bond between a and b. These are I, II, III, and IV ($\alpha\beta\alpha\beta, \alpha\beta\beta\alpha, \beta\alpha\alpha\beta, \beta\alpha\beta\alpha$). This is how we can find the right signs in the spin function [44]. We first write

$$a_1 [\alpha\beta\alpha\beta] + a_2 [\alpha\beta\beta\alpha] + a_3 [\beta\alpha\alpha\beta] + a_4 [\beta\alpha\beta\alpha]$$

Exchanging the spins on a and b, the whole expression must change its sign:

$$- a_1 [\beta\alpha\alpha\beta] - a_2 [\beta\alpha\beta\alpha] - a_3 [\alpha\beta\alpha\beta] - a_4 [\alpha\beta\beta\alpha]$$

Now we exchange the spins on c and d; the sign of the expression remains unchanged:

$$a_1 [\alpha\beta\beta\alpha] + a_2 [\alpha\beta\alpha\beta] + a_3 [\beta\alpha\beta\alpha] + a_4 [\beta\alpha\alpha\beta]$$

Since these three expressions are equal, the coefficients of the individual spin-arrays must be the same:

$$a_1 = - a_3 = a_2$$
$$a_2 = - a_4 = a_1$$
$$a_3 = - a_1 = a_4$$
$$a_4 = - a_2 = a_3$$

and the right spin function for Ψ_{ab} is

$$\frac{1}{\sqrt{4}} (\alpha\beta\alpha\beta + \alpha\beta\beta\alpha - \beta\alpha\alpha\beta - \beta\alpha\beta\alpha)$$

For the two other structure eigenfunctions we obtain similarly:

$$\Psi_{bc}: \quad \frac{1}{\sqrt{4}} (- \alpha\alpha\beta\beta - \beta\alpha\beta\alpha + \alpha\beta\alpha\beta + \beta\beta\alpha\alpha)$$

$$\Psi_{cd}: \quad \frac{1}{\sqrt{4}} (\alpha\beta\alpha\beta + \beta\alpha\alpha\beta - \alpha\beta\beta\alpha - \beta\alpha\beta\alpha)$$

In brief this procedure consists in giving opposite sign to spin-arrays, which differ by an exchange of spins in a *bond*, not otherwise.

Each spin-array with the 4! permutations of the electrons corresponds to a Slater determinant. With the notations already used we have

$$\Psi_{ab} = \frac{1}{\sqrt{4}} (\psi_I + \psi_{II} - \psi_{III} - \psi_{IV})$$

$$\Psi_{bc} = \frac{1}{\sqrt{4}} (\psi_I - \psi_{IV} - \psi_V + \psi_{VI}) \qquad (4\text{-}53)$$

$$\Psi_{cd} = \frac{1}{\sqrt{4}} (\psi_I - \psi_{II} + \psi_{III} - \psi_{IV})$$

We shall use these functions now to evaluate the matrix components in order to set up the secular equation. Since we neglect spin-orbital interactions due to the magnetic fields associated with the orbital and spin motions, the three sets of spin functions would lead to the same energy values. It would be simpler to use the first set but since we have already computed (p. 63) all the integrals with the Slater functions contained in the third set, we shall use these latter.

$$H_{ab,ab} \equiv \int \Psi_{ab} H \Psi_{ab} \, dv$$

$$= \tfrac{1}{4} \int (\psi_I + \psi_{II} - \psi_{III} - \psi_{IV}) H (\psi_I + \psi_{II} - \psi_{III} - \psi_{IV}) \, dv$$

$$= \tfrac{1}{4} [H_{I\,I} + H_{II\,II} + H_{III\,III} + H_{IV\,IV} + 2H_{I\,II} - 2H_{I\,III} - 2H_{I\,IV}$$
$$- 2H_{II\,III} - 2H_{II\,IV} + 2H_{III\,IV}]$$

$$= \tfrac{1}{4} [Q - (ac) - (bd) + Q - (ad) - (bc) + Q - (ad)$$
$$- (bc) + Q - (ac) - (bd) - 2(cd) + 2(ab) + 0 - 0$$
$$+ 2(ab) - 2(cd)]$$

$$= \tfrac{1}{4} [4Q - 2(ac) - 2(bd) - 2(ad) - 2(bc) - 4(cd) + 4(ab)]$$

Neglecting interactions between nonneighbors and putting $(ab) = (bc) = (cd) = A$ we obtain

$$H_{ab,ab} = Q - \tfrac{1}{2}A \qquad (4\text{-}54)$$

In the same way we obtain

$$H_{bc,bc} = Q \qquad (4\text{-}55)$$

and

$$H_{cd,cd} = Q - \tfrac{1}{2}A \qquad (4\text{-}56)$$

There are three mixed terms:

$$H_{ab,bc} \equiv \int \Psi_{ab} H \Psi_{bc}\, dv$$

$$= \tfrac{1}{4} \int (\psi_{\mathrm{I}} + \psi_{\mathrm{II}} - \psi_{\mathrm{III}} - \psi_{\mathrm{IV}}) H (\psi_{\mathrm{I}} - \psi_{\mathrm{IV}} - \psi_{\mathrm{V}} + \psi_{\mathrm{VI}})\, dv$$

$$= \tfrac{1}{4}[H_{\mathrm{II}} + H_{\mathrm{III}} - H_{\mathrm{III}} - 2H_{\mathrm{IIV}} - H_{\mathrm{IIIV}} + H_{\mathrm{IIIIV}} + H_{\mathrm{IVIV}} - H_{\mathrm{IV}}$$
$$\quad - H_{\mathrm{IIV}} + H_{\mathrm{IIIV}} + H_{\mathrm{IVV}} + H_{\mathrm{IVI}} + H_{\mathrm{IIVI}} - H_{\mathrm{IIIVI}} - H_{\mathrm{IVVI}}]$$

$$= \tfrac{1}{4}[Q - (ac) - (bd) - (cd) + (ab) - 0 + (ab) - (cd) + Q$$
$$\quad - (ac) - (bd) + (bc) + (bd) - (ac) - (ad) - (ad) - (ac)$$
$$\quad + (bd) + (bc)]$$

$$= \tfrac{1}{4}[2Q - 4(ac) - 2(cd) + 2(ab) + 2(bc) - 2(ad)]$$

In the same approximation as before

$$H_{ab,bc} = \tfrac{1}{2}Q + \tfrac{1}{2}A \qquad (4\text{-}57)$$

and, naturally

$$H_{bc,cd} = \tfrac{1}{2}Q + \tfrac{1}{2}A \qquad (4\text{-}58)$$

In the same way we obtain that

$$H_{ab,cd} = \tfrac{1}{2}A \qquad (4\text{-}59)$$

Furthermore

$$d_{ab,ab} = 1, \qquad d_{bc,bc} = 1, \qquad d_{cd,cd} = 1$$
$$d_{ab,bc} = \tfrac{1}{2}, \qquad d_{bc,cd} = \tfrac{1}{2}, \qquad d_{ab,cd} = 0$$

The secular equation will be as follows:

$$s_{ab}(H_{ab,ab} - Ed_{ab,ab}) + s_{bc}(H_{ab,bc} - Ed_{ab,bc}) + s_{cd}(H_{ab,cd} - Ed_{ab,cd}) = 0$$
$$s_{ab}(H_{ab,bc} - Ed_{ab,bc}) + s_{bc}(H_{bc,bc} - Ed_{bc,bc}) + s_{cd}(H_{bc,cd} - Ed_{bc,cd}) = 0$$
$$s_{ab}(H_{ab,cd} - Ed_{ab,cd}) + s_{bc}(H_{bc,cd} - Ed_{bc,cd}) + s_{cd}(H_{cd,cd} - Ed_{cd,cd}) = 0$$
$$(4\text{-}60)$$

Substituting the values obtained above:

$$s_{ab}(Q - \tfrac{1}{2}A - E) + s_{bc}(\tfrac{1}{2}Q + \tfrac{1}{2}A - \tfrac{1}{2}E) + s_{cd}(\tfrac{1}{2}A) = 0$$
$$s_{ab}(\tfrac{1}{2}Q + \tfrac{1}{2}A - \tfrac{1}{2}E) + s_{bc}(Q - E) + s_{cd}(\tfrac{1}{2}Q + \tfrac{1}{2}A - \tfrac{1}{2}E) = 0 \quad (4\text{-}61)$$
$$s_{ab}(\tfrac{1}{2}A) + s_{bc}(\tfrac{1}{2}Q + \tfrac{1}{2}A - \tfrac{1}{2}E) + s_{cd}(Q - \tfrac{1}{2}A - E) = 0$$

Introducing $(Q - E)/A = X$ we obtain

$$(X - \tfrac{1}{2}) + s_{bc}(\tfrac{1}{2}X + \tfrac{1}{2}) + \tfrac{1}{2}s_{cd} = 0$$
$$(\tfrac{1}{2}X + \tfrac{1}{2}) + s_{bc}X + s_{cd}(\tfrac{1}{2}X + \tfrac{1}{2}) = 0 \qquad (4\text{-}62)$$
$$\tfrac{1}{2} + s_{bc}(\tfrac{1}{2}X + \tfrac{1}{2}) + s_{cd}(X - \tfrac{1}{2}) = 0$$

setting $s_{ab} = 1$.
The determinant of the coefficients

$$\begin{vmatrix} X - \tfrac{1}{2} & \tfrac{1}{2}X + \tfrac{1}{2} & \tfrac{1}{2} \\ \tfrac{1}{2}X + \tfrac{1}{2} & X & \tfrac{1}{2}X + \tfrac{1}{2} \\ \tfrac{1}{2} & \tfrac{1}{2}X + \tfrac{1}{2} & X - \tfrac{1}{2} \end{vmatrix} = 0$$

leads to the equation

$$X^3 - 3X^2 + X + 1 = 0 \qquad (4\text{-}63)$$

which factors to

$$(X - 1)(X^2 - 2X - 1) = 0$$

whose roots are -0.4142, $+1$, and $+2.4142$. Thus, the triplet energy levels are

$$E_0^T = Q + 0.4142A$$
$$E_1^T = Q - A$$
$$E_2^T = Q - 2.4142A$$

For E_0^T the secular determinant becomes

$$-0.9142 + \frac{s_{bc}}{s_{ab}}0.2929 + 0.5\frac{s_{cd}}{s_{ab}} = 0$$

$$0.2929 - \frac{s_{bc}}{s_{ab}}0.4142 + \frac{s_{cd}}{s_{ab}}0.2929 = 0 \qquad (4\text{-}64)$$

$$0.5 + \frac{s_{bc}}{s_{ab}}0.2929 - \frac{s_{cd}}{s_{ab}}0.9142 = 0$$

Subtracting the third equation from the first gives

$$\frac{s_{cd}}{s_{ab}} = 1$$

and then the second equation gives

$$\frac{s_{bc}}{s_{ab}} = 1.4142$$

The condition of normalization is
$$s_{ab}^2 + s_{bc}^2 + s_{cd}^2 + 2s_{ab}s_{bc}d_{ab,bc} + 2s_{ab}s_{cd}d_{ab,cd} + 2s_{bc}s_{cd}d_{bc,cd} = 1 \qquad (4\text{-}65)$$
We obtain

$$s_{ab}^2 = 0.1464$$
$$s_{bc}^2 = 0.2929$$
$$s_{cd}^2 = 0.1464 \quad \text{(continued on p. 74)}$$

$$\tfrac{1}{2} s_{ab} s_{bc} = 0.2071$$
$$\tfrac{1}{2} s_{ab} s_{bc} = \underline{0.2071}$$
$$1.0000$$

Neglecting all but the squared terms we obtain

$$s_{ab}^2 = 0.25, \qquad s_{bc}^2 = 0.50, \qquad s_{cd}^2 = 0.25$$

This would indicate that in the lowest triplet level the structure in which the bond is in the middle is twice as important as any of the two other structures.

For E_1^T we obtain

$$s_{ab}^2 = 0.50, \qquad s_{cb}^2 = 0, \qquad s_{cd}^2 = 0.50$$

and for E_2^T again

$$s_{ab}^2 = 0.25, \qquad s_{bc}^2 = 0.50, \qquad s_{cd}^2 = 0.25$$

There is also a quintet energy level with total spin projection equal to two. It is easiest to assume that all four electrons have the same spin. Then we can disregard spin entirely. Counting only neighbor interactions the energy is

$$E^Q = Q - 3A \tag{4-66}$$

(see p. 61 or the rules on p. 62).

Finally the energy diagrams for butadiene will be as follows in the semi empirical valence-bond approximation:

$$E_Q \quad Q - 3A$$
$$E_2^T \quad Q - 2.4142A$$
$$E_1^S \quad Q - 1.732A$$
$$E_1^T: \quad Q - A$$
$$E_0^T: \quad Q + 0.4142A$$
$$E_0^S: \quad Q + 1.732A$$

So far we have neglected ionic structures, that is, structures where on at least one atom the atomic orbital entering the calculation is occupied by two electrons and on one other atom at least the atomic orbital is empty. For butadiene, for example, such structures include those shown in Fig. 4-3.

Fig. 4.3

The inclusion of such structures in valence-bond calculations will be discussed in Chapter 9.

4-6. AN EXAMPLE WITH AN ODD NUMBER OF ELECTRONS

In certain problems we have an odd number of electrons. An example would be the free radical allyl.

$$CH_2 = CH - \dot{C}H_2$$

provided the $-CH_2$ $-\dot{C}H_2$ group has trigonal hybridation with one π electron, as it probably does.

The easiest way of making valence-bond calculations in such a case is to take the molecule having one more electron (here butadiene) and consider the additional electron as a "phantom," that is to say, infinitely remote from the others. Then we can simply take the expressions for the energies of the even molecule [Eqs. (4-39) through (4-41)] and set equal to zero all the exchange integrals involving the phantom (x). Thus in our example we label a, b, and c the three carbon atoms of the allyl radical and we obtain its energy levels from those of butadiene in equating to zero all exchange integrals containing the letter d (Fig. 4-4). For butadiene we had

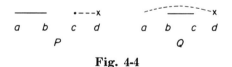

Fig. 4-4

$$H_{pp} = \tfrac{1}{4}[4Q - 2(ac) - 2(bd) - 2(ad) - 2(bc) + 4(ab) + 4(cd)]$$

Neglecting nonneighbor interactions, such as (ac), (bd), and (ad), and omitting (cd) [and (ad)] we obtain for the radical:

$$H_{pp} = Q + \tfrac{1}{2}A \qquad (4\text{-}67)$$

Similarly for structure Q we had

$$H_{QQ} = \tfrac{1}{4}[4Q - 2(ac) - 2(bd) - 2(ab) - 2(cd) + 4(bc) + 4(ad)]$$

For allyl it becomes

$$H_{QQ} = Q + \tfrac{1}{2}A \qquad (4\text{-}68)$$

(Actually P and Q become equivalent in taking d to infinity.) For the mixed term we had

$$H_{PQ} = \tfrac{1}{4}[4Q - 4(ac) - 4(bd) + 2(cd) + 2(ab) + 2(bc) + 2(ad)]$$

Now we have

$$H_{PQ} = \tfrac{1}{2}Q + A \qquad (4\text{-}69)$$

The secular equation is then

$$\begin{vmatrix} X + \frac{1}{2} & \frac{1}{2}X + 1 \\ \frac{1}{2}X + 1 & X + \frac{1}{2} \end{vmatrix} = 0 \tag{4-70}$$

$$X^2 + X + \tfrac{1}{4} - \tfrac{1}{2}X^2 - X - 1 = 0$$

$$3X^2 - 3 = 0, \qquad X = \pm 1$$

$$E_0 = Q + A, \qquad E_1 = Q - A$$

Naturally, the calculation can also be made directly without reference to the next even molecule. The three possible structures are shown in Fig. 4-5.

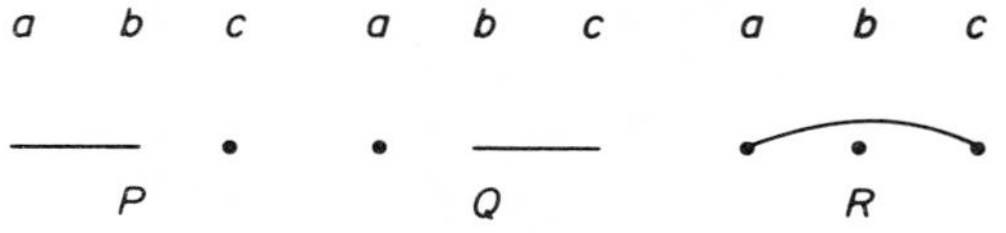

Fig. 4-5

The spin functions have to change sign when we exchange the spins of two electrons which form a bond. Thus, we have for Ψ_P

$$\frac{1}{\sqrt{2}} [\alpha\beta\alpha - \beta\alpha\alpha]$$

for Ψ_Q

$$\frac{1}{\sqrt{2}} [\alpha\beta\alpha - \alpha\alpha\beta]$$

and for Ψ_R

$$\frac{1}{\sqrt{2}} [\alpha\alpha\beta - \beta\alpha\alpha]$$

It is seen immediately that

$$\Psi_R = \Psi_P - \Psi_Q$$

Labeling the Slater functions

$$\psi_I = \frac{1}{\sqrt{3!}} (\alpha\beta\alpha)$$

$$\psi_{II} = \frac{1}{\sqrt{3!}} (\beta\alpha\alpha)$$

$$\psi_{III} = \frac{1}{\sqrt{3!}} (\alpha\alpha\beta)$$

we have

$$H_{I\,I} = Q - (ac), \quad H_{II\,II} = Q - (bc), \quad H_{III\,III} = Q - (ab)$$

$$H_{I\,II} = -(ab), \quad H_{I\,III} = -(bc), \quad H_{II\,III} = -(ac) \tag{4-71}$$

$$H_{PP} = \tfrac{1}{2}[Q - (ac) + Q - (bc) + 2(ab)] = Q + \tfrac{1}{2}A$$

neglecting interactions between non neighbors.

$$H_{QQ} = \tfrac{1}{2}[Q - (ac) + Q - (ab) + 2(bc)] = Q + \tfrac{1}{2}A \qquad (4\text{-}72)$$

$$H_{PQ} = \tfrac{1}{2}[Q - (ac) + (ab) + (bc) - (ac)] = \tfrac{1}{2}Q + A \qquad (4\text{-}73)$$

All the matrix components are the same as before. The states are actually doublets. The other set of spin functions has one α and two β.

There is also a quadruplet state. Giving α spins to all three electrons, the energy of this state is seen to be

$$Q - 2A \qquad (4\text{-}74)$$

The full energy diagram is then

$$E_0^Q: \quad Q - 2A$$
$$E_1^D: \quad Q - A$$
$$E_0^D: \quad Q + A$$

For a more rigorous proof that the various spin functions belong to a given multiplicity we refer to Eyring, Walter, and Kimball [40, p. 235].

4-7. CANONICAL STRUCTURES

Certain special problems are encountered when we apply the valence-bond method to larger molecules.

First of all, the number of possible structure eigenfunctions increases rapidly. In the homopolar, π-electronic approximation benzene has five of them. These are the well-known two Kekulé-type and three Dewar-type structures (Fig. 4-6). Now the question arises how to select a set of mutually independent structure eigenfunctions.

As we have seen in the case of four electrons, a structure with crossed links can always be written as a linear sum of two structures without crossed links, as in Fig. 4-7, where the sign depends on the assignment of signs to the individual Slater functions belonging to a given structure eigenfunction.

Rumer [45] pointed out that the structure eigenfunctions do not

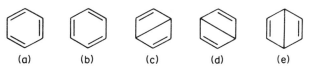

(a)   (b)   (c)   (d)   (e)

Fig. 4-6

Fig. 4-7

a canonical set with the canonical circle shown in Fig. 4–8.

depend on the spatial arrangement of the atoms[5] (although naturally the matrix components do). This means that the above rule is valid for any two pairs of electrons. Any structure eigenfunction in which two links cross can be replaced by the sum of two structure eigenfunctions in which crossing is avoided.

From this follows the well-known rule of Rumer: "Place the atoms on a closed convex curve (for example, a circle) in any order and draw all the structures where no links cross."

Pauling called these structures "canonical" [46]. It is easy to see that for benzene, for example, the five structures in Fig. 4–6 form

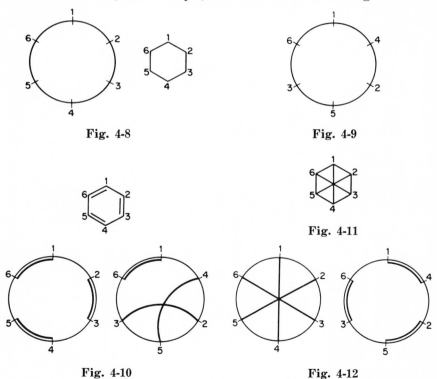

Fig. 4-8   **Fig. 4-9**

Fig. 4-11

Fig. 4-10   **Fig. 4-12**

[5] For example, it cannot be seen from a structure eigenfunction whether two atoms that are bonded together are close neighbors or not.

Since the wave function does not depend on the spatial arrangement of the atoms, the numbers may be written in any other order. Then, however, we obtain a different set of canonical structures. For example, if instead of numbering I we adopt numbering II (Fig. 4-9), we see that Kekulé-structure (a) will not be canonical (Fig. 4.10). The structure shown in Fig. 4-11, on the other hand, will not be canonical according to I but it will be according to II (Fig. 4-12)

In the case of butadiene either P and Q or P and R or Q and R can be taken as a set of canonical structures according to the numbering we adopt in the canonical circle.

Rumer, Teller, and Weyl have shown [47] that the structure eigenfunctions obtained by using Rumer's rule are not only independent from one another but form a complete set. It is just such a complete, independent set of structures that was called "canonical" (see also Eyring, Walter and Kimball. [40, p. 239]. With such a set the matrix components are usually simple.

The number of canonical structures increases rapidly with the size of the molecule. If N is the number of bonds and $2N$ the number of atoms and there is one electron on every atom it is given by the expression [48]

$$\frac{(2N)!}{N!\,(N+1)!} \qquad (4\text{-}75)$$

For naphthalene ($N = 5$) it gives 42, for anthracene ($N = 7$), 429.

Among the structures there are some which contain only bonds between close neighbors. In others there are one, two, three, . . . "long" bonds. The number of structures belonging to each category can be computed from formulas given by Wheland for various types of molecules [49].

Pauling, Brockway, and Beach [43] have defined a bond order in the valence-bond method which can be related to bond distances, bond energies, and chemical reactivity in the same semiempirical way as in the molecular orbital method.

The bond order (I_{rs}) for the bond between atom r and atom s is defined as the sum of the weight of the structures in which there is a bond between r and s.

Daudel and Pullman [50], inspired by an idea of N. Svartholm [51], defined a free valence number for atom r in the following way:

$$J_r = 1 - \sum_s I_{rs} \qquad (4\text{-}76)$$

that is, the difference between unity and the sum of the bond orders of the bonds which have one end on atom r.

The charge densities are equal to unity everywhere if polar structures are excluded, as they have been so far.

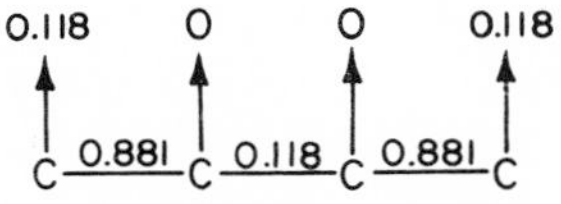

Fig. 4-13

For butadiene the diagram of bond orders and free valence numbers shown in Fig. 4-13 is obtained. Unfortunately these quantities are entirely dependent upon the choice of the set of canonical structures [52]. This is immediately seen from the example above (p. 79), where certain Kekulé-structures were rendered canonical or non canonical following the different order in which the numbers were written in the canonical circle.

Using a little chemical evidence the "reasonable" numbering usually can be easily found, although with nonalternant hydrocarbons this is not always easy [53].

The most important point is that the total energy is independent of the choice of the canonical set of structures.

Penney [54] defined bond orders which are directly linked to the energy and are equally independent from the choice of the canonical set. We are not going to discuss this problem, however.

Resonance energies can be obtained in the valence-bond method in the following way. We compute the total energy and compute the difference between it and the energy the molecule would have if it were represented by only one structure, the one of lowest energy. This is usually a Kekulé-type structure with no long bonds.

For butadiene

$$E_{res} = E_0 - E_K = Q + 1.732A - (Q + 1.5A) = 0.232A \qquad (4\text{-}77)$$

Resonance theory can be regarded as a semi-intuitive extension of the valence-bond method.

Actual calculations become impossible to carry out for large molecules. In the case of anthracene, for example, the secular determinant would be of degree 429. Various simplifications have been made, which consist usually in neglecting certain categories of structures. Structures containing two or more "long" bonds have high energies and have little weight in the ground state (see the values of the H_{PP}) although not necessarily in excited states.

We are now going to deal with the problem of computing the matrix components of the secular determinant in the case of large molecules.

4-8. RULES FOR COMPUTING THE MATRIX COMPONENTS

It is always possible to obtain the matrix components (such as H_{PP}, H_{PQ}, ...) by the method applied at the beginning of this chapter. For more than four electrons, however, this becomes very tedious.

Eyring and Kimball [55] and Pauling [56] gave methods enabling one to write down the matrix components from inspection of the structures only, without developing the structure eigenfunctions into a linear combination of Slater determinants and without regarding all the permutations in the latter.

All matrix components contain the Coulomb integral Q multiplied by a certain coefficient k and the exchange integral A multiplied by a certain coefficient l.

$$H_{XY} = \frac{1}{2^m}(kQ + lA) \qquad (4\text{-}78)$$

m being the number of bonds and $1/2^m$ the normalization factor.

We will discuss the case of singlet states, neglecting exchange integrals between nonneighbors and taking all exchange integrals between neighbors equal (A). Double or higher exchange terms will also be disregarded.

We have to determine the coefficients k and l.

It is easy to determine the coefficient of the coulombic term. Since both structure eigenfunctions are a sum of Slater functions and in a coulombic term the same electrons must be in the same orbitals before and after the Hamilton operator and, furthermore, since only terms where the same electrons have the same spin before and after the operator do not vanish, the integral Q only occurs as many times as there are Slater functions in common between the two structure eigenfunctions. No contribution can come from integrals involving two different Slater functions, since in order to have the spins matched we ought to make permutations and therefore, in any case, should not obtain coulombic integrals.

Eyring [57] gave a method to count the number of Slater functions common to two given structure eigenfunctions. Let us take again the example of butadiene and take first the integral H_{PQ} (Fig. 4-14). If in structure P atom a has α spin projection, b must have β, because a and b are bonded together. Since we are looking for a coulombic term and no permutations of the electrons are possible, a and b must have spin α and β respectively in structure Q too. Now, in Q, b and c are bonded together, thus, c must have α spin. Then c must have α spin in P too and d must have β spin. Thus, if the spin for a in P is given, the others are automatically determined. Eyring called a set of orbitals, whose spins are tied if only one of them is given, a *cycle* and introduced the notation

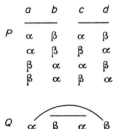

Fig. 4-14

$$\frac{a \quad c}{b \quad d}$$

where α spin is associated with the orbitals that are above the line and β spin with those which are below the line.

The Slater function corresponding to spin-array $\alpha\beta\alpha\beta$ is compatible with the bonding conditions in both P and Q. There is only one other arrangement like this, namely $\beta\alpha\beta\alpha$, where all the α are replaced by β and vice-versa. There cannot be any others, since if one of the spins is tied in the cycle all others are equally tied and only α or β can be assigned to a given orbital. Thus for H_{PQ}, $k = 2$.

The situation is somewhat different for the term H_{PP} (Fig. 4-15).

a	b	c	d
α	β	α	β
α	β	β	α
β	α	α	β
β	α	β	α

Fig. 4-15

Naturally $k = 4$ in this case, since the two structures are the same. It is interesting, however, to form cycles in this case too. If $\underline{a}$ is assigned α spin in the first structure b will have β spin, and the same in both structures. However, the spin of $\underline{c}$ can be chosen freely since c is not bonded to either a or b in any of the two structures. Thus,

$$\frac{a}{b}$$

is a cycle in itself and so is $\dfrac{c}{d}$. This multiplies by two the number of Slater functions the two structures have in common, since $\underline{c}$ can have either α or β spin.

Quite generally, if the number of cycles is i, $k = 2^i$.

In Pauling's method the cycles are called "islands." This is because Pauling superimposes the two structures in order to establish the number of orbitals whose spins can be freely chosen and in order to find the units within which the fixing of one spin ties all the others.

In our example, for P and Q the superposition gives the result

Fig. 4-16   **Fig. 4-17**

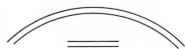

Fig. 4-18

in Fig. 4–16, which is one island; for P and P (Fig. 4–17) there are
two islands; and there are two for Q and Q (Fig. 4–18). An island
is a closed polygon which may have only two sides as in ═══. The
polygon will be closed only if there is a bond between every pair
of neighbor atoms in at least one of the two structures. Thus there
can be only two spin-arrays for any island, but the spin-arrays of
one island do not tie the spins in the other.

The sign on the coulombic integral is positive in any H_{PQ} provided Slater functions occurring in both P and Q are given the same
sign.

So, quite generally,

$$k = 2^i$$

where i is the number of "cycles" or "islands."

It is more difficult to count the number of the exchange integrals
(A) occuring in the H_{PQ}. In order to see the problem clearly let us
recall the expressions of the matrix components of the secular equation in the case of butadiene.

In the approximation stated above, and omitting the factor of
normalization, we had

$$H_{PQ} = 2Q + 2(ab) + 2(bc) + 2(cd)$$

It will be useful to remember where these various contributions
came from:

$$2(ab): \quad \begin{matrix} \alpha\beta\alpha\beta & \alpha\beta\beta\alpha \\ \beta\alpha\alpha\beta & \beta\alpha\beta\alpha \end{matrix}$$

$$2(bc): \quad \begin{matrix} \alpha\beta\alpha\beta & \beta\alpha\beta\alpha \\ \alpha\alpha\beta\beta & \beta\beta\alpha\alpha \end{matrix}$$

$$2(cd): \quad \begin{matrix} \alpha\beta\alpha\beta & \beta\alpha\alpha\beta \\ \alpha\beta\beta\alpha & \beta\alpha\beta\alpha \end{matrix}$$

where in each case the spin-arrays corresponding to the two respective Slater functions yielding the term are below one another.
To obtain an exchange integral we have to make the spins match
in all the orbitals. This can be achieved only between two Slater
functions, which differ only in the spins of two electrons in adjacent
orbitals. These Slater functions, naturally, are available for pairs of
orbitals which are part of the same cycle because cycles correspond
to the same spin-array in both structures, and spin-arrays differing
only by permuting the spins in a *bond* are always contained in the
same structure eigenfunctions. We have two exchange integrals for
any pair of orbitals bonded together, in the same cycle, since any
of the Slater functions will appear once before and once after the
Hamiltonian in the integrals of type

$$\int \psi_{\mathrm{I}} H \psi_{\mathrm{II}}\, dv = \int \psi_{\mathrm{II}} H \psi_{\mathrm{I}}\, dv$$

The sign is positive since the two Slater functions originally differ by one spin permutation, changing sign once, and then we have to make one permutation of electrons in order to match the spins, changing the sign back again.

Therefore, in H_{PQ} we have

$$l = 2 + 2 + 2 = 6$$

For H_{PP} we had

$$H_{PP} = 4Q - 2(bc) + 4(ab) + 4(cd)$$

$$-2(bc): \quad \begin{matrix} \alpha\beta\beta\alpha \\ \alpha\beta\beta\alpha \end{matrix} \qquad \begin{matrix} \beta\alpha\alpha\beta \\ \beta\alpha\alpha\beta \end{matrix}$$

$$4(ab): \quad \begin{matrix} \alpha\beta\alpha\beta \\ \beta\alpha\alpha\beta \text{ twice} \end{matrix} \qquad \begin{matrix} \alpha\beta\beta\alpha \\ \beta\alpha\beta\alpha \text{ twice} \end{matrix}$$

$$4(cd): \quad \begin{matrix} \alpha\beta\alpha\beta \\ \alpha\beta\beta\alpha \text{ twice} \end{matrix} \qquad \begin{matrix} \beta\alpha\alpha\beta \\ \beta\alpha\beta\alpha \text{ twice} \end{matrix}$$

We have two cycles or islands in this case. The integral (bc) represents an exchange between two orbitals which are adjacent but belong to different cycles. These originate, like the coulombic terms, from integrals of type

$$\int \psi_{\mathrm{I}} H \psi_{\mathrm{I}}\, dv$$

where the two Slater functions are the same. They are negative because only electrons are permuted but not the spins. Such a situation can arise only if the two orbitals have the same spin, that is, in half of the cases since the spin of c is not determined by the spin of b, these orbitals not being bonded together in either of the two structures. Half the cases means half the Slater functions, which the two structure eigenfunctions have in common. Then the contribution to l from exchanges between two adjacent atoms being in different cycles is

$$-\frac{2^i}{2}$$

Exchange integrals in islands having the form of a double bond $\left(\text{or cycles of type } \frac{a}{b} \text{ or } \frac{c}{d}\right)$ occur twice as many times because each island independently offers two possibilities. The sign is positive and the contribution to l from each island (cycle) is

$$2^i$$

Thus far we have obtained for matrix components H_{PQ} ($P = Q$ or $P \neq Q$) that

$$H_{PQ} = \frac{1}{2^n}\left[2^i Q + \left(2^i f_1 - \frac{2^i}{2}f_2\right)A\right] \tag{4-79}$$

where f_1 is the number of bonds *in* the islands and f_2 the number of adjacent orbitals between the islands. After rearrangement

$$H_{PQ} = \frac{1}{2^{n-i}}[Q + (f_1 - \tfrac{1}{2}f_2)A] \tag{4-80}$$

There is no real difference between case PP and case PQ nor between double-bondlike islands and islands of different shape. In any case a bond *in* an island contributes two exchange integrals. If, however, there are two islands, another spin becomes free and we shall have 2^2 exchange integrals, etc. Thus, the coefficient of f_1 is 2^i, the same as that in the coulombic integral.

A few examples related to the benzene molecule will make this clearer.

The superposition diagram corresponding to the structures A and A (Fig. 4-19) is shown in Fig. 4-20. Then $n = 3$, $i = 3$, $f_1 = 3$, $f_2 = 3$, and

$$H_{AA} = \frac{1}{2^3}\left[2^3 Q + \left(2^3 f_1 - \frac{2^3}{2}f_2\right)A\right] = Q + (f_1 - \tfrac{1}{2}f_2)A = Q + \tfrac{3}{2}A \tag{4-81}$$

For structures A and B (Fig. 4-21) we have the result shown in Fig. 4-22. Then $n = 3$, $i = 1$, $f_1 = 6$, $f_2 = 0$, and

$$H_{AB} = \frac{1}{2^3}[2Q + 2f_1 A] = \tfrac{1}{4}Q + \tfrac{3}{2}A \tag{4-82}$$

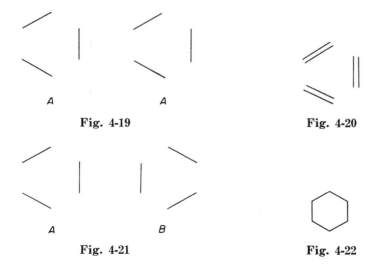

A   A

Fig. 4-19   Fig. 4-20

A   B

Fig. 4-21   Fig. 4-22

For structures A and C (Fig. 4–23)

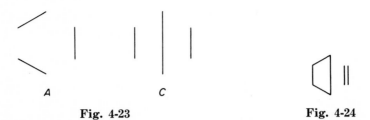

Fig. 4-23   **Fig. 4-24**

we have the result shown in Fig. 4–24. Then $n = 3$, $i = 2$, $f_1 = 4$, $f_2 = 2$, and

$$H_{AC} = \frac{1}{2^3}\left[2^2 Q + \left(2^2 f_1 - \frac{2^2}{2} f_2\right)A\right] = \tfrac{1}{2}Q + \tfrac{3}{2}A \qquad (4\text{-}83)$$

This rule is general and independent of the size of the molecule since we only admit single exchanges.

Fig. 4-25

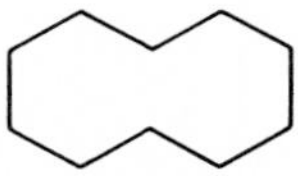

Fig. 4-26

There is, however, one possibility which is not covered by the rule. In larger molecules it may happen that we find adjacent, nonbonded orbitals within an island. As an example consider the superposition of two of the Kekulé structures of naphthalene (Fig. 4–25), which gives the result shown in Fig. 4–26. There are $2^5 = 32$ Slater functions in this case. Writing these down, one finds that there are only two among those of A which become identical with one of those of B after the interchange of the spins on the two central atoms. These are shown in Fig. 4–27. This is no news,

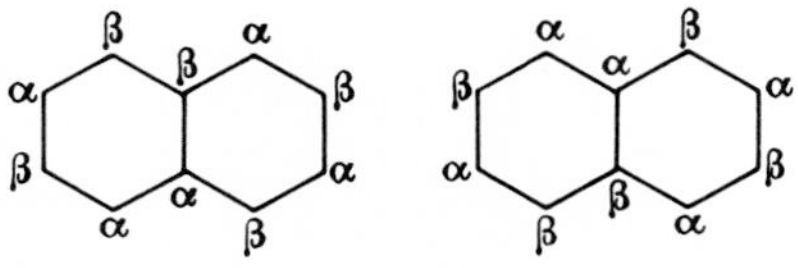

Fig. 4-27

and the number is in general 2^i as we have seen. In structure A these Slater functions have negative signs since they differ by three exchanges of spins of bonded pairs of atoms from the fully alternant one taken as positive. In B, however, the Slater-function, which is obtained by the interchange of the spins on the central atoms, is positive.[6] Therefore, the interaction term between the two is negative, but is made positive again by exchanging the two respective electrons. It follows that the exchange integral between the two central atoms is $+ 2^i$, the same as for a bond between neighbors, and should be counted in f_1. This is always so, if there are two adjacent, nonbonded atoms within an island, separated by an odd number of bonds.

We have finally

$$H_{AB} = \frac{1}{2^{5-1}} [Q + 11A] = \tfrac{1}{16} Q + \tfrac{11}{16} A \qquad (4\text{-}84)$$

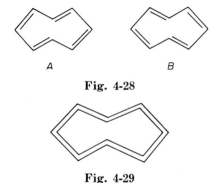

The situation is different if two adjacent, nonbonded atoms are separated by an even number of bonds. We take, as an example, the two structures of the hypothetical hydrocarbon pentalene shown in Fig. 4-28, giving the superposition diagram in Fig. 4-29. There are again two Slater functions among the $2^4 = 16$ belonging to the structure eigenfunction of A, which after the exchange of the spins on the central atoms fit B. These are shown in Fig. 4-30. Both occur with the positive sign in their respective structure eigenfunctions. The exchange of the electrons then changes the sign to negative, giving

$$- 2^i$$

In this case, however, there is, in addition, a contribution coming from those Slater functions which the two structures possess in com-

---

[6] The exchange of the spins of the two central atoms does not change the sign of the Slater function, since these two orbitals are not bonded together in these structures.

As before, the fully alternant spin function is taken as positive in both structure eigenfunctions. The following practical rule is useful: Start giving α spin to a given atom in one structure and then give β to the atom which is bonded to it, whether it is a short or a long bond. Then go on in the same direction assigning to the orbitals alternately α and β until you obtain the fully alternant spin-array.

In the other structure start assigning α to the *same* atom as in the first structure, then assign β to the atom to which it is bonded in the second structure, and continue in the direction determined in this way.

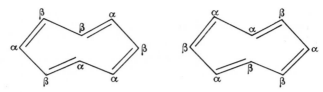

Fig. 4-30

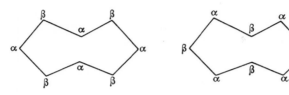

Fig. 4-31

mon (Fig. 4–31). Unlike the case of naphthalene, here in these common Slater functions the two central atoms have the same spin, giving another $- 2^i$. Together we have obtained

$$- 2 \times 2^i$$

This applies in all cases where there are adjacent nonbonded atoms, within the same island, separated by an even number of bonds. Let us call the number of such pairs of atoms f_3. Then, we have the complete general formula for the matrix component between any two structures P and Q:

$$H_{PQ} = \frac{1}{2^n} \left[2^i Q + \left(2^i f_1 - \frac{2^i}{2} f_2 - 2 \cdot 2^i f_3 \right) A \right]$$

or

$$H_{PQ} = \frac{1}{2^{n-i}} [Q + (f_1 - \tfrac{1}{2} f_2 - 2f_3) A] \qquad (4\text{–}85)$$

For more complicated cases—if, for example, the inclusion of non-neighbor interactions is desired—the reader is advised to consult the original publications of Eyring and Kimball [55,58] and Pauling [56].

The above formula applies only to singlet states. Eyring, Frost, and Turkevich published general rules for states of any multiplicity [59].

4.9 REFERENCES TO SOME FUNDAMENTAL WORKS CONCERNING THE VALENCE-BOND METHOD

Following is a list of some of the fundamental papers concerning the valence-bond method.

W. Heitler and F. London, *Z. Physik*, **44.** 455 (1927) (the original treatment of the H_2 molecule).

S. Wang, *Phys. Rev.*, **31,** 579 (1928).

J. C. Slater, *Phys. Rev.*, **38,** 1109 (1931) (where the method is developed for polyatomic molecules).

N. Rosen, *Phys. Rev.*, **38,** 2099 (1931).

S. Weinbaum, *J. Chem. Phys.*, **1,** 317 (1933).

J. Van Vleck and A. Sherman, *Rev. Mod. Phys.*, **7,** 168, 200 (1935).

Y. Sugiura, *Z. Physik*, **45,** 484 (1937).

5

Intensities of Spectral Transitions

5-1. THE EINSTEIN ABSORPTION AND EMISSION COEFFICIENTS

The intensity of *absorption* for a transition from state of energy E_n to state of energy $E_m (E_m > E_n)$ may be defined as the energy absorbed from the incident beam of $1 cm^2$ cross section per unit time. If ω_{nm} is the wave number of the incident radiation, which is isotropic and unpolarized, where $\omega_{nm} = \nu_{nm}/c$ and $\rho(\omega)$ is its radiation density,[1] meaning that $\rho(\omega) d\omega$ is the energy per unit volume in the range $d\omega$ at ω, then

$$I_{abs} = \rho(\omega) N_n B_{nm} hc\omega \Delta l \qquad (5\text{-}1)$$

where N_n is the number of atoms or molecules *per cm³* in the initial state, B_{nm} is Einstein's coefficient of absorption, which is characteristic of the atom or molecule, and Δl is the thickness of the layer (in cm), assumed thin. $\rho(\omega) d\omega$ is measured in erg cm^{-3}, while $\rho(\omega)$ is the radiant energy per wave-number interval and is measured in erg cm^{-2}. The product $N_n B_{nm} \rho(\omega)$ represents the number of photons absorbed or the number of transitions which take place per cm³ per second. The units for I_{abs} as defined above are erg $cm^{-2} sec^{-1}$, and B_{nm} has the curious units sec g^{-1}. The exciting light is supposed to contain all the frequencies contributing to the absorption band in question.

The transition is a consequence of the interaction between the electromagnetic field of the radiation and the field of the atom or

[1] For the sake of simplicity from now on the indices *n m* will be omitted from ω.

molecule. If the atom or molecule is excited it can interact with the electromagnetic field of the radiation in releasing energy to it, instead of receiving energy from it, as in absorption. It is assumed that the Einstein emission coefficient for this *induced emission* is the same as for (induced) absorption:

$$B_{nm} = B_{mn} \qquad (5\text{-}2)$$

However, the excited atom or molecule emits radiation even in the absence of an external electromagnetic field, and we have to introduce a coefficient for *spontaneous* emission:

$$A_{mn}$$

The intensity of emission is defined as the number of photons emitted by the source per second, in the absence of an external electromagnetic field. If N_m is the number of excited molecules in the source, then

$$I_{\text{em}} = N_m A_{mn} hc\,\omega \qquad (5\text{-}3)$$

The units for I_{em} are erg sec^{-1} and for A_{mn} simply sec^{-1}.

As we shall see, the ratio of A_{mn} and B_{mn} can be fairly easily calculated. The proportionality factor contains the third power of ω and, therefore, the relative contribution of the two kinds of emission varies widely according to the spectral region. According to Dirac's radiation theory [1, 2] the two phenomena are not really fundamentally different.

The values of A_{mn} and B_{mn} for a given transition are an intrinsic property of the atom or molecule and are the same whether there is thermal equilibrium or not.

If thermal equilibrium is established, the Maxwell-Boltzmann distribution law applies and makes it possible to compute the ratio of the two emission coefficients. Then the same number of molecules undergo transitions from n to m as from m to n and we can write (referring N_n and N_m to the same volume)

$$N_n B_{nm} \rho(\omega) = N_m \{A_{mn} + B_{mn}\rho(\omega)\} \qquad (5\text{-}4)$$

or

$$\frac{N_m}{N_n} = \frac{B_{nm}\rho(\omega)}{A_{mn} + B_{mn}\rho(\omega)} \qquad (5\text{-}5)$$

On the other hand the distribution law gives

$$\frac{N_m}{N_n} = \frac{e^{-E_m/kT}}{e^{-E_m/kT}} = e^{-(E_m - E_n)/kT} = e^{-hc\omega/kT} \qquad (5\text{-}6)$$

Equating (5-5) and (5-6) we obtain

$$e^{-hc\omega/kT} = \frac{B_{nm}\rho(\omega)}{A_{mn} + B_{mn}\rho(\omega)} \qquad (5\text{-}7)$$

We express the radiation density $\rho(\omega)$:

$$\rho(\omega) = \frac{A_{mn}/B_{mn}}{e^{hc\omega/kT} - 1} \tag{5-8}$$

We can now use the expression given for $\rho(\omega)$ by Planck's black-body radiation formula [60] which is

$$\rho(\omega) = 8\pi hc\omega^3 \frac{1}{e^{hc\omega/kT} - 1} \tag{5-9}$$

From (5-8) and (5-9)

$$A_{mn} = 8\pi hc\omega^3 B_{mn} \tag{5-10}$$

5-2. TRANSITION MOMENTS

Possessing this relation, we now need only compute Einstein's coefficient for induced emission or absorption. This can be done by using the time-dependent Schrödinger equation.

$$H\Psi = -\frac{h}{2\pi i}\frac{\partial \Psi}{\partial t} \tag{5-11}$$

(see Chapter 2, p. 11).

We suppose that H^0 is the Hamiltonian of the unperturbed system and that $H'(t)$ represents the perturbation due to the interaction between the system and the electromagnetic field of the radiation and carry through a time-dependent perturbation calculation. This was first done by Dirac (see [1, 2]). We shall follow the treatments given by Pauling and Wilson [9] and Pitzer [7]. The Schrödinger equation then becomes

$$H^0\Psi + H'(t)\Psi = -\frac{h}{2\pi i}\frac{\partial \Psi}{\partial t} \tag{5-12}$$

The time-dependent wave function of the perturbed system can be expanded in terms of the complete series of the wave functions of the unperturbed system, since the latter form a complete orthonormal set of functions.

$$\Psi = \sum a_k(t)\Psi_k^0 \tag{5-13}$$

the coefficients $a_k(t)$ being time-dependent. Substituting (5-13) into (5-12),

$$\sum a_k(t)H^0\Psi_k^0 + \sum a_k(t)H'(t)\Psi_k^0$$
$$= -\frac{h}{2\pi i}\sum \frac{da_k(t)}{dt}\Psi_k^0 + \sum a_k(t)\left(-\frac{h}{2\pi i}\right)\frac{\partial \Psi_k^0}{\partial t} \tag{5-14}$$

The first and last terms cancel because of (5-11) and there remains

$$\sum a_k(t)H'(t)\Psi_k^0 = -\frac{h}{2\pi i}\sum \frac{da_k(t)}{dt}\Psi_k^0 \tag{5-15}$$

We now multiply by Ψ_m^{0*} and integrate.

$$\sum a_k(t) \int \Psi_m^{0*} H'(t) \Psi_k^0 \, d\tau = -\frac{h}{2\pi i}\frac{da_m(t)}{dt} \tag{5-16}$$

On the right-hand side, since the a_k are functions of time only and not of the space coordinates represented by $d\tau$, only the term with $m = k$ remains; the others vanish because of the orthogonality of the Ψ_k^0 of which Ψ_m^0 is one.

If at $t = 0$ the system is in state n, then $a_n(0) = 1$ and all the other $a_k(0)$ are equal to zero. We assume that this is still true a very short time after $t = 0$, which is required by the transition. Then all the terms are zero at the left-hand side of (5–16) except the one with $a_n(t)$ and we can write

$$\frac{da_m(t)}{dt} = -\frac{2\pi i}{h}e^{2\pi i(E_m - E_n)t/h} \int \psi_m^* H'(t)\psi_n \, d\tau \tag{5-17}$$

where the time-dependent parts of the wave functions are now put before the sign of the integral, and under the integral there are the time-*independent* wave functions.

Integrating equation (5–17) yields a_m, and $a_m^* a_m$ can be considered as the probability that the perturbation carried the system from state E_n to E_m. This follows because the average value of the energy is

$$\bar{E} = \frac{\int \Psi^* E \Psi \, d\tau}{\int \Psi^* \Psi \, d\tau} \tag{5-18}$$

and substituting from (5–13) gives

$$\bar{E} = \frac{\sum a_k^* a_k E_k}{\sum a_k^* a_k} \tag{5-19}$$

We see that this treatment amounts to considering the electronic transition as a result of the perturbation.

At this stage we have to make precise the nature of the perturbation, i.e., find an adequate expression for $H'(t)$.

The x component of the dipole moment can be written as

$$M_x = \sum_i e_i x_i$$

where the summation extends to all the charged particles (electrons and nuclei) of the system. This quantity will vary under the perturbation and it is reasonable to assume that the product of the *instantaneous* dipole moment and the x component of the strength of the electromagnetic field is a good representation of the perturbing Hamiltonian.

$$H'(t) = F_x(\omega, t) \sum_i e_i x_i = F_x(\omega, t) M_x \tag{5-20}$$

The dipole moment is a function of the x_i and, therefore, its wave-mechanical expectation value (see Chapter 2, p. 18) for a state k is

$$(M_x)_{kk} = \int \psi_k^* M_x \psi_k \, d\tau \tag{5-21}$$

The field strength oscillates periodically in time and in space but we shall assume that it is constant all over the space occupied by the system. This is a fair approximation, since the molecular dimensions are of the order of a few angstroms while the wavelength of ultra-violet or visible light is several thousands of angstroms. (However, this assumption amounts to neglecting quadrupole radiation. See Sec. 5-6.)

The electromagnetic field of the radiation is represented by an oscillating electric vector F and an oscillating magnetic vector H which are perpendicular to one another and to the direction of propagation of the waves. They have equal magnitude provided F is measured in electrostatic units and H in electromagnetic units. It follows from Maxwell's equations that the energy density of the radiation field is equal to

$$\rho(\omega) \, d\omega = \frac{1}{8\pi} (\overline{F^2} + \overline{H^2}) = \frac{\overline{F^2}}{4\pi} \tag{5-22}$$

The near-totality of the interaction with the electrons will be due to the electric field of the radiation, the contribution of its magnetic field being negligible. This is because the force exerted on a particle of charge e by the electric field is eF but the force exerted on the same particle by the magnetic field is evH/c, where v is the velocity of the particle and c the speed of light. Since for all atomic or molecular systems $v \ll c$, the latter force is very much smaller than the former. This is linked to the fact that an electric field moves a charged particle according to its own direction but a magnetic field moves it perpendicularly to its direction. For the x component of the electric vector we can write

$$F_x(\omega, t) = 2F_x^0(\omega) \cos 2\pi c \omega t = F_x^0(e^{2\pi i c \omega t} + e^{-2\pi i c \omega t}) \tag{5-23}$$

where $2F_x^0$ is the amplitude of $F_x(\omega, t)$.

From (5-22) and (5-23), since the average value of $\cos^2 2\pi c \omega t$ is $\frac{1}{2}$, we have for the radiation density related to the x component:

$$\frac{F_x^{02}}{4\pi} \tag{5-24}$$

Then, introducing

$$\int \psi_m^* H'(t) \psi_m \, d\tau = F_x(\omega, t)(M_x)_{mn}$$

into (5-17) we obtain

$$\frac{da_m}{dt} = -(M_x)_{mn} F^0_x(\omega)\frac{2\pi i}{h}[e^{2\pi i(Em/h - En/h + c\omega)t} + e^{2\pi i(Em/h - En/h - c\omega)t}] \quad (5\text{-}25)$$

where the exponential (time-dependent) parts of (5-17) and (5-23) are taken together.

Integrated this gives

$$a_m(t) = (M_x)_{mn} F^0_x(\omega)\left[\frac{1 - e^{2\pi i(Em/h - En/h + c\omega)t}}{E_m - E_n + hc\omega} + \frac{1 - e^{2\pi i(Em/h - En/h - c\omega)t}}{E_m - E_n - hc\omega}\right]$$

$$(5\text{-}26)$$

The constants of integration were chosen in such a way that at $t = 0$, $a_m(t)$ should be zero in conformity with our previous supposition. This is what introduces the 1 in the numerators of the expressions in the brackets.

Since $a^*_m a_m$ is the probability that the transition from n to m took place, it is necessary to establish now under what circumstances (5-26) can be different from zero.

The numerators of the two fractions in the brackets vary only from 0 to 2 (the exponentials being equivalent to a sin or cos function) and since $(M_x)_{mm} F^0_x(c\omega)$ is usually small for a single frequency, the fractions are significantly different from zero only if the denominator is (near) zero.

Then in absorption $(E_m > E_n)$ we can neglect the first fraction, $(E_m - E_n)$ and $hc\omega$ having there the same sign, and the second fraction will be appreciable only for

$$hc\omega = E_m - E_n$$

which is the Bohr condition.

Similarly in emission the second fraction can be neglected and the first one will be significant only for

$$E_n - E_m = hc\omega$$

Dealing with an absorption band, we use a continuous source and we have to integrate according to ω. Only a narrow range of frequencies around the Bohr frequency will make a nonnegligible contribution, however, and we can take $-\infty$ and $+\infty$ as limits. Integrating and taking the square of (5-26) gives[2]

$$a^*_m(t)a_m(t) = 4(M_x)^2_{mn}\int [F^0_x(\omega)]^2 \frac{\sin^2 \pi t\left(\dfrac{E_m}{h} - \dfrac{E_n}{h} - c\omega\right)}{(E_m - E_n - hc\omega)^2}d\omega \quad (5\text{-}27)$$

We can take $F^0_x(\omega)$ constant across the narrow range of frequencies and using

$$\int_{-\infty}^{+\infty}\frac{\sin^2 x}{x^2}dx = \pi$$

[2] Using $\sin^2 x = \dfrac{1 - \cos 2x}{2}$

we obtain that

$$a_m^*(t)a_m(t) = \frac{4\pi^2}{h^2 c}(M_x)^2_{mn}F_x^{0^2}(\omega)t \qquad (5\text{-}28)$$

Remembering that the exciting wave is never really monochromatic but contains a small range of frequencies, and taking into account now the x, y, z components of the field strength, supposing the radiation isotropic we have

$$\rho(\omega)d\omega = \frac{1}{4\pi}[\overline{F_x^2(\omega)} + \overline{F_y^2(\omega)} + \overline{F_z^2(\omega)}]$$

$$= \frac{3}{4\pi}\overline{F_x^2(\omega)} = \frac{6}{4\pi}F_x^{0^2}(\omega) \qquad (5\text{-}29)$$

The probability of transition is

$$a_m^* a_m = B_{mn}\rho(\omega)\,d\omega t$$

or, for radiation polarized in the x direction:

$$\frac{4\pi^2}{h^2 c}(M_x)^2_{mn}F_x^{0^2}(\omega)t = B_{mn}\frac{6}{4\pi}F_x^{0^2}(\omega)t$$

hence

$$B_{mn} = \frac{8\pi^3}{3h^2 c}(M_x)^2_{mn}$$

In the general case

$$B_{mn} = \frac{8\pi^3}{3h^2 c}[(M_x)^2_{mn} + (M_y)^2_{mn} + (M_z)^2_{mn}] = \frac{8\pi^3}{3h^2 c}(M^2)_{mn} \qquad (5\text{-}30)$$

The coefficient for spontaneous emission, using (5-10), is

$$A_{mn} = 8\pi hc\omega^3 B_{mn}$$

$$= \frac{64\pi^4\omega^3}{3h}[(M_x)^2_{mn} + (M_y)^2_{mn} + (M_z)^2_{mn}] = \frac{64\pi^4\omega^3}{3h}(M)^2_{mn} \qquad (5\text{-}31)$$

where, because of ω^3, spontaneous emission is highly favored for transitions of high frequency.

At the heart of the matter are the expressions

$$(M_x)_{mn} = \int \psi_m^* \sum_i e_i x_i \psi_n\,d\tau$$

called *transition moment*. (This is, of course, not the permanent dipole moment of any of the states involved, nor their difference.)

If all three components are zero, the transition is forbidden, and its intensity is zero. If at least one of the components is nonvanishing, the transition is allowed. If only one, say the x component, is different from zero, the transition is said to be polarized according to the x axis. If two of the components, say x and y, are different from zero, the transition is polarized in the xy plane.

It is perhaps worthwhile to elaborate on this point. In the argument that lead us to the x component of the transition probability we introduced the product of the x component of the electric field strength and the x component of the variable dipole moment of the molecule. Thus, in the expression of the transition moment x represents not only the direction of the dipole moment component but also the direction in which the oscillations of the electric field vector take place, i.e., its direction of polarization. If the electric field has no component in the x direction—is polarized perpendicularly to it—no x axis-polarized transition can take place.

Let us consider a molecule with fixed orientation, as in a crystal. We could think, for example, of the naphthalene molecule with the x and y axes in the plane of the molecule and the z axis perpendicular to it (Fig. 5-1). It is known (p. 240, 342) that the first (lowest frequency) transition of naphthalene at about 3080Å is polar-

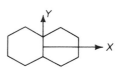

Fig. 5-1

ized in the x direction, the second one, at about 2750 Å, in the y direction. Thus, if the exciting light is polarized in the x direction (and is of the right frequency), the first band will appear but the second one will be absent, and if the light is polarized in the y direction the reverse is the case. (In both cases the direction of propagation of the light beam is the z direction, light being a transverse wave.) If light is polarized in any other direction, it will have a component in both the x and the y directions and both bands will appear with intensities depending on the angle of polarization. In general, absorption spectra are measured with unpolarized light, which contains waves polarized in all directions. Measurements in polarized light are of great help in making assignments of observed bands to transitions predicted by theoretical calculations. [Then, in Eqs. (5–29) through (5–31), $3h^2$ has to be replaced by h^2, since two components of F are then zero.]

If the molecules are randomly distributed, as in a gas or in solutions, and polarized light is used for irradiation, the individual molecules will absorb more or less according to their orientation. This is true also for every wave in unpolarized light, and using polarized or unpolarized light does not alter the intensity of absorption.

In emission spectra the molecules emit polarized light, which is observed as such if the molecules are oriented, but is observed as unpolarized light if the molecules are randomly oriented in space.

The treatment given in this chapter applies to the 0-0 band, that is, the purely electronic transition. For all other bands the complete (electronic-vibrational) wave function has to be used.

5-3. DIPOLE AND OSCILLATOR STRENGTH

We are now going to introduce some other quantities, which are often used in dealing with the intensities of band systems [61].

The transition moment components are, as stated above, of the form

$$(M_x)_{mn} = \int \psi_m^* \sum_i e_i x_i \psi_n \, d\tau$$

Often the electronic charge is written before the integral sign and then we have

$$(M_x)_{mn} = e \int \psi_m^* \sum_i x_i \psi_n \, d\tau = e Q_{mn} \tag{5-32}$$

with $Q_{nm}^2 = (Q_x^2)_{nm} + (Q_y)_{nm}^2 + (Q_z)_{nm}^2$.

So far our formulas apply to the case when both energy levels implied in the transition are nondegenerate. If the levels are degenerate (5-30) and (5-31) have to be replaced by

$$B_{mn} = \frac{8\pi^3}{3h^2 c} \frac{\sum (M^{n'm'})_{mn}^2}{g_n} \tag{5-33}$$

and

$$A_{mn} = \frac{64\pi^4 \omega^3}{3h} \frac{\sum (M^{n'm'})_{mn}}{g_m} \tag{5-34}$$

where g_n and g_m are the degeneracies of the respective initial state and n' and m' mark the sublevels belonging to degenerate levels n and m. The summation has to be extended over all possible combinations between sublevels.

Somewhat less rigorously we may suppose that all the $M^{n'm'}$ are equal. Then, if G is the degeneracy of the *final* state, 1 for non degenerate states, 2 for doubly degenerate states, and so forth,

$$B_{mn} = \frac{8\pi^3}{3h^2 c} G(M)_{mn}^2 \tag{5-35}$$

and

$$A_{mn} = \frac{64\pi^4 \omega^3}{3h} G(M)_{mn}^2 \tag{5-36}$$

The quantity

$$D_{nm} = G Q_{nm}^2$$

is called the dipole strength; its units are simply cm². It is related to Einstein's coefficients by

$$B_{mn} = \frac{8\pi^3 e^2}{3h^2 c} D_{mn} = 14.50 \cdot 10^{24} D_{mn} \tag{5-37}$$

and

$$A_{mn} = \frac{64\pi^4 \omega^3 e^2}{3h} D_{mn} = 7.24 \cdot 10^{10} \omega^3 D_{mn} \qquad (5\text{-}38)$$

From (5-1) the intensity of absorption per unit volume is

$$I'_{abs} = N_n B_{nm} \rho(\omega) hc\omega \qquad (5\text{-}39)$$

In this expression N_n and $\rho(\omega)$ are external factors depending on the conditions of the experiment, while B_{nm} and ω_{nm} are characteristic of the molecule.

Using

$$M_{mn}^2 = [(M_x)_{mn}^2 + (M_y)_{mn}^2 + (M_z)_{mn}^2]$$

we have from (5-35)

$$I'_{abs} = N_n \frac{8\pi^3}{3h^2 c} G M_{mn}^2 \rho(\omega) \, hc\,\omega \qquad (5\text{-}40)$$

or, from (5-37),

$$I'_{abs} = N_n \frac{8\pi^3 e^2}{3h^2 c} D_{nm} \rho(\omega) \, hc\,\omega \qquad (5\text{-}41)$$

Another quantity which is often used in relation to intensities is f, the oscillator strength. In classical electromagnetic theory the intensity of absorption was given by

$$I'_{abs} = N_n \pi f \frac{e^2}{m_e c} \rho(\omega) \qquad (5\text{-}42)$$

where m_e is the mass of the electron. An electron was considered as an oscillator having its own characteristic frequency which could be excited by electromagnetic waves having the same frequency (resonance). For a three-dimensional harmonic oscillator f would be equal to 1 in the above formula (it would be $\frac{1}{3}$ for a one-dimensional oscillator, $\frac{2}{3}$ for a two-dimensional one). If there is more than one electron in an atom or molecule it would be considered as a system of coupled oscillators. Then f in (5-42) would measure the *effective* number of electrons whose oscillations give rise to a given line or band in a spectrum. The sum of the f values over all the bands for a given system (which is finite in the classical theory) is equal to the number of electrons of the system. This is known as the Kuhn-Thomas sum rule [62].

The classical electromagnetic theory is, of course, no longer considered applicable to the interaction of light with atoms or molecules. However, if we compare the quantum-mechanical (5-40) and classical (5-42) formulas for I'_{abs}, we see that the latter can be made identical with the former by means of a reinterpretation of f. Then we have

$$f\frac{\pi e^2}{m_e c} = \frac{8\pi^3 \omega}{3h}GM_{nm}^2 \tag{5-43}$$

whence

$$f = \frac{8\pi^2 \omega m_e c}{3he^2}GM_{nm}^2 \tag{5-44}$$

It can be shown [63] that in this way the Kuhn-Thomas sum rule is valid in quantum mechanics, except that the number of transitions from the ground state is now infinite owing to the continuous energy levels connected with ionization.

Thus, the classical expression of I_{abs} (5-42) is valid in wave mechanics provided we use the oscillator strength as given by (5-44).

From (5-41) and (5-42) the relationship between f_{nm} and D_{nm} is

$$f_{nm} = \frac{8\pi^2 m_e c\omega}{3h}D_{nm} = 1.085\cdot 10^{11}\omega D_{nm} \tag{5-45}$$

f is a dimensionless quantity; the units for D_{nm} are cm^2. D_{nm} is often expressed in Å^2 instead of cm^2. Then in (5-45) 10^{11} has to be replaced by 10^{-5} to have the same f_{nm} value. The relation between f_{nm} and B_{nm} is

$$f_{nm} = \frac{hc^2 m_e}{\pi e^2}\omega B_{nm} = 7.483\cdot 10^{-15}\omega B_{nm} \tag{5-46}$$

One reason why oscillator strength is favored is the close connection of this quantity with polarizability and refractive index. This subject, however, will not be treated in this book. (See, for an excellent account, [8, part V].)

5-4. COMPARISON BETWEEN THEORETICAL AND EXPERIMENTAL QUANTITIES

This far all the quantities introduced to characterize intensities have been purely theoretical. Our next task is to relate these to experimentally measured intensities. It was Mulliken [64, 65] who pioneered this field.

The intensity of absorption has been expressed as (5-1):

$$I_{abs} = \rho(\omega)N_n B_{nm}hc\omega\,\Delta l \tag{5-47}$$

We can introduce into this expression the intensity of the incident light, I, which is the energy falling on 1 cm^2 per second,[3] if we multiply $\rho(\omega)\,d\omega$ by the speed of light.

$$I = c\rho(\omega)\,d\omega \tag{5-48}$$

in units erg cm^{-2} sec^{-1}. We multiply both sides of (5-47) by $d\omega$ and

[3] Or the energy per cm^{-1} interval passing through 1 cm^3 of the absorbing medium per second.

substitute (5–48) into (5–47). We obtain

$$I_{\text{abs}}\,d\omega = I N_n B_{nm} h\omega\,\Delta l \tag{5–49}$$

We now consider the passing of I through an absorbing layer which we regard as divided into thin layers Δl (Fig. 5–2). Part ΔI_1 of I will be absorbed by Δl. It will be proportional to both I and Δl,

$$\Delta I_1 = -\alpha I\,\Delta l$$

where α, the absorption coefficient, depends on the properties of the layer's material. The negative sign is used because I_1 is a decrease of I. For the second layer the incident light will be less than I and we shall have

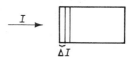

Fig. 5-2

$$\Delta I_2 = -\alpha(I - \Delta I_1)\,\Delta l$$

and so forth. In the limiting case when the layers are infinitesimal

$$dI = -\alpha I\,dl \tag{5–50}$$

hence

$$\int \frac{dI}{I} = -\int \alpha\,dl$$

and

$$\ln I = -\alpha l + C \tag{5–51}$$

The constant can be determined from the fact that if $l = 0$, $I = I_0$, and from (5–51) $C = \ln I_0$. Thus

$$\ln \frac{I}{I_0} = -\alpha l \tag{5–52}$$

or

$$I = I_0 e^{-\alpha l} \tag{5–53}$$

where I is the intensity of the transmitted light. Taking the reciprocal,

$$\ln \frac{I_0}{I} = \alpha l \tag{5–54}$$

From (5–53), if $\alpha = 1/l$, $I = I_0/e$. Thus, the absorption coefficient is the reciprocal of the layer which diminishes the incident light intensity by e. (2.7172). Its unit is cm^{-1}. Using Briggs' logarithms,

$$I = I_0 10^{-kl}$$

or

$$\log \frac{I_0}{I} = kl \tag{5–55}$$

where the new absorption coefficient k is the reciprocal of the length that would diminish I_0 ten times.

For a solution where only the solute molecules are assumed to absorb, the concentration and length play the same role and we have

$$I = I_0 10^{-\epsilon cl} \tag{5-56}$$

or

$$\log \frac{I_0}{I} = \epsilon cl \tag{5-57}$$

where c is the concentration in moles per liter and l the cell length in centimeters. Equation (5-57) is the well-known combined Beer-Bouguer-Lambert law.

ϵ is the molecular extinction coefficient whose units are liter $mole^{-1} cm^{-1}$; it is a widely used quantity in chemical spectroscopy (see Chapter 1).

The expressions for gases and solutions can be combined if we take for the concentration of the gas at 0°C at 1 atm pressure, $c = 1/22.41$ mole liter^{-1}. If, as often is the case, we want to pass from $\ln (I_0/I)$ for a gas (natural logarithms) to $\log (I_0/I)$ (Briggs' logarithms), then

$$\ln \frac{I_0}{I} = \alpha l = \log \frac{I_0}{I} \ln 10 \frac{1}{22.41} \epsilon l$$

and

$$\alpha = \frac{\ln 10}{22.41} \epsilon = 0.1028 \epsilon \tag{5-58}$$

This equality would only hold, however, if the solvent did not influence the intensity of the bands. This is never exactly the case.

Since I_0 is now the intensity of the incident light and I the intensity of the transmitted light, we may write

$$I_{abs} = I_0 - I = \Delta I$$

Hence, comparing (5-49) and (5-50) multiplying the latter by $d\omega$ we have

$$\alpha(\omega) \, d\omega = N_n B_{nm} h\omega \tag{5-59}$$

This would be true, however, only if the band were infinitesimally thin, which in reality it is not. The bands are broadened by a number of effects, natural line width, Doppler effect, Stark effect, pressure, and solvent effects. In the case of molecules, and even more so for polyatomic molecules, the states n and m contain a whole series of vibrational and rotational states. This has to be taken into account if we compare theoretical and experimental quantities. We quote from Mulliken [61]:

"We may liken the molecular spectrum, if it is continuous, to a very broad atomic line; if it has band structure, to an atomic line having fine structure. Just as the strength of a single atomic line is obtained experimentally from (and is defined by) the integral of intensity over the whole width of the line, so the strength of a molecular electronic transition can be obtained experimentally from, and be defined by, the integral of intensity over all the band-lines and the whole of the continuum belonging to the particular electronic transition."

Hence, instead of (5-50) we write

$$\int \alpha(\omega) \, d\omega = N_n B_{nm} h\omega \tag{5-60}$$

where for ω an average value is taken for approximate calculations, usually the frequency corresponding to the center of the band.

We want to introduce now the dipole strength, D. Using (5-37) we obtain

$$\int \alpha(\omega) \, d\omega = N_n \frac{8\pi^3 e^2}{3hc} D_{nm} \omega \tag{5-61}$$

and

$$D_{nm} = \frac{3hc}{N_n 8\pi^3 e^2 \omega} \int \alpha(\omega) \, d\omega \tag{5-62}$$

Numerically, since at 0°C and 1 atmosphere

$$N_n = 2.69 \times 10^{-19} \quad \text{molecules/cm}^3$$

$$D_{nm} = 3.87 \times 10^{-19} \frac{1}{\omega} \int \alpha(\omega) \, d\omega \quad \text{cm}^2 \tag{5-63}$$

For solutions we have by (5-58)

$$D_{nm} = 3.98 \times 10^{-20} \frac{1}{\omega} \int \epsilon(\omega) \, d\omega \tag{5-64}$$

The oscillator strength might be introduced as well using (5-60) and (5-46):

$$\int \alpha(\omega) \, d\omega = N_n \frac{\pi e^2}{hc^2 m_e} f_{nm} \frac{h}{\omega} \omega$$

hence

$$f_{nm} = \frac{c^2 m_e}{N_n \pi e^2} \int \alpha(\omega) \, d\omega$$
$$= 4.20 \times 10^{-8} \alpha(\omega) \, d\omega \tag{5-65}$$

For solutions we obtain

$$f_{nm} = 4.32 \times 10^{-9} \int \epsilon(\omega) \, d\omega \tag{5-66}$$

Equations (5-45) and (5-66) make it possible to compare theoretically and experimentally obtained dipole strengths or oscilator strengths and are widely used by spectroscopists.

In practice first the spectra are plotted, ϵ on the ordinate against $\omega = 1/\lambda$ on the abscissa. Then the surface underlying the extinction curve of the whole electronic band system is planimetered out, giving, usually, a result in square centimeters. From this $\int \epsilon(\omega)\, d\omega$ is obtained, taking as units for ϵ liter mole^{-1} cm^{-1} and for $\omega = 1/\lambda$ cm^{-1}.

There are several practical difficulties involved in this procedure. In most cases the choice of a representative wave number is quite difficult. The highest value of ϵ does not, in general, correspond to the 0–0 band (no change in vibrational quantum number) which theoretical calculations usually yield. There is often overlapping between neighbor band systems. Then, too, there is the inevitable problem of the "wings"; one cannot know how far to carry the integration on the two sides. Therefore, a great deal of caution is needed in dealing with intensities. However, in favorable cases, significant results can still be obtained.

If the band system, as measured experimentally, has no fine structure one might try to fit the observed band by a curve given by a known function and then obtain the underlying area by integrating the function. This leads into the problems of band shape and band width.

Gauss functions were used long ago to fit experimental curves by Bielicki and Henri [66] and especially by Kuhn and Braun [67]. The latter took the Gauss curve in the form:

$$\epsilon = \epsilon_{\max} e^{-(\Delta\omega/\theta)^2} \qquad\qquad (5\text{–}67)$$

where $\epsilon_{\max}$ is the peak value of the molecular extinction coefficient, $\Delta\omega$ the difference in cm^{-1} between the wave numbers corresponding to $\epsilon_{\max}$ and a given ϵ on the curve, and θ is a width parameter equal to the $\Delta\omega$ for which $\epsilon = \epsilon_{\max}/e$.

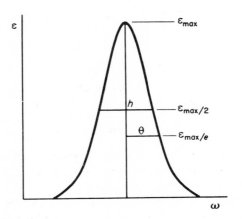

Fig. 5-3

This formula is easy to apply in the case of free-standing bands with no fine structure. We take the values of ϵ_{max} and θ from the extinction curve obtained experimentally (ϵ against $\omega = 1/\lambda$) and then from (5–67) we compute ϵ values for various $\Delta\omega$. If these ϵ values are not on the experimental curve we might vary slightly ϵ_{max} and θ to obtain a better fit.

The integral of (5–67) is

$$A = \int \epsilon(\omega)\, d\omega = \epsilon_{max} \int e^{-(\Delta\omega/h)^2}\, d\omega = \epsilon_{max} \sqrt{\pi}\; \theta \qquad (5\text{–}68)$$

Naturally, band areas obtained by this procedure can be only approximate measures of band intensity. Yet this method's simplicity makes it very useful. It shows immediately that the peak value of the molecular extinction coefficient (ϵ_{max}) is proportional to the intensity, but it can be used for comparisons between intensities of different bands only if their widths are very nearly equal. The assumption of the Gauss shape very often helps in uncovering band overlap between close-lying bands. If a band system has fine structure, then, of course, the integration has to be extended over all the bands belonging to the band system. If the partial bands still have approximate Gauss shape (corresponding to further unresolved fine structure) then the individual Gauss curve integrals can be added to give A for the whole system.

The width parameter θ we used above is, in our opinion, the simplest one to apply in practice, but the so-called half-width is much more often used. The half-width, h, is the $2\Delta\omega$ for which $\epsilon = \epsilon_{max}/2$ (h is counted both sides of ϵ_{max} while θ is counted only one side). Applying (5–67) to $\epsilon_{max}/2$ and ϵ_{max}/e we obtain the relation between the two parameters, which is $h = 2\sqrt{\ln 2}\,\theta = 1.6651\theta$ and

$$A = \epsilon_{max}(1.0645)h \qquad (5\text{–}69)$$

If two band systems overlap, we can first fit one of them by a Gauss curve, then find the difference between the latter and the observed curve, fit the difference by another Gauss-curve, etc. This procedure is largely arbitrary and there is usually more than one way of fitting an extinction curve by such "curve analysis." However, such studies may guide us in counting the number of electronic transitions making up an extinction curve and can teach us what apparent band shapes overlap can produce. Functions giving band shapes different from the Gaussian shape have also been tried [68, 69].

In recent times band-shape problems have attracted much more study in the infrared (vibrational bands) than in the ultraviolet. For a recent review of this interesting problem we refer to a work by Seshadri and Jones [71].

5-5. THE LIFETIME OF EXCITED STATES

If a molecule or an atom is in an excited state, then in the absence of an external electromagnetic field, on the average, after a time

$$\tau = \frac{1}{A_{mn}} \tag{5-70}$$

it will emit a photon. τ is called the mean lifetime of the excited state m. If there is a possibility of transitions to more than one lower-lying state we have to sum over all the possible lower states:

$$\tau = \frac{1}{\sum\limits_{n} A_{mn}} \tag{5-71}$$

The law controlling spontaneous emission is very similar to that of radioactive decay or of first-order reactions in chemical kinetics: the number of atoms or molecules which emit a photon per unit time is proportional to the number of excited molecules.

$$-\frac{dN}{dt} = kN \tag{5-72}$$

We can also write

$$-\frac{dN}{N} = k\,dt$$

$$-\int \frac{dN}{N} = \int k\,d\tau \tag{5-73}$$

$$-\ln N = kt + C$$

When $t = 0$, $C = -\ln N_0$ and therefore

$$\ln \frac{N_0}{N} = kt$$

or

$$N = N_0 e^{-kt} \tag{5-74}$$

If $k = 1/t = 1/\tau$,

$$N = \frac{N_0}{e}$$

Since in our case A_{mn} plays the role of k,

$$k \equiv A_{mn}$$

the mean lifetime appears to be the time needed to have the original number of excited molecules reduced e times.

5-6. QUADRUPOLE AND MAGNETIC DIPOLE TRANSITIONS

This far we have supposed that the emission or absorption of radiation is due to the interaction of the electric vector with the oscillating electric dipole moment of the atoms or molecules. This is substantiated by the entering of the electric dipole moment into the expression of the perturbing Hamiltonian [Eq. (5-20), p. 93] and into the transition moment. This is indeed by far the most important way of producing radiation (emission or absorption).

There are, however, other means whereby an atom or molecule might create an oscillating electromagnetic field in its environment.

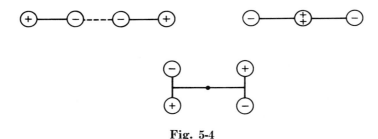

Fig. 5-4

The arrangements of electric charges in Fig. 5-4. do not have a permanent dipole moment but they do create an electrostatic field around themselves. They are said to posses a *quadrupole moment*. In the simplest possible case (the x axis passing through all four charges as in Fig. 5-4) this is given by

$$q_x = \sum e_i x_i^2 \tag{5-75}$$

This is obviously not zero even if the dipole moment, $\mu_x = \sum_i e_i x_i$, is. If the two dipoles forming the quadrupole oscillate in opposite directions, μ_x is still zero but q_x varies periodically. Emission or absorption might take place on account of this motion, and it is called *quadrupole radiation*. The intensities depend on the square of the field strength, which is much less than for dipole radiation. It can be estimated that the ratio of intensities for dipole and quadrupole radiation is about $1:10^{-5}$.

Higher electric multipoles can also give rise to radiation, but these would give even weaker bands.

An oscillating *magnetic* dipole moment can also produce radiation. We have such a case for an atom which has a nonzero total angular momentum (J), with both the total orbital and spin angular momenta

(L and S) different from zero. Such an atom has a magnetic moment whose direction is not the same as the direction of J because of the magnetic anomaly of spin (Landé-factor). Then the magnetic moment precesses with L and S around the direction of J. Thus there is a periodically changing magnetic moment. The corresponding field strength is again weak, however. In general, an oscillating magnetic moment may interact with the magnetic vector of the radiation causing emission or absorption.

The resulting bands are about as weak as in quadrupole radiation.

The chemical spectroscopist is unlikely to encounter such bands and, therefore, they have been mentioned only briefly. The more interested reader might consult Kauzman's *Quantum Chemistry* [8, pp. 611, 654]. (See also Herzberg [72, pp. 53, 111]).

5-7. NUMERICAL EXAMPLES

Let us take a very strong absorption band with $\epsilon_{max} = 100,000$ and a half-width $h = 5000 \, cm^{-1}$, whose maximum is located at 40,000 cm^{-1} (2500 Å).

The Gauss-curve approximation would give for the band area

$$A = \int \epsilon(\omega) \, d\omega = \epsilon_{max}(1.0645)h$$
$$= 10^5 \times 5000 \times 1.0645 = 5.32 \times 10^8 \text{ liter mole}^{-1}cm^{-1}.$$

Supposing that both the initial and final states are nondegenerate we obtain from (5–66) that

$$f_{nm} = 4.32 \times 10^{-9} \times 5.32 \times 10^8 = 2.30$$

Such high oscillator strengths seldom occur. Indeed bands with f values of a few tenths have to be considered as strong bands.

The dipole strength of this transition is [Eq. 5–64]

$$D_{nm} = 3.98 \times 10^{-20} \times 0.25 \times 10^{-4} \times 5.32 \times 10^8$$
$$= 5.29 \times 10^{-16} \quad cm^2 = 5.29 \, Å^2.$$

We can check these values using (5–45).

$$f_{nm} = 1.085 \times 10^{11} \, \omega D_{nm}$$
$$= 1.085 \times 10^{11} \times 4 \times 10^4 \times 5.29 \times 10^{-16}$$
$$= 2.30$$

From (5–37) and (5–38) we obtain Einstein's coefficients:

$$B_{nm} = 14.50 \times 10^{24} \times 5.29 \times 10^{-16} = 7.671 \times 10^9 \quad \text{sec g}^{-1}$$
$$A_{mn} = 7.24 \times 10^{10} \times 64 \times 10^{12} \times 5.29 \times 10^{-16} = 2.45 \times 10^9 \quad \text{sec}^{-1}$$

The average lifetime of the excited state is

$$\tau = \frac{1}{A_{mn}} = 0.41 \times 10^{-9} \quad \text{sec}$$

The value of the ϵ_{max} varies between zero and several hundred thousand. We take as a second example a band with $\epsilon_{max} = 10$, a half-width of $100 \, \text{cm}^{-1}$, located at $20,000 \, \text{cm}^{-1}$ ($5000 \, \text{Å}$), in the visible. Then

$$A = \int \epsilon(\omega) \, d\omega = 10 \times 1.0645 \times 100 = 1.06 \times 10^{-3} \, \text{liter mole}^{-1} \text{cm}^{-1}$$

$$f_{nm} = 4.32 \times 10^{-9} \times 1.06 \times 10^{3} = 4.58 \times 10^{-6}$$

$$D_{nm} = 3.98 \times 10^{-20} \times 0.5 \times 10^{-4} \times 1.06 \times 10^{3}$$
$$= 2.11 \times 10^{-21} \quad \text{cm}^{2} = 2.11 \times 10^{-5} \text{Å}^{2}$$

Checking by (5-45) gives

$$f_{nm} = 1.085 \times 10^{11} \omega D_{nm} = 1.085 \times 10^{11} \times 2 \times 10^{4} \times 2.11 \times 10^{-21}$$
$$= 4.58 \times 10^{-6}$$

$$B_{nm} = 14.50 \times 10^{24} \times 2.11 \times 10^{-21}$$
$$= 3.06 \times 10^{4} \quad \text{sec g}^{-1}$$

$$A_{mn} = 7.24 \times 10^{10} \times 8 \times 10^{12} \times 2.11 \times 10^{-21}$$
$$= 1.22 \times 10^{3} \quad \text{sec}^{-1}$$

and

$$\tau = 0.82 \times 10^{-3} \quad \text{sec}$$

This band is a very weak band. It is important to point out, however, that such weak bands are responsible for the visible color of many dissolved compounds. The colored complex ions of Fe^{++}, Fe^{+++}, Co^{+++}, Ni^{++}, Cu^{++}, Cr^{+++}, and so on are in this class as are some dyestuffs.

Among highly forbidden bands, such as singlet-triplet transitions, there are ϵ_{max} values of the order of 10^{-3} or 10^{-4} ($\log \epsilon_{max} = -3$ or -4). These are usually too weak to make a solution colored (see Chapter 15).

It is perhaps interesting to state here for comparison that infrared bands, i.e., bands due to purely vibrational transitions, have ϵ_{max} values between 0 and 1000. Thus we see that although on the average ultraviolet and visible bands tend to be much stronger than infrared bands, there are numerous ultraviolet bands which are weaker than many infrared bands.

6

The Classification of Electronic States

This subject is a classical one and its treatment here could hardly differ greatly from previous treatments. An attempt will be made, however, to give a brief review of this field introducing some of the main principles. It will be based on the fundamental works of Hund [73], Wigner and Witmer [74], White [75], and Herzberg [76, 77].

Although little use will be made in this book of atomic spectra, the subject will be developed here to some extent since it is needed as an introduction to the study of molecular spectra.

6-1 ATOMS. CASE OF ONE ELECTRON

As is well known, the total wave function of an electron in an atom contains four quantum numbers.

$$n = 1, 2, 3, \ldots$$

the principal quantum number;

$$l = 0, 1, \ldots, (n - 1)$$

the azimuthal quantum number;

$$m_l = 0, \pm 1, \pm 2, \ldots, \pm l$$

the magnetic quantum number; and

$$m_s = \pm\tfrac{1}{2}$$

the quantum number of the spin projection in a given direction. The spin quantum number itself is always

$$s = \tfrac{1}{2}$$

In the case of the hydrogen atom or the hydrogenlike ions such as He$^+$, Li^{++}, Be^{+++}, and so on, the energy depends only on the principal quantum number,

$$E_n = -\frac{2\pi^2 m_e e^4 Z^2}{n^2 h^2}, \qquad n = 1, 2, 3, \ldots \qquad (6\text{-}1)$$

For other atoms the energy depends on both n and l. The shape of the charge distribution is determined by l. For the same l the size of the orbital increases with increasing n.

In the absence of an external field the energy is the same for any value of m_l compatible with a given value of l. The orbitals having the same n and l but different values of m_l differ only in their orientation in space, and every state is $2l$ times degenerate, $(2l + 1)$ being the number of values m_l can take. In a magnetic or electric field, however, the motion of the electrons will be influenced by the field, and its energy will depend on the orientation of its orbital with respect to the field direction, that is to say on m_l, and the degeneracy will be removed.

From the point of view of the classification of spectral states l is by far the most important quantum number. The reason is that it measures the angular momentum of the electron (it is connected with the azimuthal angular part of the wave function).

The angular momentum is the vector product of the linear momentum (or simply momentum)

$$\mathbf{p} = m\mathbf{v}$$

where m is the mass of the particle, $\mathbf{v}$ its velocity, and $\mathbf{r}$ its distance from a fixed point about which the particle is moving.

$$\mathbf{M} = m[\mathbf{v}, \mathbf{r}] = [\mathbf{p}, \mathbf{r}]$$

and

$$|\mathbf{M}| = m|\mathbf{v}||\mathbf{r}|\sin\alpha$$

where $\mathbf{M}$, $\mathbf{v}$ and $\mathbf{r}$ are vector quantities, $|\mathbf{M}|$, $|\mathbf{v}|$ and $|\mathbf{r}|$ their magnitudes, and α the angle between the radius vector and the velocity vector. The direction of the angular momentum is perpendicular to both $\mathbf{v}$ and $\mathbf{r}$, whose sense is such that $\mathbf{r}$, $\mathbf{v}$, and $\mathbf{M}$ form a right-handed system. Its magnitude is numerically

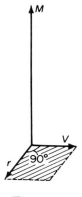

Fig. 6-1

equal to the area of the parallelogram formed by **p** and **r**. (Fig. 6-1) is an example with $\alpha = 90°$.

In wave mechanics the magnitude of the angular momentum of an electron is equal to

$$\sqrt{l(l + 1)}\,\frac{h}{2\pi} \tag{6-2}$$

In the Bohr theory it was $l(h/2\pi)$ [40, p. 39]. (Cf. the solution of the θ equation for the hydrogen atom.) It is interesting to note that the Planck constant

$$h = 6.6239 \times 10^{-27} \quad \text{erg sec}$$

has the dimensions of an angular momentum (ML^2T^{-1}). Since classically the total energy of the electron is

$$E = \tfrac{1}{2}\,m_e v^2 + E_{\text{pot}}$$

and

$$\frac{1}{2}\,m_e v^2 = \frac{M^2}{2m_e r^2} = \frac{M^2}{2I}$$

I being the moment of inertia, we can write that

$$E = \frac{M^2}{2I} + E_{\text{pot}} \tag{6-3}$$

This means that although the angular momentum is linked to the energy the two are not a measure of one another. The energy difference between states of given l values may vary widely according to the cases.

It may appear at first sight that speaking about angular momenta for the motion of an electron in an atom contradicts Heisenberg's uncertainty principle. Not so, however. The space coordinate conjugated with the angular momentum is the angle of rotation, and this is completely uncertain because of the rotational symmetry of the charge distribution. Therefore, the angular momentum is perfectly well determined, and we can still think of the atom as containing electrons rotating around the nucleus [72, p. 48].

The angular momentum due to the orbital motion and characterized by l is not the only kind of angular momentum the electron possesses. The interpretation of the fine structure of the spectral lines and the behavior of the atom in a magnetic field (experiment of Stern and Gerlach, Zeeman effect) impose "spin" upon us, which is usually visualized as the rotation of the electron around its own axis. The spin quantum number is

$$s = \tfrac{1}{2}$$

and the corresponding angular momentum

$$\sqrt{s(s+1)}\ \frac{h}{2\pi}$$

This vector can be parallel or antiparallel with respect to a given direction.

With both orbital and spin angular momenta (mechanical momenta) a magnetic moment is associated, since the motions are those of electrically charged particles. The orbital motion of the electron is conditioned by the electrical forces between the nucleus and the electron (and the other electrons in polyelectronic atoms) but its spin is not, being an intrinsic property of the electron. Spin is *not* affected by an electric field. Spin and orbital motion influence each other, however, by their magnetic moments.

The magnetic moment due to the orbital motion (in electromagnetic units) is

$$\mu_l = -\frac{e}{2m_ec}\frac{h}{2\pi}\sqrt{l(l+1)} \tag{6-4}$$

where m_e is the mass of the electron, e its charge, and c the speed of light. If $l = 0$ there is no magnetic moment as there is no angular momentum. If $l = 1$ the magnetic moment is equal to one Bohr magneton, which is taken as the unit of the magnetic moment in atomic problems. The direction of the magnetic moment is the opposite of the direction of the angular momentum because of the negative charge of the electron.

The magnetic moment associated with spin is, anomalously, not half of a Bohr magneton but a whole one.

$$\mu_s = -\frac{2e}{2m_ec}\frac{h}{2\pi}\sqrt{s(s+1)} \tag{6-5}$$

The spin must orient itself with respect to the angular momentum, provided $l \neq 0$. Only two orientations are possible, parallel and antiparallel to l, with quantum numbers for the total angular momentum taking the values $j = l + \frac{1}{2}$ or $j = l - \frac{1}{2}$ with magnitude

$$\sqrt{j(j+1)}\ \frac{h}{2\pi}$$

The total magnetic moment is

$$\mu_j = -\frac{e}{2m_ec}\frac{h}{2\pi}\sqrt{j(j+1)}\ g \tag{6-6}$$

where g is called the Landé factor and takes into account the magnetic anomaly of spin [72, p. 106] (see below).

6-2 ATOMS. CASE OF MORE THAN ONE ELECTRON

We might still assign to each electron individually a constant orbital angular momentum characterized by quantum number l_i. This is justified if we consider that each electron is moving in the field of the nucleus and the other electrons, this field being approximately spherically symmetrical.

The angular momenta of the different electrons are not independent of each other but influence each other by mutual coulombic repulsion and the interaction of the related magnetic moments. To obtain their resultant we have to add them vectorially. According to quantum mechanics the resultant, too, is quantized.[1] With two electrons

$$L = (l_1 + l_2), (l_1 + l_2 - 1), (l_1 + l_2 - 2), \ldots, |l_1 - l_2| \qquad (6\text{-}7)$$

Negative values have no sense for an angular momentum; only its components in a given direction may be positive or negative. If we have more than two electrons we still put them together according to the rules of vector addition, or we may first obtain the L values corresponding to two of them and add to each one the l of the third one using (6-7) and so forth.

For example, if we have

$$l_1 = 1, \qquad l_2 = 2, \qquad l_3 = 3$$

we obtain

$$L_{12} = 3, 2, \text{ and } 1$$

and then

$$L_{123} = \begin{cases} 6, 5, 4, 3, 2, 1, 0 \\ 5, 4, 3, 2, 1 \\ 4, 3, 2 \end{cases}$$

where, as can be seen, the different L values may have different statistical weights.

When we obtain a certain L from the l_i of the individual electrons the length and mutual orientation of the l_i are fixed, but they could turn around the direction of L leaving the latter completely unchanged

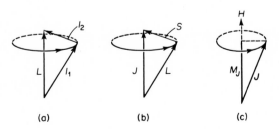

(a)   (b)   (c)

Fig. 6-2

[1] That is, if we resolved the Schrödinger-equation for a polyelectronic atom we should find that the angular momentum again has only certain quantized values.

[Fig. 6-2 (a)]. This motion actually does take place, as we can see when we take into account that the relative positions of the electrons and, therefore, the forces acting upon them vary because of their respective motions; it is called a *precession*. If the precession is comparably fast, or faster than the revolutions of the individual electrons the l_i will not even approximately characterize the motion; the related angular momenta will no longer be well-defined quantities. However, their resultant will be well defined and L still indicates the total angular momentum of the electrons.

L is a quantum number taking only integral values or zero. The angular momentum itself is equal to

$$\sqrt{L(L + 1)}\,\frac{h}{2\pi}$$

and the related magnetic moment is

$$\mu_L = -\frac{e}{2m_e c}\frac{h}{2\pi}\sqrt{L(L + 1)} \tag{6-8}$$

The spins of the different electrons interact by their magnetic moments. The resultant spin quantum number, if there are N electrons, will be

$$S = \frac{N}{2}, \frac{N}{2} - 1, \ldots, \frac{1}{2} \text{ or } 0.$$

according to whether N is odd or even. The total spin angular momentum will be

$$\sqrt{S(S + 1)}\,\frac{h}{2\pi}$$

and the related magnetic moment

$$\mu_S = -\frac{2e}{2m_e c}\frac{h}{2\pi}\sqrt{S(S + 1)} \tag{6-9}$$

The spin is not affected by the electric field of the electrons but it interacts with the magnetic moment due to their orbital motion. Thus, the angular momenta measured by L and S will orient themselves with respect to each other, giving a total angular momentum measured by quantum number

$$J = L + S, L + S - 1, L + S - 2, \ldots, |L - S|$$

Again the vectors corresponding to L and S can and do turn around the direction of the total angular momentum, executing another (L, S) precession [Fig. 6-2 (b)]. The momenta related to L and S lose their meaning if the precession is fast.

The length of the angular momentum vector related to J is given by

$$\sqrt{J(J+1)}\,\frac{h}{2\pi}$$

and the corresponding magnetic momentum is

$$\mu_J = -\frac{e}{2m_e c}\frac{h}{2\pi}\sqrt{J(J+1)}\,g \tag{6-10}$$

The Landé factor depends on J, L, and S separately. It is equal to

$$g = 1 + \frac{J(J+1) + S(S+1) - L(L+1)}{2J(J+1)}$$

The deduction is simple and it is given, for example, by Herzberg [72, p. 109].

In an external magnetic field the atomic magnet will interact with the field. According to quantum mechanics it cannot take an arbitrary direction with respect to the field. Space quantization will take place so that the component of the total angular momentum in the direction of the external field (H) can take the values measured by

$$M_J = J, J-1, J-2, \ldots, -J$$

the length of the component being given by

$$M_J \frac{h}{2\pi}$$

It should be noticed here that the latter expression contains simply M_J, not $\sqrt{M_J(M_J+1)}$. This is related to differences between the solutions of the two angular parts of the Schrödinger equation. Thus, while the greatest length of the total angular momentum is $\sqrt{J(J+1)}(h/2\pi)$, the greatest possible length of its projection on the direction of H is only $J(h/2\pi)$. As a consequence the total angular momentum can never lie exactly in the field direction. Gyromagnetic interactions will again make the total angular momentum vector precess with a constant component around the H direction [Fig. 6-2 (c)]. If this precession is rapid, J will lose its meaning as a quantum number characterizing the motion of the electrons, but M_J and the component will still be well defined. This last precession is called Larmor precession, and its frequency increases with increasing interaction between the external field and the atomic magnet. It plays an important role in electron paramagnetic resonance spectroscopy.

In a magnetic field, if $J \neq 0$, the energy of the atoms will be different for different M_J values because of the different orientation of the total angular momentum of the atom with respect to the field. Therefore in a magnetic field the electronic energy levels and the related spectral lines, usually located in the ultraviolet or visible part of the spectrum, will split (Zeeman effect). On the other hand, transitions become possible between the levels separated by the magnetic field. These energy differences depend on the strength of the external magnetic field, i.e., on the will of the experimenter. The transitions between these usually close-lying levels give rise to lines in the microwave region. Their study is the subject of electron paramagnetic resonance spectroscopy. (The name is related to the fact that only atoms with $J \neq 0$ are paramagnetic; $J = 0$ indicates the absence of an atomic magnet.)

For a more detailed discussion of the Zeeman effect we again refer to Herzberg's book [72]. The spectral lines usually also split in an electric field (Stark effect); however, there is no complete analogy between the two effects. The Stark effect will be briefly mentioned later in relation to diatomic molecules.

Returning to the atom in a field-free space, the energy differences corresponding to different values of L will be greater the stronger the (l, l) interactions between the different electrons. The strength of this interaction is proportional to the velocity of the (l, l) precession. The (L, S) interaction is usually weaker and the related precession slower; thus, the multiplet-splitting (due to spin) is generally much less than the difference between levels corresponding to different L values. This type of coupling where the individual l_i interact so strongly with each other that they give a resultant L, and the individual s_i interact so strongly with each other that they give a resultant S, and then L and S through a weaker coupling give a resultant J, is called Russell-Saunders coupling.

The following question is well justified: would it not be just as logical to presume that the l_i of one individual electron is coupled with the spin, s_i, of the same electron to give a resultant j_i and then the j_i of the individual electrons would interact (less strongly) to give a resultant total angular momentum with quantum number J?

The answer is that there are cases where this latter type of coupling, (j, j) coupling, describes the conditions better than Russell-Saunders coupling. All depends on the relative strengths of the interactions between the l_i and the s_i. In small atoms, where, on the average, the different electrons are close to each other, the interactions between them will be generally strong and Russell-Saunders coupling will apply. In large atoms, where the distances between the electrons are often large, the interactions between the l_i and s_i of the same electron will be relatively stronger and (j, j) coupling applies. The situation might change from one atom to the other or even from one

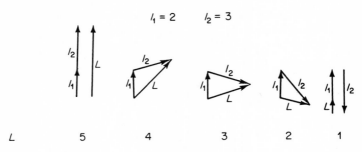

Fig. 6-3

energy level of a given atom to the other. Intermediate cases are also possible where the (l, l) and (s, s) coupling and the (l, s) coupling are of comparable strength.

In (j, j) coupling L and S are not defined at all but J (and its projection in the direction of an external field, M_J) are, of course, well defined. The number of terms and the J values are the same in both types of coupling, but the relative positions of the terms differ.

Now, we are going to discuss an example in order to illustrate these conditions. Let us have two electrons with, say, $l_1 = 2$ and $l_2 = 3$.

In Russell-Saunders coupling we have (Fig. 6–3).

$$L = 5, 4, 3, 2, 1 \quad \text{and} \quad S = 1 \text{ or } 0$$

Thus for every L there will be a triplet and a singlet. The possible J values, for the different values of L, are given below.

$$
\begin{array}{lll}
L = 5, & S = 0, & J = 5, \\
L = 5, & S = 1, & J = 6, 5, 4 \\
L = 4, & S = 0, & J = 4 \\
L = 4, & S = 1, & J = 5, 4, 3 \\
L = 3, & S = 0, & J = 3 \\
L = 3, & S = 1, & J = 4, 3, 2 \\
L = 2, & S = 0, & J = 2 \\
L = 2, & S = 1, & J = 3, 2, 1 \\
L = 1, & S = 0, & J = 1 \\
L = 1, & S = 1, & J = 2, 1, 0 \\
\end{array}
$$

Thus J may have values from 6 to 0 for triplets and 5 to 1 for singlets. The number of values J may have is $(2S + 1)$ for any given value of L. $(2S + 1)$ is called the multiplicity. (However, if $S > L$, $(2L + 1)$ is the *real* measure of multiplicity even if $(2S + 1)$ is kept for reasons of consistency.) For the projection in a given direction, in each case, $M_J = J, J - 1, \ldots, -J$. It is seen that M_J can have $2J + 1$ different values.

As we know, electronic states having quantum number

$$L = 0, 1, 2, 3, 4, \ldots$$

are called

$$S, P, D, F, G, \ldots$$

states, respectively. Spectral terms are symbolized by one of these letters and an upper left index giving the multiplicity $(2S + 1)$ and a lower right index giving the value of J. For example,

$$^3P_0$$

is a term with $L = 1$, $(2S + 1) = 3$, hence $S = 1$ and $J = 0$.

In (j, j) coupling with $l_1 = 2$ and $l_2 = 3$ we have

$$j_1 = \tfrac{5}{2} \text{ or } \tfrac{3}{2} \qquad \text{and} \qquad j_2 = \tfrac{7}{2} \text{ or } \tfrac{5}{2}$$

for the two electrons respectively. From these we obtain the following J values for the total angular momentum using $J = (j_1 + j_2)$, $(j_1 + j_2 - 1), \ldots, |j_1 - j_2|$:

j_1	j_2	J
$\tfrac{5}{2}$	$\tfrac{7}{2}$	$6, 5, 4, 3, 2, 1$
$\tfrac{5}{2}$	$\tfrac{5}{2}$	$5, 4, 3, 2, 1, 0$
$\tfrac{3}{2}$	$\tfrac{7}{2}$	$5, 4, 3, 2$
$\tfrac{3}{2}$	$\tfrac{5}{2}$	$4, 3, 2, 1$

These are the same J values as the ones obtained in Russell-Saunders coupling. Since L and S are not defined we cannot distinguish between singlets and triplets. The term symbols used in Russell-Saunders coupling cannot be applied either. We can speak only of (j_1, j_2) terms which split into components when (j, j) interaction is taken into account.

6-3 SELECTION RULES FOR ATOMIC SPECTRA

As shown in Chapter 5, the intensities of spectral lines are proportional to the square of the transition moment

$$\int \psi' \sum_i e_i r_i \psi'' \, d\tau$$

If it is possible to show that this quantity is zero for a whole category of transitions we say that we have a selection rule. In atomic spectroscopy the selection rules are connected with the values of the quantum numbers which enter the expressions of the angular momenta.

We think of atoms as having spherical symmetry. Then if we execute an inversion through the origin of the coordinates, which is also a center of symmetry, the Hamilton operator (and the potential function in it) clearly do not change, since the forces acting between the particles are still the same. This is also true for the square of the wave function which measures the electron density in a given volume element, otherwise the potential would have changed. The wave function itself may remain unchanged or change its sign upon inversion; accordingly it is called "even" or "odd." In the transition moment integral r_i (and all the x_i, y_i, z_i) changes sign upon inversion and

$$\psi' r_i \psi'' \, d\tau$$

is, therefore, an odd function if both ψ' and ψ'' are either odd or even. This implies that for every volume element $d\tau$ which makes a positive contribution to the integral there will be a volume element which makes an equal but negative contribution to it and, therefore, the integral will be zero. This is already clear if we consider that the transition moment is an intrinsic property of the atom and a purely geometrical (symmetry) operation cannot possibly change it. (A symmetry operation is always equivalent to a change of coordinate system.) However, only zero can simultaneously change sign and remain the same. Thus, we are led to the very important conclusion that the transition moment is zero and the transition forbidden between two states having both even or both odd wave functions.

If ψ' and ψ'' are one even and the other odd, the transition moment integral will keep its sign upon inversion. Even states are usually noted by g (German *gerade*, even), odd states by u (*ungerade*, odd). Then the selection rule (called the Laporte rule) is

$$g \not\leftrightarrow g, \quad u \leftrightarrow g, \quad g \leftrightarrow u, \quad u \not\leftrightarrow u$$

where $\leftrightarrow$ stands for allowed and $\not\leftrightarrow$ for forbidden.

This is a very general selection rule for dipole radiation which is valid not only for spherical symmetry but whenever there is a center of symmetry (see Chapter 7). It is valid in the case of degenerate wave functions too.

Inversion as a symmetry operation (also called *reflection at the center*) consists of joining each point to the center and then producing the line for an equal distance on the other side. This is the same as changing the signs of all the x_i, y_i, z_i for all the particles. In spherical coordinates the inversion is obtained by changing θ to $(180° - \theta)$, and ϕ to $(180° + \phi)$, while $\cos \theta$, $\cos \phi$, and $\sin \phi$ change sign but $\sin \theta$ does not.

Now if we look at the hydrogenlike wave functions on p. 15 we see immediately that they are even for $l = 0, 2, 4$ but odd for $l = 1, 3, 5, \ldots$. If there are two or more electrons we can take the total wave function as a product of the one-electron wave functions, although this is only approximately true. Then, the total wave function will be odd or even when $\sum l_i$ is odd or even.

Besides this selection rule the following are generally valid:

1. $\Delta J = 0, \pm 1$; excepting $J = 0 \not\to J = 0$.
2. $\Delta M_J = 0, \pm 1$; excepting $M_J = 0 \not\to M_J = 0$ if $\Delta J = 0$.
3. $\Delta L = 0, \pm 1$ (for one electron $\Delta l = \pm 1$).
4. $\Delta S = 0$.
5. $\Delta l = \pm 1$ for the electron making the quantum jump.

Rule 1 holds for any type of coupling since J is well defined in both (L, S) and (j, j) coupling. It would become approximate in weak magnetic fields and break down in strong ones, since then J loses its meaning as a quantum number measuring angular momenta and only its component on the field direction (M_J) remains well defined. This selection rule is rigorous for dipole radiation in the absence of an external field.

Rule 2 operates only when the atoms are in an external field, since otherwise the states belonging to a given J all have the same energy whatever the value of M_J. This rule is the most important one for the discussion of the Zeeman effect. In *very* strong magnetic fields even M_J loses its meaning as a quantum number since then the coupling between H and L on the one hand and H and S on the other is so strong that L and S are no longer coupled together but have individually constant components in the direction of H (Paschen-Back effect). Then the selection rules are

$$\Delta M_L = 0, \pm 1 \quad \text{and} \quad \Delta M_S = 0$$

It might even happen that the coupling between the individual l_i and s_i breaks down and they couple individually with the external magnetic field with components

$$m_l = l, (l - 1), (l - 2), \ldots, -l$$

and $m_s = \pm \frac{1}{2}$. The above selection rules then apply to the individual electrons.

If we had (j, j) coupling to start with, the individual j may not couple together to give a resultant J but rather couple with the external field with components

$$m_j = j, (j - 1), (j - 2), \ldots, -j$$

Then rule 1 applies to the individual j.

Rules 3 and 4 apply only for Russell-Saunders coupling since only there are L and S defined. For only one electron the selection rule is $\Delta l = \pm 1$.

The rule $\Delta S = 0$ is called the *prohibition of intercombinations*, prescribing that the total spin quantum number cannot change in the transition. The reason is that the complete eigenfunctions in the transition moment integral are a product of a function depending only on the space coordinates and a spin function, provided the coupling between spin and orbital motion is neglected. Then we can integrate first over the spin coordinates, obtaining zero for states of different multiplicity because of the orthogonality of the spin functions. The well-known division of the terms of helium into singlets and triplets which do not combine with each other is the classical example of this. The rule loses its validity with the departure from Russell-Saunders coupling. It is generally rigorous for light atoms but not for heavy atoms. For example, the mercury 2537 Å line, which is due to an intercombination, is so intense that it is often used for irradiation purposes.

Rule 5 applies when, as in most cases, only one electron makes the transition. For example let us have $l_1 = 1$, $l_2 = 3$, and $L = 2$ in the initial state. A transition to a state with $l_1 = 3$, $l_2 = 3$, and $L = 3$ would be allowed by the selection rule for L, but it is forbidden because l_1 changes by two units. The validity of this rule depends on how far the total wave function can be considered as a simple product of one-electron wave functions. It is, of course, compatible with the more general Laporte rule.

It is possible that in a transition two or more electrons jump simultaneously, although lines due to such transitions are expected to be much weaker than those due to one-electron jumps. For the first electron we have the rule

$$\Delta l_1 = \pm 1$$

However, this cannot apply for the second electron, since then the wave functions of the initial and final states would be both even or both odd. Therefore, the complementary selection rule is

$$\Delta l_2 = 0, \pm 2$$

It is somewhat disturbing to beginners that forbidden bands are seldom really and totally absent from the spectrum. More usually they appear as weak lines. The reasons for this are not difficult to understand, however. They are twofold. First, selection rules are obtained by calculations referring to one, isolated atom. Now, in reality the atoms are subject to the electric and magnetic field of other atoms. Second, even for the isolated atom the selection rules are often the result of approximate calculations. In particular, the presumed coupling conditions seldom hold exactly. Furthermore, all the abovementioned selection rules refer to dipole radiation. A line forbidden for dipole radiation may be allowed for quadrupole (or higher multipole) and magnetic dipole radiation (see Sec. 5-6).

We do not intend to develop here the selection rules for the latter cases, but it is interesting to note that the very important $g \not\longleftrightarrow g$, $u \longleftrightarrow u$, $g \longleftrightarrow u$ rule's exact opposite holds for quadrupole radiation. This is because the transition moment is then

$$\int \psi' \, r^2 \psi'' \, d\tau$$

where r^2 always keeps its sign with respect to inversion and thus ψ' and ψ'' must either be both even or both odd, or else the integral vanishes. The situation is similar for magnetic dipole radiation.

For further details we refer to Herzberg's book [72, p. 53].

A few examples will be given now in order to illustrate the selection rules treated in this chapter.

1. In its ground state, the configuration of the helium atom is $1s^2$ and the corresponding term is $^1S_0$. The lowest excited states have configuration $1s2s$. There may be a triplet and a singlet, since the spins are free then, the principal quantum number being different for the two electrons. The transition from the ground state to the triplet is of type

$$^3S_1 \leftarrow {}^1S_0$$

This is strictly forbidden as an intercombination by selection rule $\Delta S = 0$ and also, but less strictly, by the rule $\Delta l = \pm 1$ for the electron which makes the jump.

The transition to the singlet is forbidden too, although somewhat less strictly, by $\Delta l = \pm 1$ and by $J = 0 \not\longleftrightarrow J = 0$. The other selection rules of p. 121 are satisfied in both cases.

2. Lithium, in its ground state, has configuration $1s^2 2s$. The term is $^2S_{1/2}$. It is formally a doublet term because $(2S + 1) = 2$, but in reality $S = J = +\frac{1}{2}$ or $-\frac{1}{2}$ are the same since $L = 0$ and there is no orbital angular momentum according to which the spin could be oriented. (This is general for S terms.) The lowest excited state is $1s^2 2p\,^2P_{3/2}$ or $^2P_{1/2}$, a real doublet. It is important to note that there is no selection rule for the principal quantum number, and Δn might well be zero. The transition is of type

$$^2P_{3/2,1/2} \leftarrow {}^2S_{1/2}$$

It is allowed according to all the selection rules and it is responsible for the well-known red doublet of lithium. The origin of the yellow D lines of sodium is similar, and the other alkali metals also have similar lines.

3. The ground-state configuration for a carbon atom is $1s^2 2s^2 2p^2$. From this at first sight six terms could result, with $L = 2, 1,$ or 0.

$$^3D \qquad {}^1D$$
$$^3P \qquad {}^1P$$
$$^3S \qquad {}^1S$$

In reality some of these contradict the Pauli principle since two electrons turn out to have all four quantum numbers the same and have to be ruled out. This often happens when we have two or more so-called equivalent electrons, which have n and l the same in an incompletely closed shell. This somewhat complicated topic will not be pursued here [72, p. 130]. Only ^3P, ^1D, and ^1S remain. Of these, ^3P has the lowest energy, corresponding to the ground state. This is in conformity with Hund's rule: "Of the terms given by equivalent electrons, those with greatest multiplicity lie deepest, and of these the lowest is that with the greatest L." (A proof of this is found in F. Hund's *Linien Spektren* [74, p. 124].) Qualitatively one can understand that because of the Pauli principle, the more electrons have the same spin the greater will be the tendency of the system to spread out, thereby increasing its stability.

The ^1D and ^1S terms lie only slightly above ^3P and if transitions to these were allowed, carbon atoms could absorb visible light. They are forbidden, however, because of the Laporte rule. Since all three terms belong to the same configuration, $\sum l_i$ is obviously the same for all of them (namely 2). Thus these transitions would be of $g \longleftrightarrow g$ type and are forbidden. This is quite generally valid for terms originating from the same configuration. On this basis the lowest excited states of carbon to which transitions are allowed originate from the $1s^2 2s^2 2p 3s$ configuration.

For further examples we refer to specialized works on atomic spectra [72, 74, 79].

We must include a remark on the Stark effect.

The splitting of spectral lines is observed in electric fields as well as in magnetic fields, but the rules governing the two phenomena are different. The fundamental difference originates in the fact that, although the atom (with $J \neq 0$) is a natural magnetic dipole, it is not an electric dipole. It may be remembered in this respect that no magnetic "monopoles" exist in nature, positive and negative magnetism appearing always jointly, but of course there exist particles having positive or negative electric charges only.

As we have already seen, in a magnetic field the splitting is proportional to the strength of the magnetic field (H). In an electric field the splitting will be propotional to the square of the electric field (F^2). This can be understood in the following way.

In a magnetic field the change in the energy of the atom is equal to the product of H and the magnetic dipole moment of the atom.

In an electric field it is equal to the product of F and the electric dipole moment of the atom. In the latter case, however, the dipole moment itself will be created by the field which polarizes the atom separating the centroids of the positive and negative charges. The magnitude of the electric dipole moment created by the field will depend on the orientation of the angular momentum of the atom with respect to the field but it will be in every case proportional to the field strength F. Thus the splitting depends on F^2.

The components of the angular momentum characterized by J can take values characterized by

$$M_J = J, J - 1, J - 2, \ldots, -J$$

just as in a magnetic field and the energies corresponding to the different values of M_J will be different. The energies corresponding to terms differing only by the sign of M_J will be, however, the same. This is because replacing M_J by $-M_J$ is the same as reversing the directions of motion of all the electrons and would not change the electric dipole created by the field. Thus the number of term components in the electric field is only $J + \frac{1}{2}$ or $J + 1$, according to whether J is half integral or integral, not $2J + 1$.

If the field is sufficiently strong, the coupling of L and S with the field direction will be stronger than the coupling between L and S, and J will not be defined. Then L and S will be quantized independently with respect to the field direction with constant components M_L and M_S. States with

$$|M_L| = L, L - 1, \ldots, 0$$

will have different energies. For every value of M_L, M_S can take values equal to $S, S - 1, \ldots, -S$. If $M_L \neq 0$, states with different M_S will have different energies. Since then there is a magnetic moment associated with L.

6-4 DIATOMIC MOLECULES

The case of diatomic molecules bears a certain analogy to the case of the atoms in an electric field. The electronic charge distribution in atoms has spherical symmetry, but in diatomic molecules it possesses only axial symmetry. Whatever the exact electronic distribution around the atomic cores and in the region of the bond, we can take the line connecting the two nuclei as a preferred direction representing an electric field. Naturally, coupling conditions vary from one molecule to the other, but in the most frequent case the diatomic molecule is comparable to an atom under Stark effect in a strong electric field.

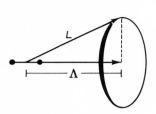

Fig. 6-4

Then we first compute the L values corresponding to all the electrons of the molecule. A precession of L will take place about the internuclear axis with constant component $M_L(h/2\pi)$ (Fig. 6-4). For a given value of L this constant component can take the values

$$M_L = L, L - 1, L - 2, \ldots, -L$$

As in the case of atoms, states differing only by the sign of M_L have the same energy, no matter whether the molecule is homoatomic or heteroatomic. All that counts is that the dipole is created by the field and the reversing of the direction of rotation does not change it.

Therefore, the absolute value of M_L is taken as a new quantum number:

$$\Lambda = |M_L|$$

with the magnitude of the related angular momentum component being $\Lambda(h/2\pi)$. This quantum number is the basis of the nomenclature for electronic states of diatomic molecules. If $\Lambda = 0, 1, 2, 3, 4 \ldots$, the state is

$$\Sigma, \Pi, \Delta, \Phi, \Gamma, \ldots$$

All states, except Σ states, are doubly degenerate because $+M_L$ or $-M_L$ give the same Λ. Since the coupling of L with the line connecting the nuclei is strong, usually states with different Λ values have significantly different energies.

The spin is not affected by the electric field, but its magnetic moment will interact with the magnetic field which lies in the direction of the internuclear axis. If $\Lambda = 0$, there is no such field, but there will be one if $\Lambda \neq 0$, i.e. for $\Pi, \Delta, \Phi, \ldots$ states. If $\Lambda \neq 0$, the resultant spin vector S will precess around the internuclear axis with constant component $M_S(h/2\pi)$. For molecules we replace M_S by Σ which can take values

$$\Sigma = S, S - 1, S - 2, \ldots, -S$$

The magnetic moment is not created by the field; adding it to or subtracting it from the field yield different energies.

The total angular momentum in the direction of the field is measured by

$$\Omega = |\Lambda + \Sigma|$$

The multiplicity due to spin is $(2S + 1)$ as in the case of atoms, since Σ can have $(2S + 1)$ different values (not $2\Sigma + 1$). If $\Lambda = 0$, the spin will not be oriented and Σ and Ω will not be defined at all. However, $(2S + 1)$ will still be called the multiplicity of the term.

The term notation is similar to that used for atoms. For example, in

$$^3\Pi_2$$

we have a term with $\Lambda = 1$; the upper index $3 = 2S + 1$ is for the multiplicity (triplet), with $S = 1$. The lower index is the Ω value for the particular term, here $\Lambda = 1$ and $\Sigma = 1$.

If L and S are not entirely uncoupled by the field a J vector will be defined, and its constant components on the direction of the internuclear axis will again be measured by Ω. Then Λ and Σ lose their meanings and the usual nomenclature cannot be used. More complicated cases, however, will not be treated here.

The scheme described above may seem to be relatively simple. The main question, however, remains to be answered. It is all right to say, for example, that *if* L has a given value then Λ has certain values—but how do we determine L in a molecule? Indeed, how do we know the l_i values for the "individual" electrons? In general, what is the relation between the states of the molecule and the states of its atoms? One way of handling this problem is to think of the molecule as being obtained by bringing together the whole atoms of which it is built, and then to ask what molecular states will result from the states of the *separated atoms*.

Another way of attacking the problem is to start, not with infinite internuclear distance, but with zero internuclear distance. We first make the two nuclei "coalesce" into a *united atom*, which is the one having as its Z number the sum of the nuclear charges of the two atoms. For example, the united atom of the hydrogen molecule is the helium atom, the united atom of the LiH molecule is the beryllium atom, and so on. Then we split the united atom and see what molecular states result from its states.

In the method of the separated atoms if we have two atoms with quantum numbers L_1, S_1 and L_2, S_2, respectively, at infinite distance, then when we bring them together at molecular distance an electric field is produced in the direction of the line connecting the nuclei, and L_1 and L_2 will orient themselves with respect to this direction, with components M_{L_1} and M_{L_2} giving a resultant

$$\Lambda = |M_{L_1} + M_{L_2}|$$

Since M_{L_i} can take the values

$$M_{L_i} = L_i, L_i - 1, L_i - 2, \ldots, -L_i$$

a large number of states might result. For example, if $L_1 = 2$ and $L_2 = 3$, that is to say one atomic state is a D state, the other an F state, we can have $|M_{L_1}| = 2, 1$, or 0 and $|M_{L_2}| = 3, 2, 1$, or 0, whence $\Lambda = 5, 4, 3, 2, 1$, or 0, with $\Sigma^+, \Sigma^-, \Pi, \Delta, \Phi, \Gamma, H$ terms. Generally each term is obtained by more than one combination of the M_{L_1} and M_{L_2}, with different statistical weights. (For Σ^+ and Σ^- see p. 129.)

The spin is not influenced by the electric field; thus, every state can be obtained with $(2S + 1)$ multiplicities corresponding to any of the values

$$S = (S_1 + S_2), (S_1 + S_2 - 1), (S_1 + S_2 - 2), \ldots, |S_1 - S_2|$$

Taking all possible combinations of all the L_i and S_i of the separated atoms we obtain all the terms of the molecule.

In the united atom approximation, again an electric field is produced in the direction of the internuclear axis when the united atom is split. Then the L of the united atom will orient itself with respect to the field with possible components

$$\Lambda = |M_L| = L, L - 1, L - 2, \ldots, 0$$

The spin, S, of the united atom remains the same when the molecule is formed. For example, from a ^3P state of the beryllium atom (with, for example, configuration $1s^2 2s 2p$) we obtain for the LiH molecule $^3\Pi$ or $^3\Sigma$ states since $L = 1$, and $\Lambda = 1$ or 0. Using all the L of the united atom we obtain all the terms of the corresponding molecule.

For obvious reasons this approximation will be good only for molecules with short internuclear distances, such as hydrides.

We have supposed in dealing with both methods that the internuclear field is strong enough to uncouple L and S. If this is not so, a total angular momentum vector J has to be defined and oriented according to the field direction to give Ω values. However, this subject will not be followed up here.

There is a third method of obtaining the molecular terms from the atomic terms, which gives more insight into the nature of molecular states than either of the two others. The underlying idea is similar to that of the molecular orbital method.

We consider that each electron has an orbital in the core constituted by the nuclei, and we shall add the electrons to the core one by one just as in the case of atoms. Then we shall proceed to determine the term values from the electron configuration.

Let us start with only one electron. (In the simple case of H_2^+ we actually have only one.) We shall use lower-case letters instead of capital letters as in the case of atoms.

If

$$\lambda = 0, 1, 2, 3, 4, \ldots$$

we speak of $\sigma, \pi, \delta, \phi, \gamma, \ldots$ orbitals. A σ electron has zero angular momentum component in the direction of the internuclear line, a π electron $h/2\pi$, a δ electron $2h/2\pi$, and so on. If there is more than one electron the individual λ_i add algebraically (with the same sign or opposite sign) since they are all projections in the same direction. Table 6–1 gives a few examples.

TABLE 6–1

Electrons	λ_1	λ_2	Λ	Term
$\sigma\sigma$	0	0	0	Σ
$\sigma\pi$	0	1	1	Π
$\sigma\delta$	0	2	2	Δ
$\sigma\phi$	0	3	3	Φ
$\pi\pi$	1	1	2, 0	$\Delta, \Sigma^+, \Sigma^-$
$\pi\delta$	1	2	3, 1	Φ, Π
$\pi\phi$	1	3	4, 2	Γ, Δ
$\delta\delta$	2	2	4, 0	$\Gamma, \Sigma^+, \Sigma^-$
$\delta\phi$	2	3	5, 1	H, Γ

The significance of Σ^+ and Σ^- is the following.

Because of the axial symmetry of diatomic molecules, it is convenient to assign cylindrical coordinates to the electrons. If the internuclear axis coincides with the z axis, these are z_i, ρ_i, and ϕ_i, where ρ_i is the distance from the axis and ϕ_i the azimuth. Now, the electronic wave function may or may not change sign if we replace all the ϕ_i by their negatives, i.e., we reflect the wave function with respect to any plane containing the nuclei (in group-theoretical language: operation σ_v). The ϕ_i-dependent part of the wave function may be, for example, in the case of two electrons, $\sin(\phi_2 - \phi_1)$ or $\cos(\phi_2 - \phi_1)$. The former changes sign upon reflection at any plane containing the internuclear axis (Σ^-), the second does not (Σ^+). These terms correspond to different energies if they result from *other* than σ electrons (from two π, or two δ electrons, etc.). If both electrons are σ electrons the term is a Σ term with no superscript,[2] since then the wave function has no angular dependence. (See p. 180.)

For $\Pi, \Delta, \ldots$ terms it is also possible to write wave functions, which change or keep their signs with respect to a reflection in a plane through the nuclei. The difference is that these states are all doubly degenerate because of $\Lambda = \pm M_L$, while Σ states are not. This has the consequence that for $\Pi, \Delta, \ldots$ terms the two wave functions correspond to exactly the same energies. Thus, the above distinction is introduced only for Σ terms.

[2] Although certain authors use Σ^+ in this case too.

In a higher approximation we have to take into account the fact that, there exists for molecules another angular momentum due to molecular rotation. The interaction of the electronic motion and nuclear rotation might split the Π, Δ, ... states into two components of slightly different energy and then we can have Π^+, $\Pi^-\Delta^+$, Δ^-, ... terms as well. We shall not elaborate on this point, however.

For further information the reader might consult Wigner and Witmer [80] and Herzberg [81, pp. 213, 217, 317].

So far we have supposed that the λ_i of the electrons are known. For more insight we might trace them back again to either the separate atoms or the united atom.

If an electron had $n = 1$ and $l = 0$ in the united atom, on splitting of the latter it will become a $1s\sigma$ electron, where the symbols, in this order, represent n, l, and λ. An electron which was $2p$ in the united atom may have $\lambda = 0$ or $\lambda = 1$ in the molecule, or $2p\sigma$ and $2p\pi$, respectively. A $3d$ electron may become $3d\sigma$, $3d\pi$, or $3d\delta$. The order of increasing energy is usually $1s\sigma$, $2s\sigma$, $2p\sigma$, $2p\pi$, $3s\sigma$, $3p\sigma$, $3p\pi$, ... According to the Pauli principle two electrons can occupy the same orbital only if they have opposite spin projection. Therefore at most two electrons can occupy a σ orbital, and $(1s\sigma)^2$ or $(2p\sigma)^2$ represent closed shells. In other than σ orbitals there are four places because $\lambda = \pm m_l$ and for each of these there are two possible values for the spin projection. Thus $(2p\pi)^4$ or $(3d\delta)^4$, for example, are closed shells.

In the approximation of separated atoms we use a notation where the value of λ comes first and is followed by the n and l values in one of the separated atoms. If they are different an index indicates the atom to which the electron originally belonged. If, for an electron in atom A, l was equal to 0 and n to 1 ($1s$ electron) it becomes $\sigma 1s_A$. If an electron was a $2p$ electron in atom A it will be either $\sigma 2p_A$ or $\pi 2p_A$, and so on. Again closed shells are obtained with two electrons for σ orbitals and four electrons for π, δ, ... orbitals. It is important to realize that the n and l numbers the electron has in one of the separated atoms are not, in general, the same it would have in the united atom. Correlation diagrams between the two systems were established. Such diagrams are given, for example, in Herzberg's [81, pp. 328, 329] and Coulson's books [11, pp. 97, 105].

An example will help further elucidate these conditions. We choose the N_2 molecule. The united atom of N_2 is the atom with 14 nuclear charges, which is silicon. In its ground state, Si has the configuration

$$\text{Si}\, 1s^2 2s^2 2p^6 3s^2 3p^2$$

This yields for N_2 the following configuration:

$$N_2(1s\sigma)^2(2s\sigma)^2(2p\sigma)^2(2p\pi)^4(3s\sigma)^2(3p\sigma)^2$$

Since all electrons are in closed shells, Λ must be equal to zero and the term must be a singlet Σ term[3], $^1\Sigma_g$.

Using the approximation of the separated atoms we have

$$N[K(2s)^2(2p)^3] + N[K(2s)^2(2p)^3]$$
$$\rightarrow N_2[KK(\sigma_g 2s)^2(\sigma_u 2s)^2(\sigma_g 2p)^2(\pi_u 2p)^4]$$

or

$$N_2[KK(z\sigma)^2(y\sigma)^2(x\sigma)^2(w\pi)^4]$$

Here K stands for $(\sigma 1s)^2$. These electrons can be taken as being very close to their original nuclei, tightly bound, and essentially unperturbed by the molecule formation. g and u, as before, stand for even and odd and are used only for homonuclear molecules which do possess a center of symmetry.

An important point is that the two atoms contribute, for example, four $2s$ electrons which, of course, cannot go all to one $(\sigma 2s)$ shell.

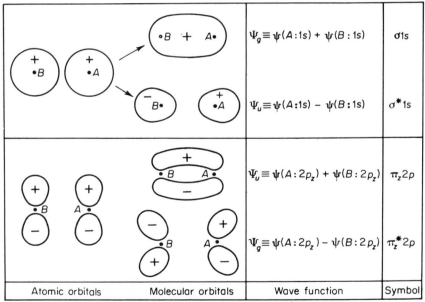

Atomic orbitals	Molecular orbitals	Wave function	Symbol
		$\Psi_g \equiv \psi(A:1s) + \psi(B:1s)$	$\sigma 1s$
		$\Psi_u \equiv \psi(A:1s) - \psi(B:1s)$	$\sigma^* 1s$
		$\Psi_u \equiv \psi(A:2p_z) + \psi(B:2p_z)$	$\pi_z 2p$
		$\Psi_g \equiv \psi(A:2p_z) - \psi(B:2p_z)$	$\pi_z^* 2p$

Attractive and repulsive σ, σ^* and π, π^* molecular orbitals and their formation from atomic orbitals

Fig. 6-5

[3] Closed shells always give $^1\Sigma$ or $^1\Sigma^+$ terms. In the case of equivalent electrons (n and l the same) the Pauli principle has to be taken into account when we derive the terms corresponding to a given configuration [81, p. 336].

On the other hand, s electrons can only become σ electrons in the molecule. Now, when we form the molecular orbitals from the two atomic orbitals we obtain two molecular orbitals. These are (p. 25)

$$\phi_1 = \frac{1}{\sqrt{N_1}}(\psi_A + \psi_B) \quad \text{and} \quad \phi_2 = \frac{1}{\sqrt{N_2}}(\psi_A - \psi_B)$$

The first of these is symmetrical with respect to inversion (g), the second one is antisymmetrical (u) as can be seen in Fig. 6–5 taken from Coulson [11]. Similarly from p electrons we obtain two σ and two π molecular orbitals. The order of increasing energy is, at least for the first row of the periodic system,

$$\sigma_g 1s < \sigma_u 1s < \sigma_g 2s < \sigma_u^* 2s < \sigma_g 2p < \pi_u 2p < \pi_g^* 2p < \sigma_u^* 2p$$
$$K \qquad K \qquad z\sigma \qquad y\sigma \qquad x\sigma \qquad w\pi \qquad v\pi \qquad u\sigma$$

Since n and l have no exact meanings except for very large inter-nuclear distances, Mulliken introduced the notation using simply z, y, x, ..., which indicate the order of increasing energy without implying anything relative to the quantum numbers in the separated atoms [82]. The term is again $^1\Sigma_g$ in our example.

Orbitals marked by an asterisk are antibonding, i.e., they have the negative sign in $\phi = \psi_A \pm \psi_B$. Thus for N_2 the bonding power of $z\sigma$ is approximately balanced by $y\sigma$ and there remain three pairs of electrons in $x\sigma$ and $w\pi$, giving a triple bond.[4] Generally single, double, and triple bonds correspond to σ^2, $\sigma^2\pi^2$, and $\sigma^2\pi^4$, respectively.

Concerning the $(w\pi)$ or $(v\pi)$ levels, these can be formed of p_x or p_y atomic orbitals; accordingly two of the electrons in the closed shell are π_y and two π_x (if the internuclear axis lies in the z axis), both having, of course, $\lambda = 1$.

As a second example we take the NO molecule. The united atom $(7 + 8 = 15)$ is phosphorus:

$$P \, 1s^2 2s^2 2p^6 3s^2 3p^3$$

This gives for NO:

$$NO \, (1s\sigma)^2 (2s\sigma)^2 (2p\sigma)^2 (2p\pi)^4 (3s\sigma)^2 (3p\sigma)^2 (3p\pi)$$

Only one electron is in an open shell and the term is therefore $^2\Pi$.

Using the approximation of separated atoms, we obtain

$$N[1s^2 2s^2 2p^3] + O[1s^2 2s^2 2p^4]$$
$$\rightarrow NO[KK(\sigma 2s)^2 (\sigma^* 2s)^2 (\sigma 2p)^2 (\pi 2p)^4 (\pi^* 2p)]$$
$$\equiv NO[KK(z\sigma)^2 (y\sigma)^2 (x\sigma)^2 (w\pi)^4 (v\pi)]$$

and the term is again $^2\Pi$. The bonding in NO is of a complicated

---

[4] The question is sometimes asked: how is it that certain bonding orbitals have energies higher than certain antibonding orbitals? We have to remember in this respect that this sequence follows the total energies of the orbitals of which the bonding energies are just a fraction.

nature: a triple bond minus a single electron in an antibonding orbital. Because of the latter the molecule is paramagnetic.

The oxygen molecule has a triplet ground state (as has the oxygen
atom). The united atom is sulphur, and the configuration for O_2 is
the same as for NO except that there are two electrons in $(3p\pi)$.
Since even then there remain two empty places in that shell, the
spins are free and we might have either a singlet or a triplet state.
According to Hund's rule the triplet will have the lower energy. The
term could be $^3\Delta$ or $^3\Sigma$ but a Δ term would imply $m_{l_1} = m_{l_2}$; thus,
all four quantum numbers would be the same (equivalent electrons).
This would contradict the Pauli principle. Actually the ground term
of O_2 is $^3\Sigma_g^-$. The separated atom treatment would again give the
same configuration as for NO except $(v\pi)^2$. This gives a double bond
for O_2 and again $^3\Sigma_g$, by a similar reasoning.

A molecular orbital for homodiatomic molecules is g or u, if the
united atom orbital to which it reduces is g or u, since in the atom
the nucleus is in the center of symmetry and the $g—u$ property is
independent from the internuclear distance. As we have seen before
(p. 121), an atomic wave function is g or u according as $\sum_i l_i$ is
even or odd.

The subject which has been briefly treated in this chapter is one
of the major topics of Herzberg's *Spectra of Diatomic Molecules*. A
shorter but very useful description can be found in Coulson's *Valence*
[11, pp. 91–110].

6-5 SELECTION RULES FOR THE ELECTRONIC SPECTRA
OF DIATOMIC MOLECULES

Selection rules are predictions concerning the value of the transition moment integral

$$\int \psi' \sum_i e_i r_i \psi'' \, d\tau$$

where ψ' is the eigenfunction of the excited state and ψ'' that of
the ground state (see Sec. 5-2).

For molecules, unlike atoms, the electronic wave function is not
the total wave function and the latter can be thought of as being
in first approximation, essentially a product of an electronic, a vibrational, and a rotational wave function. There are selection rules which
refer to the total wave functions, and others which apply to the
electronic (or vibrational or rotational) wave function.

The *total* wave function is called positive if it conserves its sign
when the signs of the Cartesian coordinates of all electrons and nuclei

forming the molecule are replaced by their negatives. It is called negative if it changes sign upon the same operation (inversion, or reflection at the origin). In spherical coordinates the inversion means replacing θ by $\pi - \theta$ and ϕ by $\pi + \phi$.

Now the transition moment has to be invariant (in both sign and magnitude) with respect to any change that leaves the potential energy—and with it the charge distribution—unchanged. This applies to any symmetry operation or coordinate transformation, and an inversion is equivalent to changing from a right-handed to a left-handed coordinate system. Therefore, since the inversion certainly changes the sign of the coordinate (x or y or z) in the transition moment integral, $\psi' \psi''$ must also change its sign, that is, one of the two wave functions has to be positive, the other negative, otherwise the transition moment must vanish. From this follows the general selection rule applying to the total wave function:

$$+ \longleftrightarrow -, \quad\quad + \longleftrightarrow\!\!\!/\, +, \quad\quad - \longleftrightarrow\!\!\!/\, -$$

This rule is valid whether the two atoms are the same or not.

For two identical nuclei we have two supplementary rules. In this case exchanging the two nuclei, i.e., replacing x_1, y_1, z_1 by x_2, y_2, z_2 respectively, clearly does not affect the potential function. Therefore, the square of the total wave function must remain the same, allowing the sign of the wave function to remain the same or to change. Wave functions that remain unchanged are called symmetrical in the nuclei, those that change are called antisymmetrical. Since the interchange of the nuclei cannot affect the dipole moment, ψ' and ψ'' must behave the same way or else the transition moment vanishes. From this follows the selection rule:

$$\text{sym} \longleftrightarrow \text{sym}, \quad \text{anti} \longleftrightarrow \text{anti}, \quad \text{sym} \longleftrightarrow\!\!\!/\, \text{anti}$$

Both of the selection rules above concern the total wave function. However, interchanging the nuclei is the same as carrying out first an inversion of *all* particles on the origin and then an inversion of the electrons only. The *electronic* wave function can again keep or change its sign with respect to inversion, giving even and odd states (g and u), as in the case of atoms. The dipole moment component in the transition moment will change its sign upon this inversion, and thus ψ' must keep and ψ'' must change its sign or vice versa. We have again the

$$g \longleftrightarrow\!\!\!/\, g, \quad u \longleftrightarrow\!\!\!/\, u, \quad g \longleftrightarrow u$$

selection rule concerning the *electronic* wave function. This rule applies only to homoatomic diatomic molecules (and also to polyatomic molecules with a center of symmetry), since for two different atoms the sym $\longleftrightarrow$ sym, etc. rule is clearly meaningless. Selection rules applying to the electronic (or vibrational or rotational) wave function have to be in accordance with the selection rules applying to the total wave function, which is the one that enters into the expression of the transition moment. It can be seen that

> For g states $+$ terms are sym
> For g states $-$ terms are anti
> For u states $+$ terms are anti
> For u states $-$ terms are sym

Other selection rules are related to the angular momenta. It is necessary to take into account the electronic angular momenta as well as the angular momentum due to the rotation of the molecule as a whole. Then, if J is the quantum number of the *total* angular momentum we have the general rule that[5]

$$\Delta J = 0, \pm 1, \qquad \text{except } J = 0 \not\longleftrightarrow J = 0$$

Other rules apply to Ω, Λ, Σ, and S if the related angular momenta are well defined, and this depends on the coupling conditions. These in turn depend (among others) upon the interaction of rotation and electronic motion. Four typical cases are distinguished, called "Hund's cases." These are described, for example, in Herzberg's *Spectra of Diatomic Molecules* [81, p. 218], and will not be treated here.

In the most frequent case the coupling between rotation and electronic motion is weak and Λ is well defined. Then we have

$$\Delta\Lambda = 0, \pm 1$$

If the total spin vector is defined, the rule

$$\Delta S = 0$$

holds for intercombinations, and if its projection on the internuclear axis is defined, the rule

$$\Delta\Sigma = 0$$

also holds, as well as $\Delta\Omega = 0, \pm 1$.

Another selection rule has to be added for Σ^+ and Σ^- terms. The upper $+$ or $-$ indices refer to a reflection in any plane containing the nuclei (σ_v) and *not* to inversion at the origin of all particles. The rule is:

$$\Sigma^+ \longleftrightarrow \Sigma^+, \qquad \Sigma^- \longleftrightarrow \Sigma^-, \qquad \Sigma^+ \not\longleftrightarrow \Sigma^-$$

and it is valid for either homoatomic or heteroatomic molecules. (Both Σ^+ and Σ^- combine with Π states.)

[5] However, $\Delta J = 0$ is forbidden for $\Omega = 0 \longleftrightarrow \Omega = 0$.

6-6 PARALLEL AND PERPENDICULAR BANDS

An important distinction between two band types can be reached when we prove selection rule

$$\Sigma^+ \longleftrightarrow \Sigma^+, \qquad \Sigma^- \longleftrightarrow \Sigma^-, \qquad \Sigma^+ \longleftrightarrow\!\!\!/\, \Sigma^-$$

We take the case of two different atoms.

Let us suppose that the internuclear axis is in the z axis and consider the three components of the transition moment:

$$\int \psi' M_x \psi'' \, d\tau, \qquad \int \psi' M_y \psi'' \, d\tau, \qquad \int \psi' M_z \psi'' \, d\tau$$

These integrals are different from zero only if they are unchanged for any symmetry operation. The only one for which Σ^+ and Σ^- behave differently is a reflection in a plane containing both nuclei (σ_v). Therefore, since M_z does not change for this latter operation, ψ' and ψ'' must be either both changed or both unchanged if a reflection in *any* such plane is to have the z component of the transition moment different from zero.

The components containing M_x and M_y then vanish because x and y change sign for a reflection in the yz and xz planes, respectively. Thus we see that $\Sigma^+ \longleftrightarrow \Sigma^+$ and $\Sigma^- \longleftrightarrow \Sigma^-$ transitions are allowed, but only if the transition moment is in the direction of the internuclear axis.

For $\Sigma^+ \longleftrightarrow \Sigma^-$ transitions all three components are zero. This is obvious for the component containing M_z, but it is also true for those containing M_x and M_y since M_x and M_y keep their signs for a reflection in planes xz and yz, respectively, making the integrals change sign—and vanish.

Quite generally, then, $\Sigma \longleftrightarrow \Sigma$ transitions are allowed only with a transition moment along the internuclear axis, and the corresponding bands are, therefore, called parallel bands. All bands corresponding to transitions with $\Delta\Lambda = 0$ are parallel bands.

Similar reasoning leads to the conclusion that $\Sigma^+ \longleftrightarrow \Pi$ or $\Sigma^- \longleftrightarrow \Pi$ transitions are allowed only if the transition moment is perpendicular to the internuclear axis. If the nodal plane for the Π electrons is, for example, the yz plane, then $\Sigma^+ \longleftrightarrow \Pi$ is allowed only with M_x, which changes sign at a reflection in the yz plane. $\Sigma^- \longleftrightarrow \Pi$ is allowed only with M_y. (Both wave functions change sign in yz but only Σ^- changes in xz. Therefore, M_x would lead to a change of sign upon reflection in yz, and M_z in xz.)

In general, $\Delta\Lambda = \pm 1$ gives perpendicular bands.

The distinction between parallel and perpendicular bands is important for the rotational fine structure of electronic band systems. The selection rule becomes $\Delta J = \pm 1$ for $^1\Sigma \longleftrightarrow \, ^1\Sigma$ but remains $\Delta J = 0, \pm 1$ for other types of bands. As a consequence we have only P and R branches for the former but P, Q, and R branches for the latter. The Q branches are strong only for perpendicular transitions, however.

6-7 RYDBERG AND SUB-RYDBERG TRANSITIONS

The distinction between Rydberg and sub-Rydberg bands is probably more important for the chemical spectroscopist than any other type of classification introduced so far.

Rydberg transitions are analogous to the electronic transitions of atoms. Generally, they lie in the far ultraviolet (wavelengths shorter than 2000 Å). These bands form series converging towards a frequency which corresponds to the energy of ionization of the molecule. The frequencies of the Rydberg bands can be expressed by Rydberg-like formulas as in the case of atoms. For these transitions the excited electron is, on the average, far from the nuclei, and the rest of the molecule can then be regarded approximately as a point. Dissociation of the *excited* molecule would leave at least one atom in an excited state.

A typical example is the transition from the ground state, $1s\sigma^2 \, ^1\Sigma_g^+$, to excited states $1s\sigma np\sigma \, ^1\Sigma_u^+$ or $1s\sigma np\pi \, ^1\Pi_u$ for the hydrogen molecule, where $n = 1, 2, 3, \ldots$ is the principal quantum number for a hydrogen atom, and united atom nomenclature is used. If we dissociate the molecule in its ground state, the transition becomes a $1s \longleftrightarrow np$ transition in one of the atoms, which is more or less profoundly perturbed in the molecule. Bands due to Rydberg transitions are usually very intense.

Sub-Rydberg transitions are typically molecular transitions, which cannot occur in atoms. Most of them lie in the ultraviolet and in the visible part of the spectrum. Their frequencies cannot be expressed by Rydberg formulas. They are usually due to electrons forming chemical bonds and would disappear if the atoms were separated at infinite distance. For this reason sub-Rydberg bands are expected .to be weaker than Rydberg bands, although there are significant exceptions.

The possibility of sub-Rydberg transitions is connected with the fact that more than one electronic state can be formed from two (or more) unexcited atomic wave functions (see pp. 25, 37). The transitions between them are sub-Rydberg transitions. An example is the transition between the state having wave function

$$\phi_1 = \frac{1}{\sqrt{N_1}} (\psi_A + \psi_B)$$

and the state having wave function

$$\phi_2 = \frac{1}{\sqrt{N_2}} (\psi_A - \psi_B)$$

of the hydrogen molecule in the LCAO MO approximation, where ψ_A and ψ_B are $1s$ atomic orbitals.

Almost all spectral bands known to chemists are such sub-Rydberg transitions. Among them there is a category of relatively strong bands called *charge-transfer* bands. In the valence-bond approximation these imply the transfer of a significant amount of electronic charge from one atom of a molecule to another. An extreme case is when a whole electron is transferred as a result of a transition such as

$$Na^+ Cl^- \xrightarrow{h\nu} Na + Cl$$

For a homopolar molecule, like H_2, the polar structures

$$H^+ \quad H^-, \qquad H^- \quad H^+$$

will make a much greater contribution to the excited state than to the ground state, and we can still speak of charge transfer.

In the molecular orbital approximation a charge transfer band corresponds to a transition from a bonding to an antibonding orbital. These facts were first recognized by Mulliken [83, 84] and will be discussed in more detail in Chapter 15.

The so-called $\pi \to \pi^*$ transitions of aromatic and other conjugated molecules, which are in the visible or the ultraviolet regions (7000–2000 Å), are all sub-Rydberg bands of the charge-transfer[6] type. All sub-Rydberg bands are not of the charge-transfer type, however.

6-8 A REMARK ON POLYATOMIC MOLECULES

Linear molecules can be treated in essentially the same way as diatomic ones.

In other polyatomic molecules, however, we cannot, in general, find a naturally preferential direction like the internuclear axis in the linear molecules. (Diatomic molecules are, of course, linear.) Therefore, although we can still speak about $\sigma, \pi, \ldots$ orbitals for the individual electrons, we cannot define meaningful angular momenta for the whole system. (A fundamental discussion of this is found in Kauzman's *Quantum Chemistry* [8, p. 259].) Under these circumstances the selection rules will be based almost exclusively on the symmetry properties of the molecules, which have a great influence on transition moments.

---

[6] In the more general sense.

On this rests the extremely great importance of group theory for the understanding of molecular spectra. We shall take up this subject in some detail in the next chapter.

The prohibition of intercombinations between states of different multiplicity is valid for molecules built of light atoms, and so is Hund's rule (see p. 124).

The Laporte rule (p. 120) is also valid for molecules possessing a center of symmetry (such as benzene, or *trans*-butadiene).

The concept of Rydberg and sub-Rydberg transitions is as important for polyatomic as for diatomic molecules.

7

Selection Rules and the Symmetry
of Molecules

As was shown in the previous chapter, spectral intensities depend essentially on transition moments, which, for dipole radiation, are

$$\int \psi' \sum e_i \, x_i \psi'' \, d\tau$$

and similarly for the y and z components. If these are zero, the band has zero intensity; it is forbidden. Now, in many cases the symmetry properties of the wave functions enable us to predict that certain types of transition will be forbidden. We have already encountered such "selection rules." All selection rules based on symmetry are based on the following simple facts:

1. The wave functions must have symmetry properties compatible with the symmetry properties of the molecule.
2. The transition moment must be invariant with respect to any symmetry operation. If there is even one symmetry operation with respect to which the transition moment changes its sign, it is equal to zero.[1]

Therefore we must study the symmetry properties of molecules. This will require an elementary treatment of group theory, whose importance for molecular spectroscopy cannot be exaggerated.

[1] For the generalization of this law in the case when both ψ' and ψ'' are degenerate, see p. 166.

140

7-1. SYMMETRY ELEMENTS

We must state at the outset that we shall be dealing with the symmetry of individual molecules, not with the symmetry of crystals, although, naturally, there are many points common to the two problems.

There are essentially five types of symmetry elements.

1. *Planes of symmetry.* These are usually designated by σ. The related symmetry *operation* is a reflection at the plane. This is similar to reflection in a mirror and consists simply of exchanging the atoms, which are at opposite sides of the plane at equal distances from it. The plane is a plane of symmetry if this operation leaves the aspect of the molecule unchanged. All nuclei occur in pairs except those in the plane.

The water molecule, for example, has two planes of symmetry. One passes through the oxygen and bisects the HOH angle. The other is the plane of the three nuclei.

The naphthalene molecule has three mutually perpendicular symmetry planes, as is easily seen; and so on.

2. *Axes of rotation.* The operation, C_p, is a rotation around a p-fold axis, where $p = 1, 2, 3, \ldots$, and the rotation is by $360°/p$ (C stands for cyclic).

A one-fold axis means no symmetry at all. A two-fold axis, C_2, means that after a rotation of $180°$ around the axis we obtain a configuration indistinguishable from the original one.

The water molecule has one two-fold axis passing through the oxygen. It lies in the line of intersection of its two planes of symmetry. *Cis-* and *trans*-butadiene both have a two-fold axis, but while for the former it lies in the plane of the molecule, for the latter it is perpendicular to it.

The naphthalene molecule has three mutually perpendicular two-fold axes.

The chloroform molecule has one three-fold axis, C_3, passing through the carbon and hydrogen nuclei. 1, 3, 5-trichlorobenzene has one three-fold axis, perpendicular to the plane of the benzene ring. For C_3 the angle of rotation is $120°$; for C_4 it is $90°$; for C_5, $72°$; and for C_6, $60°$. Benzene is an example of the latter. Any linear (and diatomic) molecule has a C_∞ axis which lies along the line passing through the nuclei, the angle of rotation being infinitesimal or any other angle.

p successive rotations make a full circle and are called C_p, $(C_p)^2$,

$(C_p)^3, \ldots, (C_p)^{p-1}, C_p^p \equiv E$. Each atom that is not on the axis occurs p times in the molecule.

3. *Center of symmetry* (i). The corresponding symmetry operation is called reflection at the *center*, or inversion. If we draw a straight line from any nucleus through the center and then continue it, there will be an identical nucleus at an equal distance from the center at the opposite side. Exchanging atoms related in this manner would leave the aspect of the molecule unchanged.

This operation is equivalent to changing the signs of all Cartesian coordinates of all the nuclei.

Trans-butadiene, benzene, naphthalene, and so on have a center of symmetry. (There can never be more than one.)

4. *Rotation-reflection axes* (S_p). If we carry out a rotation by an angle of $360°/p$ and then a reflection at a plane perpendicular to this axis and the molecule's appearance is unchanged, we have a p-fold rotation-reflection axis. The axis is not, in general, a symmetry axis of the molecule, nor is the plane necessarily a plane of symmetry. Operation S_2 is equivalent to an inversion (i). It consists in a rotation of $180°$ around an axis and a reflection at a plane perpendicular to the axis.

The boat form of cyclooctane has a four-fold rotation-reflection axis, S_4. The same axis is also a two-fold rotation axis, C_2, but *not* a C_4. The chair form of cyclohexane has a six-fold rotation-reflection axis, S_6, which at the same time is C_3 but *not* C_6.

If the molecule has a plane of symmetry perpendicular to C_2, C_4, or C_6, these axes are naturally S_2, S_4, and S_6 at the same time. There are higher reflection-rotation axes. Symmetrical linear molecules have an S_∞ axis.

For *odd* values of p (S_3 or S_5), the rotation-reflection axis *is* necessarily also a rotation axis of the same order (C_3, C_5) and the plane perpendicular to S_3 or S_5 is always a plane of symmetry. (Because of the lack of alternance in the positions of the nuclei we cannot have them alternately "up" or "down," for example. There always will be two contiguous "ups" or "downs.")

5. The identity, or "do-nothing," operation (E) must also be included. Otherwise the set of symmetry operations one can carry through on a given geometrical figure would not form a group in the mathematical sense (see below).

7-2. POINT GROUPS

There are many molecules (or in general, geometrical figures) which possess more than one symmetry element. Not every combination is possible, however. On the other hand, the presence of certain symmetry elements implies the presence of certain other symmetry elements. All symmetry elements of a molecule have one thing in common—they leave *at least* one point of the molecule unchanged. There are a limited number of sets of such symmetry elements. They are called *point groups*. In any of these groups the successive carrying out of two symmetry operations leads to the same result as *one* other symmetry operation, which is also a member of the group. The point groups will be briefly reviewed now. The notations will be those which Schönflies introduced into crystallography.

Some of our examples are taken from Herzberg [77, p. 5–12], who gave a very complete description of the point groups.

I. Groups with Axes Only. 1. *Only* one *axis of rotation*. These are the cyclic groups, C_p. The notation for the groups is the same as for the axis itself, although bold face type is often used for the groups.

When we look for examples, the difficulty is not to find molecules that have a p-fold axis but to find molecules that have *only* a p-fold axis.

C_1: No symmetry at all (except E). This is the case of about 90 per cent of the known molecules.

C_2: H_2O_2 is a probable example. The two hydroxyl groups are in (approximately) mutually perpendicular planes. The two-fold symmetry axis is perpendicular to the O—O line at its center and stands at .(approximately) 45° to any of the two H—O—O planes [86]. 1,1-dichloroethylene *would* belong to this group if the two groups were twisted with respect to one another by an angle other than 90°.

C_3: 1,1,1-trichoroethane would be an example if the two groups were twisted with respect to one another by an angle that is neither 60° nor 120°. Artificial examples could be found similarly for higher values of p. [77].

2. *Only* one *rotation-reflection axis* S_p

$S_2 \equiv C_i$: The only symmetry element is a two-fold rotation-reflection axis which is equivalent to a center of symmetry. *Trans*-1, 2-dichloro-1, 2-dibromoethane is an example. [77]

S_4: It implies C_2.

S_6: It implies C_3 and i.

S_3 and S_5 are not defined since they imply C_3 and C_5 and a plane perpendicular to the axis (C_{3h}, C_{5h}; see below).

3. *Dihedral groups*, D_p. There is one main p-fold axis, and perpendicular to it there are p other *two*-fold axes at equal angles to one another.

$D_1 \equiv C_2$.

D_2 is also called V (German *Vierergruppe*). It has three mutually perpendicular two-fold axes but no planes of symmetry.

D_3 has one three-fold axis and three two-fold axes but no planes of symmetry.

C_∞ or D_∞ cannot be imagined without planes of symmetry.

II. Groups with Symmetry Axes and Symmetry Planes but No More Than One Axis Three-fold or Higher. The axis of highest order is thought of as being vertical.

1. *Groups C_{pv}.* There is only *one* axis (p-fold) but there are p vertical planes (σ_v), the axis lying in their line of intersection. Many molecules belong to these groups.

C_{1v} is usually called C_s. It has no axis but it does have a plane of symmetry. Benzanthracene[2] is an example.

C_{2v}: *Cis*-butadiene, water, boat form of cyclohexane.

C_{3v}: NH_3, chloroform.

$C_{\infty v}$: HCN or any linear, heteroatomic molecule.

2. *Groups C_{ph}.* There is only one axis and one plane perpendicular to it ("horizontal" plane σ_h). i is implied if p is even.

C_{2h}: *Trans*-butadiene.

3. *Groups D_{pd}.* There is one p-fold axis and p two-fold axes perpendicular to it. In addition there are p vertical planes of symmetry (σ_d) which bisect the angles between two successive two-fold axes. (The index d stands for diagonal.)

D_{2d} is also called V_d. Allene is an example: $H_2C{=}C{=}CH_2$. In this molecule the two CH_2 groups lie in mutually perpendicular planes because of digonal hybridization at the central carbon atom. (The π bond is π_y in one of the bonds, π_z in the other.) These two planes are the symmetry planes and the two C_2 bisect the angle between them. In the direction of the third C_2 there is also an S_4 rotation-reflection axis.

D_{3d}: The staggered form of ethane, where the two CH_3 groups are twisted by 60°. The chair form of cyclohexane (S_6, i).

4. *Groups D_{ph}.* There are the following symmetry elements in these groups: one p-fold axis, p two-fold axes at angles $360°/2p$ perpendicular to the p-fold axis, p vertical planes (σ_v) each containing the p-fold axis and one of the two-fold axes, and one horizontal plane (σ_h) containing all the two-fold axes. If p is even we also have S_p and i.

There are no D_{pv} groups different from the D_{ph}. The only way of *not* having σ_h

[2] It is not really coplanar because of the mutual repulsion between the hydrogens in 9 and 1'.

in a dihedral group having other planes of symmetry is to have σ_d instead of σ_v.

$D_{1h} \equiv C_{2v}$.

D_{2h}, also called V_h: Ethylene, naphthalene, anthracene, and so on.

D_{3h}: "Eclipsed" ethane, *sym*-trichlorobenzene.

D_{6h}: benzene.

$D_{\infty h}$: acetylene, CO_2.

III. Groups with More Than One Three-fold or More Than Three-fold axes. These are called *cubic* groups in opposition to the axial groups which have been described under I and II.

1. *Groups T, T_d, and T_h.* In group T there are four three-fold axes and three mutually perpendicular two-fold axes but no planes of symmetry.

In group T_d, besides the symmetry elements possessed by group T there are six planes of symmetry (σ_d), each one through a pair of three-fold axes.

The regular tetrahedron belongs to this group as well as CH_4, CCl_4, the NH_4^+ ion, etc.

In group T_h there is, in addition, a center of symmetry.

2. *Groups O and O_h.* These are the octahedral groups. In O there are three mutually perpendicular four-fold axes, four three-fold axes, and six other two-fold axes, but no planes of symmetry.

In group O_h there are, in addition, nine planes and a center of symmetry, and the C_4 are S_4 at the same time.

Both regular octahedron and cube belong to group O_h as do many inorganic octahedral complex ions—for example, $[Co(NH_3)_6]^{3+}$.

3. *Groups I and I_h.* These are the icosahedral groups. In I there are six five-fold axes, ten three-fold axes, and fifteen two-fold axes; in I_h there are also a center and many planes of symmetry. No known molecule belongs to these groups.

The correspondence between the Schönflies notation and the Herman-Mauguin notation, which is more often used by crystallographers, may be found in books such as Robertson's *Organic Crystals and Molecules* [87, p. 44], or Wheatley's *The Determination of Molecular Structure* [88, p. 18].

7-3. ELEMENTS OF GROUP THEORY

As we shall see, symmetry point groups constitute groups in the mathematical sense. Therefore, we shall recall now those elements of group theory which the chemical spectroscopist is likely to encounter in his work. An excellent short review is found in Eyring, Walter, and Kimball's *Quantum Chemistry* [40], another in Margenau and Murphy's *The Mathematics of Physics and Chemistry* [89]. An even shorter but useful treatise was given by Reid [90]. References to the original literature are given at the end of this chapter.

The present description follows the pattern of the one by Eyring, Walter, and Kimball, whose symbols are kept. However, examples and some further explanation will be added in order to make it more easily accessible to chemists.

A group is a set of elements A, B, C, ... with a law of combination such that the product AB of any two elements A and B and also the square of any element is a member of the set. This is the most important characteristic of a group.

The number of the elements forming the group may be finite or infinite and the law of combination may be *any* operation, the word "product" being used to designate the result of two successive operations.

The following three conditions, are equally stringent:

(a) The group must contain a unit element E for which $EA = AE = A$ for every element of the group.

(b) The associative law holds: $A(BC) = (AB)C$.

(c) Every element has an inverse, $X = A^{-1}$, also a member of the group, for which $AX = AA^{-1} = A^{-1}A = E$.

One of the usual examples is the set of all integers including zero with addition as the law of combination. The unit element is zero and the inverse of every element is its negative.

Another well-known example is the set of the four numbers ± 1, $\pm i$. The law of combination is multiplication and the unit element is 1. The inverse of $+1$ is $+1$, the inverse of -1 is -1, the inverse of $+i$ is $-i$, and the inverse of $-i$ is $+i$.

It is of the utmost importance for the whole of molecular spectroscopy that every symmetry point group is a group in the mathematical sense, satisfying the four conditions stated above.

As a first simple example let us take point group C_{2v} to which *cis*-butadiene belongs. The elements of the group are

1. the identity operation, E;

2. a rotation by $180°$ around the axis, which we put in the direction of the z axis, C_2;

3. a reflection in the xz plane, which is the plane of the molecule, σ_v, and

4. a reflection in the xy plane (σ_v') which is perpendicular to the plane of the molecule and contains the two-fold axis (see Fig. 7–8).

The law of combination is simply the successive carrying out of two of these symmetry operations. This, according to the definition of a group, must lead in every case to the same result as the operation corresponding to just one other element of the group.

A table of multiplication can be constructed where the product of any two operations can be found at the intersection of the corresponding row and column (see Table 7–1).

TABLE 7–1

	E	C_2	σ_v	σ_v'
E	E	C_2	σ_v	σ_v'
C_2	C_2	E	σ_v'	σ_v
σ_v	σ_v	σ_v'	E	C_2
σ_v'	σ_v'	σ_v	C_2	E

The commutative law is not, in general, valid for groups.[3] If it is, as in this example, the group is called *Abelian*. (Note that in this example E seems to be the same as σ_v. This ceases to be so, however, if we let the carbon atoms carry their π orbitals) Figure 7–1 is an example of the successive carrying out of two operations. The $+$ or $-$ signs stand for positions above and below the plane of the molecule, respectively.

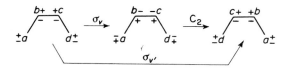

Fig. 7-1

A somewhat more complicated example is group C_{3v}. The chloroform molecule, $CHCl_3$, belongs to this group. The three chlorines are at the corners of an equilateral triangle. The possible symmetry operations, i.e., the elements of the group, are

1. the identity operation, E;
2. a clockwise rotation by 120° with respect to the three-fold axis which passes through the carbon and the hydrogen atoms, C_3;
3. a counterclockwise rotation around the same axis, C_3';
4. a reflection at the plane containing C, H, and Cl_a and bisecting the Cl_b-Cl_c distance (Fig. 7–2);
5. a reflection at the plane containing C, H, and Cl_b and bisecting the Cl_a-Cl_c line;

[3] That is, the product of two successive operations *does* depend on the order in which these operations are carried out.

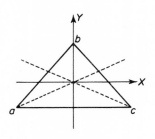

Fig. 7-2

6. a reflection at the plane containing C, H, and Cl_c and bisecting the Cl_a-Cl_b line.

The positions of the atoms for operations 4, 5 and 6 have to be taken as in Fig. 7-2.

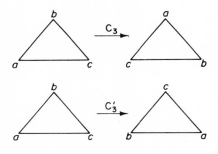

Fig. 7-3

Operations 2 and 3 are not the same. Looking at Fig. 7-3 it is seen immediately that they do not exchange the same nuclei.

(For group C_{2v}, our first example, a rotation C_2 exchanges the same nuclei in either direction.)

The multiplication table for group C_{3v} is shown in table 7-2.

TABLE 7-2

	E	C_3	C_3'	σ_v^a	σ_v^b	σ_v^c
E	E	C_3	C_3'	σ_v^a	σ_v^b	σ_v^c
C_3	C_3	C_3'	E	σ_v^c	σ_v^a	σ_v^b
C_3'	C_3'	E	C_3	σ_v^b	σ_v^c	σ_v^a
σ_v^a	σ_v^a	σ_v^b	σ_v^c	E	C_3	C_3'
σ_v^b	σ_v^b	σ_v^c	σ_v^a	C_3'	E	C_3
σ_v^c	σ_v^c	σ_v^a	σ_v^b	C_3	C_3'	E

One example of carrying out successive operations is given in Fig. 7–4. In general, the product of a reflection and a rotation is another reflection, the product of two rotations is the identity or another rotation, and the product of two reflections is the identity or a rotation.

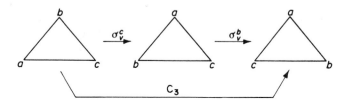

Fig. 7-4

Several new features appear in the last table of multiplication (Table 7–2). The commutative law obviously does not apply; the group is *not* Abelian.

The identity operation, the two rotations, and the three reflections clearly represent different types of operations. They are said to belong to three different *classes*. E is a class by itself, C_3 and C_3' form another class, and σ_v^a, σ_v^b, and σ_v^c still another class. If two operations belong to the same class, it is always possible to find a new coordinate system in which they go over to one other. For example, σ_v^b represents a reflection in the yz plane. Had we put y in the direction of σ_v^a, this latter would represent the reflection in the yz plane.

The more precise definition of a class can be given as follows:

If P, Q, and X are elements of the same group, X^{-1} is the inverse of X, and $X^{-1}PX = Q$, then P and Q are conjugate with each other. The set of elements conjugate with each other form a class.

For the group C_{3v}

$$\begin{array}{ccc}
the\ inverse\ of\ E & is & E \\
\text{''} & C_3 & \text{''} & C_3' \\
\text{''} & C_3' & \text{''} & C_3 \\
\text{''} & \sigma_v^a & \text{''} & \sigma_v^a \\
\text{''} & \sigma_v^b & \text{''} & \sigma_v^b \\
\text{''} & \sigma_v^c & \text{''} & \sigma_v^c
\end{array}$$

E is always a class by itself since $X^{-1}EX = X^{-1}X = E$ for any element X. C_3 and C_3' form a class since

$$\begin{array}{ll}
EC_3E = C_3 & \qquad EC_3'E = C_3' \\
C_3'C_3C_3 = C_3 & \qquad C_3'C_3'C_3 = C_3' \\
C_3C_3C_3' = C_3 & \qquad C_3C_3'C_3' = C_3'
\end{array}$$

$$\sigma_v^a C_3 \sigma_v^a = C_3' \qquad\qquad \sigma_v^a C_3' \sigma_v^a = C_3$$
$$\sigma_v^b C_3 \sigma_v^b = C_3' \qquad\qquad \sigma_v^b C_3' \sigma_v^b = C_3$$
$$\sigma_v^c C_3 \sigma_v^c = C_3' \qquad\qquad \sigma_v^c C_3' \sigma_v^c = C_3$$

all elements having been tried. [The order of forming the products is, for example, in the case of $\sigma_v^a C_3 \sigma_v^a$: first multiply by the element of the right (from the row of the table) the element of the middle (from the column) and obtain σ_v^c. Then multiply by σ_v^c (from the row) σ_v^a (from the column) and obtain C_3'.]

It can be shown in the same manner that σ_v^a, σ_v^b, and σ_v^c from a class.

If the group is Abelian the commutative law applies. Therefore

$$X^{-1}PX = X^{-1}XP = EP = P$$

for any element X, and every element is a class by itself. This was the case of our first example, the group C_{2v}.

Any group can be separated into classes, none of which contains elements in common with other classes.

A group whose elements are all contained in another group is called a subgroup. In group C_{2v} E and C_2 form a subgroup and also E and σ_v or E and σ_v'. In group C_{3v}, E, C_3, and C_3' form a subgroup and also E and σ_v^a, E and σ_v^b, or E and σ_v^c. E is, of course, a subgroup by itself.

7-4. MATRICES AND SYMMETRY OPERATIONS

There are two equivalent ways of describing symmetry operations. We may keep the coordinate system fixed and change the position of the nuclei as required by the given symmetry operation (position transformation), or we may keep the molecule fixed and make a coordinate transformation instead. It is good to remember this even though we shall apply only the first method.

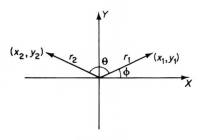

Fig. 7-5

Symmetry operations like rotations and reflections are conveniently described mathematically by making use of the matrix language. First we shall study the effect of such operations on a single vector (Fig. 7-5). We take the vector of length r in the xy plane and we carry out a rotation by an angle θ. This will carry the point (x_1, y_1) defined by the vector to point (x_2, y_2).

Then we can write for the old coordinates:

$$x_1 = r \cos \phi, \qquad y_1 = r \sin \phi \tag{7-1}$$

and for the new coordinates:

$$x_2 = r \cos (\phi + \theta) = r \cos \phi \cos \theta - r \sin \phi \sin \theta = x_1 \cos \theta - y_1 \sin \theta$$
$$y_2 = r \sin (\phi + \theta) = r \sin \phi \cos \theta + r \cos \phi \sin \theta = x_1 \sin \theta + y_1 \cos \theta \tag{7-2}$$

Using matrix notation we can write

$$\begin{pmatrix} x_2 \\ y_2 \end{pmatrix} = \begin{pmatrix} \cos \theta & -\sin \theta \\ \sin \theta & \cos \theta \end{pmatrix} \begin{pmatrix} x_1 \\ y_1 \end{pmatrix} \tag{7-3}$$

where the vectors r_1 and r_2 are written in the form of column vectors made up by their components, and the rule of matrix multiplication applies.[4]

The matrix of transformation is unitary since its determinant gives

$$\cos^2 \theta + \sin^2 \theta = 1$$

This is generally so for matrices representing rotations, reflections, and inversions. Generally, if the vector is defined in n-dimensional space and its components are $x_1, x_2, x_3, \ldots, x_n$ we can write for transformed coordinates $x'_1, x'_2, \ldots, x'_n$:

$$x'_1 = a_{11} x_1 + a_{12} x_2 + \cdots + a_{1n} x_n$$
$$x'_2 = a_{21} x_1 + a_{22} x_2 + \cdots + a_{2n} x_n$$
$$\cdots \cdots \cdots \cdots \cdots \cdots \cdots \cdots \cdots \cdots \cdots$$
$$x'_n = a_{n1} x_1 + a_{n2} x_2 + \cdots + a_{nn} x_n \tag{7-4}$$

Alternative notations are

$$x'_j = \sum_k a_{jk} x_k, \qquad k, j = 1, 2, \ldots, n \tag{7-5}$$

---

[4] In three dimensions if the z axis is perpendicular to the plane of rotation this becomes

$$\begin{pmatrix} \cos \theta & -\sin \theta & 0 \\ \sin \theta & \cos \theta & 0 \\ 0 & 0 & 1 \end{pmatrix}$$

where j is the index for the row and k for the column, or

$$x' = \boldsymbol{a}x$$

where a is the matrix of transformation

$$\boldsymbol{a} = \begin{pmatrix} a_{11} & a_{12} & \cdots & a_{1n} \\ a_{21} & a_{22} & \cdots & a_{2n} \\ \cdots\cdots\cdots\cdots\cdots\cdots \\ a_{n1} & a_{n2} & \cdots & a_{nn} \end{pmatrix} \tag{7-6}$$

If this transformation is followed by another transformation with

$$x'' = \boldsymbol{b}x' \qquad \text{or} \qquad x_i'' = \sum_j b_{ij}x_j'$$

then the combined result of the two can be obtained by one other transformation:

$$x'' = \boldsymbol{c}x \qquad \text{or} \qquad x_i'' = \sum_k c_{ik}x_k$$

Thus

$$x_i'' = \sum_j b_{ij}x_j' = \sum_j \sum_k b_{ij}a_{jk}x_k = \sum_k c_{ik}x_k \tag{7-7}$$

Hence the components of the product matrix $\boldsymbol{c} = \boldsymbol{ba}$ are

$$c_{ik} = \sum_j b_{ij}a_{jk} \tag{7-8}$$

This is just the rule of matrix multiplication.

7-5. REPRESENTATIONS

Two groups, G and G', are said to be *isomorphic* if to each element, A, B, C,..., of G there corresponds an element, A', B', C',... of G', so that if $AB = C$ then also $A'B' = C'$ for all products. Isomorphic groups have the same table of multiplication. In the general case two or more elements of G' may correspond to one element of G.

If the elements of, say, group G' are square matrices it is called a *representation* of group G. The order of the matrices is called the *dimension* (or degree) of the respresentation.

It is always possible to find a representation for a symmetry point group if we take the symbols a, b, c,... standing for the nuclei as the components of a vector, which we take in the form of a column vector, and then build matrices which multiplied by it bring about the same permutation of letters as the individual symmetry operations.

For *cis*-butadiene (C_{2v}), for example, we can write (with Figs. 7-6):

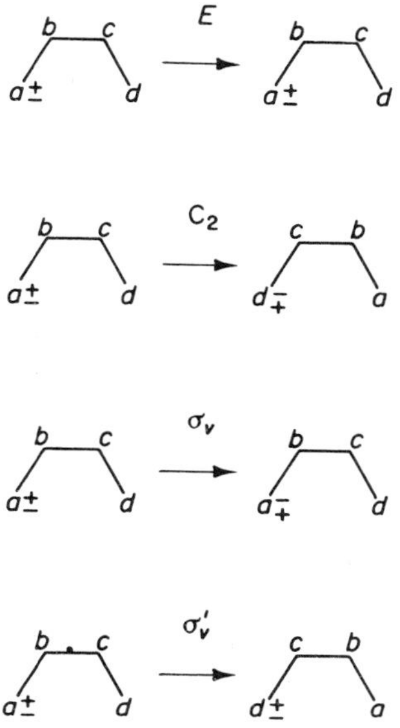

$$E: \quad \begin{bmatrix} a \\ b \\ c \\ d \end{bmatrix} = \begin{bmatrix} 1 & 0 & 0 & 0 \\ 0 & 1 & 0 & 0 \\ 0 & 0 & 1 & 0 \\ 0 & 0 & 0 & 1 \end{bmatrix} \begin{bmatrix} a \\ b \\ c \\ d \end{bmatrix}$$

$$C_2: \quad \begin{bmatrix} \overline{d} \\ \overline{c} \\ \overline{b} \\ \overline{a} \end{bmatrix} = \begin{bmatrix} 0 & 0 & 0 & -1 \\ 0 & 0 & -1 & 0 \\ 0 & -1 & 0 & 0 \\ -1 & 0 & 0 & 0 \end{bmatrix} \begin{bmatrix} a \\ b \\ c \\ d \end{bmatrix}$$

$$\sigma_v: \quad \begin{bmatrix} \overline{a} \\ \overline{b} \\ \overline{c} \\ \overline{d} \end{bmatrix} = \begin{bmatrix} -1 & 0 & 0 & 0 \\ 0 & -1 & 0 & 0 \\ 0 & 0 & -1 & 0 \\ 0 & 0 & 0 & -1 \end{bmatrix} \begin{bmatrix} a \\ b \\ c \\ d \end{bmatrix}$$

$$\sigma_v': \quad \begin{bmatrix} d \\ c \\ b \\ a \end{bmatrix} = \begin{bmatrix} 0 & 0 & 0 & 1 \\ 0 & 0 & 1 & 0 \\ 0 & 1 & 0 & 0 \\ 1 & 0 & 0 & 0 \end{bmatrix} \begin{bmatrix} a \\ b \\ c \\ d \end{bmatrix} \qquad (7\text{-}9)$$

Fig. 7-6

The original permutation is at the right-hand side, and the new permutation at the left-hand side is obtained by matrix multiplication. For example, σ_v' replaces a by d, therefore 1 is written at the intersection of row a and column d, etc. The minus signs above the letters mean that what was above the plane of the molecule before carrying out the operation is below it afterwards.

It can be easily verified that the four matrices follow the table of multiplication of group C_{2v}. For example, $\sigma_v \sigma_v' = C_2$; accordingly

$$\begin{bmatrix} -1 & 0 & 0 & 0 \\ 0 & -1 & 0 & 0 \\ 0 & 0 & -1 & 0 \\ 0 & 0 & 0 & -1 \end{bmatrix} \begin{bmatrix} 0 & 0 & 0 & 1 \\ 0 & 0 & 1 & 0 \\ 0 & 1 & 0 & 0 \\ 1 & 0 & 0 & 0 \end{bmatrix} = \begin{bmatrix} 0 & 0 & 0 & -1 \\ 0 & 0 & -1 & 0 \\ 0 & -1 & 0 & 0 \\ -1 & 0 & 0 & 0 \end{bmatrix}$$

For chloroform (C_{3v}) the following matrices constitute a representation (cf. Fig. 7-7):   (7-10)

$$E: \quad \begin{bmatrix} a \\ b \\ c \\ d \\ e \end{bmatrix} = \begin{bmatrix} 1 & 0 & 0 & 0 & 0 \\ 0 & 1 & 0 & 0 & 0 \\ 0 & 0 & 1 & 0 & 0 \\ 0 & 0 & 0 & 1 & 0 \\ 0 & 0 & 0 & 0 & 1 \end{bmatrix} \begin{bmatrix} a \\ b \\ c \\ d \\ e \end{bmatrix}$$

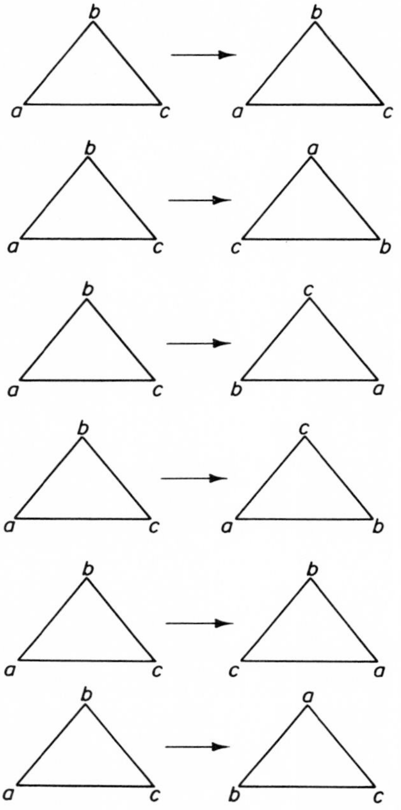

Fig. 7-7

$$C_3: \begin{bmatrix} c \\ a \\ b \\ d \\ e \end{bmatrix} = \begin{bmatrix} 0 & 0 & 1 & 0 & 0 \\ 1 & 0 & 0 & 0 & 0 \\ 0 & 1 & 0 & 0 & 0 \\ 0 & 0 & 0 & 1 & 0 \\ 0 & 0 & 0 & 0 & 1 \end{bmatrix} \begin{bmatrix} a \\ b \\ c \\ d \\ e \end{bmatrix}$$

$$C_3': \begin{bmatrix} b \\ c \\ a \\ d \\ e \end{bmatrix} = \begin{bmatrix} 0 & 1 & 0 & 0 & 0 \\ 0 & 0 & 1 & 0 & 0 \\ 1 & 0 & 0 & 0 & 0 \\ 0 & 0 & 0 & 1 & 0 \\ 0 & 0 & 0 & 0 & 1 \end{bmatrix} \begin{bmatrix} a \\ b \\ c \\ d \\ e \end{bmatrix}$$

$$\sigma_v^a: \begin{bmatrix} a \\ c \\ b \\ d \\ e \end{bmatrix} = \begin{bmatrix} 1 & 0 & 0 & 0 & 0 \\ 0 & 0 & 1 & 0 & 0 \\ 0 & 1 & 0 & 0 & 0 \\ 0 & 0 & 0 & 1 & 0 \\ 0 & 0 & 0 & 0 & 1 \end{bmatrix} \begin{bmatrix} a \\ b \\ c \\ d \\ e \end{bmatrix}$$

$$\sigma_v^b: \begin{bmatrix} c \\ b \\ a \\ d \\ e \end{bmatrix} = \begin{bmatrix} 0 & 0 & 1 & 0 & 0 \\ 0 & 1 & 0 & 0 & 0 \\ 1 & 0 & 0 & 0 & 0 \\ 0 & 0 & 0 & 1 & 0 \\ 0 & 0 & 0 & 0 & 1 \end{bmatrix} \begin{bmatrix} a \\ b \\ c \\ d \\ e \end{bmatrix}$$

$$\sigma_v^c: \begin{bmatrix} b \\ a \\ c \\ d \\ e \end{bmatrix} = \begin{bmatrix} 0 & 1 & 0 & 0 & 0 \\ 1 & 0 & 0 & 0 & 0 \\ 0 & 0 & 1 & 0 & 0 \\ 0 & 0 & 0 & 1 & 0 \\ 0 & 0 & 0 & 0 & 1 \end{bmatrix} \begin{bmatrix} a \\ b \\ c \\ d \\ e \end{bmatrix}$$

Letters d and e stand for the carbon and the hydrogen atoms and remain at their places for all the operations. Again the six matrices obey the table of multiplication of group C_{3v}. For example, $C_3'\sigma_v^a = \sigma_v^b$; accordingly:

$$\begin{bmatrix} 0 & 1 & 0 & 0 & 0 \\ 0 & 0 & 1 & 0 & 0 \\ 1 & 0 & 0 & 0 & 0 \\ 0 & 0 & 0 & 1 & 0 \\ 0 & 0 & 0 & 0 & 1 \end{bmatrix} \begin{bmatrix} 1 & 0 & 0 & 0 & 0 \\ 0 & 0 & 1 & 0 & 0 \\ 0 & 1 & 0 & 0 & 0 \\ 0 & 0 & 0 & 1 & 0 \\ 0 & 0 & 0 & 0 & 1 \end{bmatrix} = \begin{bmatrix} 0 & 0 & 1 & 0 & 0 \\ 0 & 1 & 0 & 0 & 0 \\ 1 & 0 & 0 & 0 & 0 \\ 0 & 0 & 0 & 1 & 0 \\ 0 & 0 & 0 & 0 & 1 \end{bmatrix}$$

Other representations can easily be found. We can simply assign the unit matrix (i.e., 1) to each symmetry operation.

	E	C_2	σ_v	σ_v'
C_{2v}:	1	1	1	1

This representation does obey the multiplication table. It is a trivial one but by no means unimportant.

Other simple representations are found if we change some of the signs (Table 7-3).

TABLE 7-3

C_{2v}:		E	C_2	σ_v	σ_v'
	Γ_1	1	1	1	1
	Γ_2	1	1	-1	-1
	Γ_3	1	-1	1	-1
	Γ_4	1	-1	-1	1

The individual representations are noted by Γ_i. It can be verified easily that they all obey to the table of multiplication. On the other hand

$$1 \qquad -1 \qquad -1 \qquad -1$$

does not conform to the table of multiplication and, therefore is not a representation.

For C_{3v} two one-dimensional representations can be written down just as easily.

	E	C_3	C_3'	σ_v^a	σ_v^b	σ_v^c
Γ_1	1	1	1	1	1	1
Γ_2	1	1	1	-1	-1	-1

We find a two-dimensional representation if we take the matrices of transformation of the vector determined by the Cartesian coordinates, x_1 and y_1, of one of the nuclei a, b, or c. For E we obtain from

$$\begin{pmatrix} x_2 \\ y_2 \end{pmatrix} = \begin{pmatrix} \cos\theta & -\sin\theta \\ \sin\theta & \cos\theta \end{pmatrix} \begin{pmatrix} x_1 \\ y_1 \end{pmatrix}$$

with $\theta = 0$

$$\begin{pmatrix} 1 & 0 \\ 0 & 1 \end{pmatrix}$$

For C_3, with $\theta = -120°$ we obtain

$$\begin{pmatrix} -\dfrac{1}{2} & \dfrac{\sqrt{3}}{2} \\ -\dfrac{\sqrt{3}}{2} & -\dfrac{1}{2} \end{pmatrix}$$

Correspondingly for C_3', putting $\theta = 120°$ we have

$$\begin{pmatrix} -\dfrac{1}{2} & -\dfrac{\sqrt{3}}{2} \\ \dfrac{\sqrt{3}}{2} & -\dfrac{1}{2} \end{pmatrix}$$

The matrix for σ_v^b can be written down directly as

$$\begin{pmatrix} -1 & 0 \\ 0 & 1 \end{pmatrix}$$

since this operation gives

$$x_2 = -x_1 + (0 \times y_1) \quad \text{and} \quad y_2 = y_1 + (0 \times x_1)$$

The matrices for the two other reflections are obtained from the table of multiplication ($\sigma_v^a = C_3 \sigma_v^b$ and $\sigma_v^c = C_3' \sigma_v^b$) and we have the following set of matrices, forming a representation:

$$\Gamma_3: \quad \overset{E}{\begin{pmatrix} 1 & 0 \\ 0 & 1 \end{pmatrix}} \overset{C_3}{\begin{pmatrix} -\frac{1}{2} & \frac{\sqrt{3}}{2} \\ -\frac{\sqrt{3}}{2} & -\frac{1}{2} \end{pmatrix}} \overset{C_3'}{\begin{pmatrix} -\frac{1}{2} & -\frac{\sqrt{3}}{2} \\ \frac{\sqrt{3}}{2} & -\frac{1}{2} \end{pmatrix}} \overset{\sigma_v^a}{\begin{pmatrix} \frac{1}{2} & \frac{\sqrt{3}}{2} \\ \frac{\sqrt{3}}{2} & -\frac{1}{2} \end{pmatrix}} \overset{\sigma_v^b}{\begin{pmatrix} -1 & 0 \\ 0 & 1 \end{pmatrix}} \overset{\sigma_v^c}{\begin{pmatrix} \frac{1}{2} & -\frac{\sqrt{3}}{2} \\ -\frac{\sqrt{3}}{2} & -\frac{1}{2} \end{pmatrix}}$$

The table of multiplication is obeyed. For example, $C_3 C_3' = E$ and also

$$\begin{pmatrix} -\frac{1}{2} & \frac{\sqrt{3}}{2} \\ -\frac{\sqrt{3}}{2} & -\frac{1}{2} \end{pmatrix} \begin{pmatrix} -\frac{1}{2} & -\frac{\sqrt{3}}{2} \\ \frac{\sqrt{3}}{2} & -\frac{1}{2} \end{pmatrix} = \begin{pmatrix} 1 & 0 \\ 0 & 1 \end{pmatrix}$$

Many other representations may be found. For example we might consider the three Cartesian coordinates of each nucleus. The matrices of transformation under the symmetry operations that correspond to them form a representation. Their dimension would be 12 for butadiene and 15 for chloroform. This type of representation is very important in the theory of vibrations.

It is felt, however, that there must be a fundamental difference between representations like the ones we noted by Γ_i and those which were obtained by the permutations of the letters $a, b, c, \ldots$, attached to the nuclei or those which are based on their coordinates.

First we suppose that we have found a representation, which consists of matrices

$$e', a', b', c', \ldots$$

If we multiply these matrices by another matrix β from the right, and then multiply its reciprocal β^{-1} by the product, we have carried out a so-called similarity transformation. Now, it may be shown that the matrices obtained by such transformations

$$e'' = \beta^{-1} e' \beta; \quad a'' = \beta^{-1} a' \beta; \quad b'' = \beta^{-1} b' \beta; \quad \ldots \qquad (7\text{-}11)$$

also form a representation of the same group, the same matrix being used for all members. [40] This means that if

$$a' b' = d' \qquad (7\text{-}12)$$

we also have

$$a'' b'' = d'' \qquad (7\text{-}13)$$

To prove this it is sufficient to substitute the related expressions from (7–11) into (7–13):

$$\beta' a' \beta \beta^{-1} b' \beta = \beta^{-1} d' \beta \qquad (7\text{-}14)$$

Using the associative law we have

$$\beta^{-1} a' b' \beta = \beta^{-1} d' \beta \qquad (7\text{-}15)$$

since $\beta\beta^{-1} = E$. Then we multiply from the left by β and from the right by β^{-1} and obtain

$$a' b' = d' \qquad (7\text{-}16)$$

Thus we arrived at a true statement from (7–13), which is, therefore, seen to be valid.

It is always possible to find new representations from a given one by similarity transformations. In many cases it is possible to find a similarity transformation that transforms *all* the matrices e', $a', b', c', \cdots$ into the form

$$a'' = \beta^{-1} a^1 \beta = \left\{ \begin{array}{ccccc} a_1'' & 0 & 0 & - & - \\ 0 & a_2'' & 0 & - & - \\ 0 & 0 & a_3'' & - & - \\ - & - & - & - & - \end{array} \right\}$$

$$\qquad (7\text{-}17)$$

$$b'' = \beta^{-1} b^1 \beta = \left\{ \begin{array}{ccccc} b_1'' & 0 & 0 & - & - \\ 0 & b_2'' & 0 & - & - \\ 0 & 0 & b_3'' & - & - \\ - & - & - & - & - \end{array} \right\}$$

and so on, where the $a_i'', \ldots, b_i'', \ldots$ are square matrices and there are only zeros outside of the squares. If a matrix capable of carrying through such a "reduction" can be found, the representation consisting of the original matrices $e', a', b', c', \ldots$ is called *reducible*.

If $a'' b'' = d''$, then it is also true that

$$a_i'' b_i'' = d_i'' \qquad (7\text{-}18)$$

This follows from the law of matrix multiplication and from the fact that only components located in squares with the same value of i meet each other. Thus $e_1'', a_1'', b_1'', c_1'', \ldots$ form a representation

and so do $e_2'', a_2'', b_2'', c_2'', \ldots$ It is possible that some of these representations can be further reduced by similarity transformations. However,
in a few steps we can always reduce the original representation
completely into representations which cannot be reduced further by
any similarity transformation.

These latter representations are said to be *irreducible*, and every
group has a determined number of them. Γ_1, Γ_2, Γ_3, and Γ_4 for
group C_{2v} are all irreducible and so are Γ_1, Γ_2, and Γ_3 for group
C_{3v}; and, as we shall see below, no others exist. They are all of
dimension $l = 1$, except Γ_3 for C_{3v}, which has dimension $l = 2$.

The other representations mentioned in this chapter are reducible.
In general, any reducible representation is a linear combination of
irreducible representations:

$$\Gamma = a_1\Gamma_1 + a_2\Gamma_2 + \cdots + a_n\Gamma_n \qquad (7\text{-}19)$$

This is, of course, not a simple sum but an expression showing how
many times a given Γ_i occurs in Γ. The a_i are positive integers or
zero, i.e., a given irreducible representation may occur in a reducible
one once, more than once, or not at all.

It is of considerable interest in both wave mechanics and spectroscopy to know how many times a given irreducible representation
occurs in a reducible one. In order to obtain a general relationship
to this effect we must first make some general observations on
unitary matrices.

If $\Gamma_i(R)$ is the matrix corresponding to operation R and if
$\Gamma_i(R)_{mn}$ is the mn component of the matrix, then we have

$$\sum_R \Gamma_i(R)_{mn}\Gamma_i(R)_{mn} = \frac{h}{l_i} \qquad (7\text{-}20)$$

$$\sum_R \Gamma_i(R)_{mn}\Gamma_j(R)_{m'n'} = 0; \qquad i \neq j \qquad (7\text{-}21)$$

and

$$\sum_R \Gamma_i(R)_{mn}\Gamma_i(R)_{m'n'} = 0; \qquad m \neq m' \text{ or/and } n \neq n' \qquad (7\text{-}22)$$

In words,

1. the sum of the squares of a given component mn taken over
   all the matrices of one given representation is equal to the
   ratio of the order of the group to the dimension of the representation;
2. the sum of the products of a given component mn of one
   matrix with any component $m'n'$ of another matrix or another
   component of the same matrix taken over all operations R is
   equal to zero,

We are not going to prove these relations here. Instead we are going to check them on the examples already dealt with in this chapter.

Taking first the four irreducible representations of group C_{2v} (p. 155) we see that

$$\sum_R \Gamma_1(R)_{11}\Gamma_1(R)_{11} = 4$$

and similarly for Γ_2, Γ_3, and Γ_4;

$$\sum_R \Gamma_1(R)_{11}\Gamma_2(R)_{11} = 0$$

and similarly for any choice of indices.

Taking the three irreducible representations of C_{3v} (pp. 155, 156) we obtain

$$\sum_R \Gamma_1(R)_{11}\Gamma_1(R)_{11} = 6$$

$$\sum_R \Gamma_2(R)_{11}\Gamma_2(R)_{11} = 6$$

$$\sum_R \Gamma_3(R)_{11}\Gamma_3(R)_{11} = \tfrac{6}{2} = 3$$

and also

$$\sum_R \Gamma_3(R)_{12}\Gamma_3(R)_{12} = 3$$

$$\sum_R \Gamma_3(R)_{21}\Gamma_3(R)_{21} = 3$$

$$\sum_R \Gamma_3(R)_{22}\Gamma_3(R)_{22} = 3$$

On the other hand,

$$\sum_R \Gamma_1(R)_{11}\Gamma_2(R)_{11} = 0$$

$$\sum_R \Gamma_1(R)_{11}\Gamma_3(R)_{11} = 1\cdot 1 - 1\cdot\tfrac{1}{2} - 1\cdot\tfrac{1}{2} + 1\cdot\tfrac{1}{2} - 1\cdot 1 + 1\cdot\tfrac{1}{2} = 0$$

$$\sum_R \Gamma_3(R)_{11}\Gamma_3(R)_{22} = 1\cdot 1 + \tfrac{1}{2}\cdot\tfrac{1}{2} + \tfrac{1}{2}\cdot\tfrac{1}{2} - \tfrac{1}{2}\cdot\tfrac{1}{2} - 1\cdot 1 - \tfrac{1}{2}\cdot\tfrac{1}{2} = 0$$

and so forth.

These relations can be combined into one equation, called the *orthogonality relation*,

$$\sum_R \Gamma_i(R)_{mn}\sqrt{\frac{l_i}{h}}\,\Gamma_j(R)_{m'n'}\sqrt{\frac{l_j}{h}} = \delta_{ij}\delta_{mm'}\delta_{nn'} \qquad (7\text{-}23)$$

where all three δ are equal to 1 if the two indices are the same, and are zero otherwise. Equation (7-23) is generally valid for all nonequivalent irreducible representations of any group. *Nonequivalent* means that the representations differ by more than a similarity transformation. The proof of (7-23) is somewhat involved. It may be found, for example, in Appendix VI of Eyring, Walter, and Kimball's *Quantum Chemistry* [40].

In three-dimensional space, two vectors A and B with components A_1, A_2, A_3 and B_1, B_2, B_3 are said to be orthogonal if

$$A_1 B_1 + A_2 B_2 + A_3 B_3 = 0$$

Only three independent mutually orthogonal vectors can be constructed in three-dimensional space. Similarly in n-dimensional space for two orthogonal vectors $A_1 B_1 + A_2 B_2 + \cdots + A_n B_n = 0$ and only n independent mutually orthogonal vectors can be constructed.

We can use this fact to compute the number of irreducible representations a group might have. From (7–21) and (7–22) it is at once clear that

$$\Gamma_i(R_1)_{mn}, \quad \Gamma_i(R_2)_{mn}, \quad \cdots, \quad \Gamma_i(R_h)_{mn}$$

can be considered as the components of an h-dimensional vector where h is the order of the group, i.e., the number of its elements. Such a vector is orthogonal to any other such vector obtained by another choice of m and n in the same irreducible representation or any such vector obtained from a different irreducible representation. If the dimension of a given irreducible representation is l there are obviously l^2 vectors obtainable from it. Since the number of independent orthogonal vectors in an h dimensional space is h we can write that

$$\sum_i l_i^2 = h \tag{7-24}$$

For the group C_{2v},

$$l_1 = l_2 = l_3 = l_4 = 1$$

for $\Gamma_1, \Gamma_2, \Gamma_3$, and Γ_4. Hence

$$l_1^2 + l_2^2 + l_3^3 + l_4^2 = 4 = h$$

and we cannot have more irreducible representations.

For the group C_{3v}

$$l_1 = 1, \qquad l_2 = 1, \qquad l_3 = 2$$

for Γ_1, Γ_2, and Γ_3, respectively. Hence

$$l_1^2 + l_2^2 + l_3^2 = 1 + 1 + 4 = 6$$

Since $h = 6$ we again have all the irreducible representations of the group and there cannot be any others.

All other representations are reducible into a linear cambination of these irreducible representations.

AN EXAMPLE OF REDUCING A MATRIX

The matrix

$$\beta = \begin{pmatrix} \dfrac{1}{\sqrt{3}} & \dfrac{1}{\sqrt{2}} & \dfrac{1}{\sqrt{6}} \\[2mm] \dfrac{1}{\sqrt{3}} & -\dfrac{1}{\sqrt{2}} & \dfrac{1}{\sqrt{6}} \\[2mm] \dfrac{1}{\sqrt{3}} & 0 & -\sqrt{\dfrac{2}{3}} \end{pmatrix}$$

reduces the matrix

$$\begin{pmatrix} 0 & 0 & 1 \\ 0 & 1 & 0 \\ 1 & 0 & 0 \end{pmatrix}$$

in the following way:

$$\begin{pmatrix} \frac{1}{\sqrt{3}} & \frac{1}{\sqrt{3}} & \frac{1}{\sqrt{3}} \\ \frac{1}{\sqrt{2}} & -\frac{1}{\sqrt{2}} & 0 \\ \frac{1}{\sqrt{6}} & \frac{1}{\sqrt{6}} & -\sqrt{\frac{2}{3}} \end{pmatrix} \begin{pmatrix} 0 & 0 & 1 \\ 0 & 1 & 0 \\ 1 & 0 & 0 \end{pmatrix} \begin{pmatrix} \frac{1}{\sqrt{3}} & \frac{1}{\sqrt{2}} & \frac{1}{\sqrt{6}} \\ \frac{1}{\sqrt{3}} & -\frac{1}{\sqrt{2}} & \frac{1}{\sqrt{6}} \\ \frac{1}{\sqrt{3}} & 0 & -\sqrt{\frac{2}{3}} \end{pmatrix}$$

$$= \begin{pmatrix} \frac{1}{\sqrt{3}} & \frac{1}{\sqrt{3}} & \frac{1}{\sqrt{3}} \\ \frac{1}{\sqrt{2}} & -\frac{1}{\sqrt{2}} & 0 \\ \frac{1}{\sqrt{6}} & \frac{1}{\sqrt{6}} & -\sqrt{\frac{2}{3}} \end{pmatrix} \begin{pmatrix} \frac{1}{\sqrt{3}} & 0 & -\sqrt{\frac{2}{3}} \\ \frac{1}{\sqrt{3}} & -\frac{1}{\sqrt{2}} & \frac{1}{\sqrt{6}} \\ \frac{1}{\sqrt{3}} & \frac{1}{\sqrt{2}} & \frac{1}{\sqrt{6}} \end{pmatrix}$$

$$= \begin{pmatrix} 1 & 0 & 0 \\ 0 & \frac{1}{2} & -\frac{\sqrt{3}}{2} \\ 0 & -\frac{\sqrt{3}}{2} & -\frac{1}{2} \end{pmatrix}$$

7-6. THE CHARACTER

The trace, i.e., the sum of the diagonal elements of a matrix, is called the *character* in group theory, and it is the most important quantity in practical applications. For the ith irreducible representation and operation R it is equal to

$$\chi_i(R) = \sum_m \Gamma_i(R)_{mm} \qquad (7\text{-}25)$$

For one-dimensional representations the character, of course, is the same as the matrix itself ($+1$ or -1 in the examples we have so far treated).

It can easily be shown [40, p. 182] that the character is unchanged by a similarity transformation. For example: in Γ_3 of group C_{3v}, C_3 is the reciprocal of C_3'. To $C_3 \sigma_v^b C_3'$ corresponds

$$\begin{pmatrix} -\frac{1}{2} & \frac{\sqrt{3}}{2} \\ -\frac{\sqrt{3}}{2} & -\frac{1}{2} \end{pmatrix} \begin{pmatrix} -1 & 0 \\ 0 & 1 \end{pmatrix} \begin{pmatrix} -\frac{1}{2} & -\frac{\sqrt{3}}{2} \\ \frac{\sqrt{3}}{2} & -\frac{1}{2} \end{pmatrix}$$

$$= \begin{pmatrix} -\dfrac{1}{2} & \dfrac{\sqrt{3}}{2} \\ -\dfrac{\sqrt{3}}{2} & -\dfrac{1}{2} \end{pmatrix} \begin{pmatrix} \dfrac{1}{2} & \dfrac{\sqrt{3}}{2} \\ \dfrac{\sqrt{3}}{2} & -\dfrac{1}{2} \end{pmatrix} = \begin{pmatrix} \dfrac{1}{2} & -\dfrac{\sqrt{3}}{2} \\ -\dfrac{\sqrt{3}}{2} & -\dfrac{1}{2} \end{pmatrix}$$

and the character of σ_v^b remains 0. Therefore, elements belonging to the same class have the same character. The table of characters for group C_{3v} is then

	E	$2C_3$	$3\sigma_v$
Γ_1	1	1	1
Γ_2	1	1	-1
Γ_3	2	-1	0

Only the $+1$ and -1 have descriptive meaning. 2 and 0 are just the traces of the transformation matrices and not the matrices themselves.

If we apply the orthogonality relation to the diagonal elements only, we obtain that

$$\sum_R \Gamma_i(R)_{mm} \Gamma_j(R)_{m'm'} = \frac{h}{l_j} \delta_{ij} \delta_{mm'} \tag{7-26}$$

where $l_j \leq l_i$.

We introduce the characters in summing over m and m', while $\delta_{mm'}$ can be equal to unity l_j times. Thus, we obtain that

$$\sum_R \chi_i(R)\chi_j(R) = h\delta_{ij} \tag{7-27}$$

This means that the characters of the different irreducible representations form an orthogonal set of vectors as their matrices themselves.

Sum (7-27) is taken over all operations belonging to a group. It can be transformed into a sum over the classes if we remember that operations belonging to the same class have the same character. It can be seen when this is done that there are only as many irreducible representations as there are classes (3 for C_{3v}).

If we regard a reducible representation, then, for a given operation

$$\chi(R) = \sum_j a_j \chi_j(R) \tag{7-28}$$

since the reduction is obtained by a similarity transformation, which does not change the character; a_j is the number of times the jth irreducible representation occurs in the reducible representation.

Since $\chi(R)$ is just a linear combination of the $\chi_j(R)$ we can use (7-28) and write, if $\chi_i(R)$ is the character of operation R in Γ_i,

$$\sum_R \chi(R)\chi_i(R) = \sum_R \sum_j a_j \chi_j(R)\chi_i(R) = ha_i \tag{7-29}$$

This is because only for $i = j$ is there a nonzero contribution. Thus the number of times Γ_i occurs in the reducible representation Γ is equal to

$$a_i = \frac{1}{h} \sum_R \chi(R)\chi_i(R) \tag{7-30}$$

This a most important relation from the point of view of the spectroscopist. It enables one to tell the number of times an irreducible representation occurs in a reducible one by knowing only the characters.

It is time now to make the junction between formal group theory and spectral problems treated by wave-mechanical methods.

7-7. FORMING A BASIS FOR A REPRESENTATION

We say that in our previous examples the symbols $a, b, c, d, \ldots$, which stand for the nuclei, form a basis for the reducible representations (7-9) and (7-10) because the latter were obtained by carrying out the operations of the respective groups interchanging these symbols.

Similarly the $3N$ Cartesian coordinates (if N is the number of nuclei) form a basis for another reducible representation in each case. The dimension of the representation depends on the basis chosen.

The four π-electron orbitals of butadiene of which molecular orbitals can be built (see Chapter 3) also form a basis for a representation, which is actually the same as (7-9) since we have distinguished between "up" and "down" with respect to operation σ_v. In doing this we took into account the important property of the π-electrons which consists of changing sign at a reflection in their nodal plane. Thus the matrices forming this representation are the same as in (7-9). Only in the column vectors is

$$a = \psi_a, \quad b = \psi_b, \ldots$$

Let us now examine *one* of the π-molecular orbitals of butadiene —for example

$$\phi_2 = 0.6015\psi_a + 0.3717\psi_b - 0.3717\psi_c - 0.6015\psi_d \tag{7-31}$$

(see p. 40).

If we carry through the operations of group C_{2v} we find the following:

$$E: \quad E\phi_2 = \phi_2$$
$$C_2: \quad C_2\phi_2 = \phi_2$$

Here, since ψ_a is replaced by $-\psi_d$, and ψ_b by $-\psi_c$, the MO, ϕ_2, would change sign. However, the AO themselves all change sign because of the antisymmetry of the π-electron orbitals with respect to the plane of the molecule, and ϕ_2 remains finally unchanged.

$$\sigma_v: \quad \sigma_v\phi_2 = -\phi_2$$

The change of sign occurs because of the abovementioned property of the π-electrons.

$$\sigma'_v: \quad \sigma'_v\phi_2 = -\phi_2$$

The change of sign occurs because of the signs in the MO.

Thus, we see that ϕ_2 transforms under the operations of the group as irreducible representation Γ_2.

E	C_2	σ_v	σ'_v
1	1	-1	-1

It may be said, too, that this representation was generated by applying the operations of the group to ϕ_2 and that ϕ_2 forms a basis for Γ_2.

In the valence-bond method the structure eigenfunctions form the basis for a reducible representation, as will be shown in Chapter 9.

7-8. THE EFFECT OF SYMMETRY OPERATIONS ON (ELECTRONIC) WAVE FUNCTIONS

In the Schrödinger equation the potential energy function and the electronic distribution as represented by the square of the total wave function clearly cannot change under symmetry operations, since the latter interchange only like particles. These and the Hamilton operator must have the full symmetry of the molecule. In other words, they have to conform to the totally symmetrical representation ($+1$ everywhere).

This leaves, however, certain possibilities open to the wave functions themselves.

For nondegenerate wave functions the problem is easily settled. They can only remain unchanged or just change sign under symmetry operations. If we carry out two successive symmetry operations the result will be the same as would be obtained through one other operation, and a representation will be generated which is also of dimension one. Thus, a nondegenerate wave function transforms like one of the one-dimensional irreducible representations of the group to which the molecule belongs. (Example: MO ϕ_2 of butadiene in the previous paragraph.)

For a doubly degenerate state the situation is more complicated.

Let ϕ_I and ϕ_{II} form a degenerate pair of wave functions belonging to the same state. Then any linear combination of ϕ_I and ϕ_{II} is an acceptable solution of the wave equation for the same energy. A symmetry operation may leave a wave function belonging to a degenerate pair unchanged, or may just change its sign, or may change it into a linear combination of the two functions forming the pair. Indeed any pair of orthogonal linear combinations—and there are an infinity of them—might be taken as the "original" pair.

Suppose now that by a symmetry operation ϕ_I and ϕ_{II} are transformed into ϕ'_I and ϕ'_{II}. This operation can be described in matrix language such as

$$\begin{pmatrix} \phi'_I \\ \phi'_{II} \end{pmatrix} = \begin{pmatrix} d_{11} & d_{12} \\ d_{21} & d_{22} \end{pmatrix} \begin{pmatrix} \phi_I \\ \phi_{II} \end{pmatrix} \tag{7-32}$$

or

$$\begin{aligned} \phi'_I &= d_{11}\phi_I + d_{12}\phi_{II} \\ \phi'_{II} &= d_{21}\phi_I + d_{22}\phi_{II} \end{aligned} \tag{7-33}$$

It may happen even for degenerate wave functions that the non diagonal elements of this matrix are equal to zero. Then

$$\phi'_I = \pm\phi_I \qquad \text{and} \qquad \phi'_{II} = \pm\phi_{II}$$

since the wave functions must be normalized. However, for rotations around axes of third or higher order this is not the case.

For two successive operations the matrix product of the two matrices will be equal to the matrix of the operation which is the product of the two. Thus, a representation is generated. The dimension of this representation is two and it is necessarily irreducible, since if it were reducible it could be reduced only to one-dimensional representations, which clearly cannot represent degenerate wave functions (for example Γ_3 for C_{3v}).

In general, every wave function transforms like an irreducible representation of the group to which the molecule belongs, and the dimension of the representation is equal to the degree of degeneracy of the related state.

The importance of these considerations is immediately clear from the following.

Consider an integral such as

$$\int \phi_A H \phi_B \, d\tau = \int \phi_A E \phi_B \, d\tau = E \int \phi_A \phi_B \, d\tau \tag{7-34}$$

where ϕ_A and ϕ_B are molecular wave functions and, therefore, transform like irreducible representations of the related group, and H transforms like the totally symmetrical representation. This integral being an intrinsic property of the molecule, (energy, in this case) its value cannot change upon a symmetry operation. Hence, it can be different from zero only if it remains invariant (as to sign and value) under *all* symmetry operations belonging to the group, or at least can be expressed as a sum of terms of which at least one is invariant. The latter case occurs when both ϕ_A and ϕ_B belong to more than one-dimensional representations (are degenerate). In other words, the integral as a whole must transform like Γ_1 or as a reducible representation containing the totally symmetrical irreducible representation.

Thus, we are able to predict from the symmetry properties of the wave functions, and without actually evaluating the integral, whether it will be zero or different from zero.

We need one more concept here. Under the integrals of interest to us, the functions are simply multiplied by each other. Hence, if we want to know the transformation properties of the product we have to take the ordinary product of the corresponding matrices, called the *direct product*, and not the product obtained by the law of matrix multiplication.

The following is an example of such a direct product:

$$\begin{pmatrix} a_{11} & a_{12} \\ a_{21} & a_{22} \end{pmatrix} \times \begin{pmatrix} b_{11} & b_{12} \\ b_{21} & b_{22} \end{pmatrix}$$

$$= \begin{pmatrix} a_{11}b_{11} & a_{11}b_{12} & a_{12}b_{11} & a_{12}b_{12} \\ a_{11}b_{21} & a_{11}b_{22} & a_{12}b_{21} & a_{12}b_{22} \\ a_{21}b_{11} & a_{21}b_{12} & a_{22}b_{11} & a_{22}b_{12} \\ a_{21}b_{21} & a_{21}b_{22} & a_{22}b_{21} & a_{22}b_{22} \end{pmatrix} \qquad (7\text{--}35)$$

It is seen that every matrix component of the one matrix is multiplied by every component of the other matrix. If the original matrices are of order m and n, the direct product is of order mn.

Matrices of this type may be representations of group G of order m and group G' of order n; then the direct product $G \times G'$ is a representation of a group of order mn.

The character of the direct product is seen to be

$$(a_{11}b_{11} + a_{11}b_{22} + a_{22}b_{11} + a_{22}b_{22}) = (a_{11} + a_{22})(b_{11} + b_{22}) \quad (7\text{--}36)$$

This is quite general: the character of the direct product (P) of two matrices $(A$ and $B)$ is the product of the characters of these matrices.

$$\chi(P) = \chi(A)\chi(B) \qquad (7\text{--}37)$$

This is a most important relation.

If we look at the characters of group C_{2v} (p. 155) and we multiply together the characters of the same operation we see immediately that

$$\Gamma_1\Gamma_2 = \Gamma_2, \qquad \Gamma_3\Gamma_3 = \Gamma_1$$
$$\Gamma_2\Gamma_3 = \Gamma_4, \qquad \Gamma_3\Gamma_4 = \Gamma_2$$

and so forth. For group C_{3v} (p. 162)

$$\Gamma_1\Gamma_1 = \Gamma_1, \qquad \Gamma_2\Gamma_2 = \Gamma_1$$
$$\Gamma_1\Gamma_2 = \Gamma_2, \qquad \Gamma_2\Gamma_3 = \Gamma_3$$
$$\Gamma_1\Gamma_3 = \Gamma_3, \qquad \Gamma_3\Gamma_3 = \Gamma_1 + \Gamma_2 + \Gamma_3$$

In general, the direct product of two nondegenerate irreducible representations is also a nondegenerate irreducible representation, the direct product of a nondegenerate and of a degenerate irreducible representation is a degenerate irreducible representation, and the direct product of two degenerate irreducible representations is a reducible representation. The product $\Gamma_3\Gamma_3$ is an example of the latter case. The characters of the direct product are

$$E \quad 2C_3 \quad 3\sigma_v$$
$$4 \quad 1 \quad 0$$

which are easily seen to result from $\Gamma_1 + \Gamma_2 + \Gamma_3$. This type of decomposition is usually found by simple trial and error. We now return to

$$\int \phi_A H \phi_B \, d\tau$$

Since H belongs to Γ_1 we must have

$$\Gamma_A\Gamma_B = \Gamma_1$$

or, for degenerate representations.

$$\Gamma_A\Gamma_B = \sum_i a_i\Gamma_i$$

where the sum contains Γ_1 so that a part of the integral is invariant with respect to all symmetry operations—or else the integral vanishes.

The same holds for an integral such as

$$\int \phi_A \phi_B \, d\tau$$

It is easily seen from the character tables of pp. 169–176 that if the characters are real the two wave functions must belong to the same irreducible representation, so that this condition is fulfilled and the integral is different from zero.

Such integrals very often occur in wave-mechanical problems and especially in the secular determinants to which approximate methods usually lead. It is a great simplification if we can tell a priori that some of them are zero.

The importance of these considerations is equally great when we are dealing with transition moments. Using x, instead of M_x we have the simplified expression

$$\int \phi_A x \phi_B \, d\tau \qquad (7\text{-}38)$$

for the x component of a transition moment. The coordinate x will transform itself according to an irreducible representation of the group.

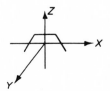

Fig. 7-8

Under the operations of group C_{2v}, for example, with the coordinate system for *cis*-butadiene shown in Fig. 7-8, x transforms the following way:

$$\begin{aligned}
E: &\quad \text{unchanged} \\
C_2: &\quad \text{changes sign} \\
\sigma_v: &\quad \text{unchanged} \\
\sigma_v': &\quad \text{changes sign.}
\end{aligned}$$

Thus, it is seen that x transforms like Γ_3. Then, the direct product of the irreducible representations to which ϕ_A and ϕ_B belong must also be Γ_3 in order to have the whole integral transform like Γ_1. As a consequence the transition is allowed with x polarization, if one of the wave functions belongs to Γ_1 and the other to Γ_3 or for $\Gamma_2 \longleftrightarrow \Gamma_4$. The selection rules for y and z may be obtained similarly.

Under C_{3v} symmetry z transforms like Γ_1 (it lies in the direction of the three-fold axis). On the other hand, x and y under operation C_3 will transform into a linear combination of the two and, therefore, belong to the degenerate representation. We try only three cases:

$\Gamma_1 \rightarrow \Gamma_2$: according to z this corresponds to $\Gamma_1 \Gamma_1 \Gamma_2 = \Gamma_2$ and is forbidden; according to x and y it corresponds to $\Gamma_1 \Gamma_3 \Gamma_2 = \Gamma_3$ and is forbidden.[5]

$\Gamma_2 \rightarrow \Gamma_3$: according to z this corresponds to $\Gamma_2 \Gamma_1 \Gamma_3 = \Gamma_3$ and is forbidden; according to x and y it corresponds to $\Gamma_2 \Gamma_3 \Gamma_3$ giving characters $4, 1, 0$. Hence $\Gamma_2 \Gamma_3 \Gamma_3 = \Gamma_1 + \Gamma_2 + \Gamma_3$ and is allowed since the sum contains Γ_1.

[5] Or any direction in the xy plane.

$\Gamma_3 \rightarrow \Gamma_3$: according to z this corresponds to $\Gamma_3 \Gamma_1 \Gamma_3 = \Gamma_1 + \Gamma_2 + \Gamma_3$ and is allowed; according to x and y it corresponds to $\Gamma_3 \Gamma_3 \Gamma_3$ giving characters $8, -1, 0$. Thus $\Gamma_3 \Gamma_3 \Gamma_3 = \Gamma_1 + \Gamma_2 + 3\Gamma_3$ and is allowed.

Direct products were tabulated for all symmetry point groups. (See Herzberg [77, pp. 125–131]; Wilson, Decius, and Cross [91, p. 331].)

7-9. TABLES OF CHARACTERS

The characters of the irreducible representations of all symmetry point groups were computed many years ago and may be found in many publications. An especially careful and complete presentation is given in Wilson, Decius, and Cross', *Molecular Vibrations* [91], and many useful comments are found in Eyring, Walter, and Kimball's *Quantum Chemistry* [40, p. 380].

The presentation in Tables 7-4 through 7-12 is essentially the same as in [91] except that quantities needed only for the treatment of vibrational spectra are omitted.

A certain amount of comment. is required.

One-dimensional representations are indicated by A, if the character is $+1$ for a rotation around the principal axis, or by B, if it is -1 (B is not used for cubic groups). Two-dimensional representations are indicated by E, and three-dimensional ones by F. If there is more than one representation of a given type, indices are used to distinguish them. Then A_1 is always the totally symmetrical representation.

TABLE 7–4 Character Tables of C_s, C_i,
and the Cyclic Groups C_p
$(p = 2, 3, 4, 5, 6)$

C_s	E	σ_h	
A'	1	1	T_x, T_y
A''	1	-1	T_z

C_i	E	i	
A_g	1	1	
A_u	1	-1	T

C_2	E	C_2	
A	1	1	T_z
B	1	-1	T_x, T_y

C_3	E	C_3	C_3^2	$\epsilon = e^{2\pi i/3}$
A	1	1	1	T_z
E	$\begin{cases} 1 \\ 1 \end{cases}$	$\begin{matrix} \epsilon \\ \epsilon^* \end{matrix}$	$\left. \begin{matrix} \epsilon^* \\ \epsilon \end{matrix} \right\}$	(T_x, T_y)

C_4	E	C_4	C_2	C_4^3	
A	1	1	1	1	T_z
B	1	-1	1	-1	
E	$\left\{\begin{matrix}1\\1\end{matrix}\right.$	$\begin{matrix}i\\-i\end{matrix}$	$\begin{matrix}-1\\-1\end{matrix}$	$\left.\begin{matrix}-i\\i\end{matrix}\right\}$	(T_x, T_y)

C_5	E	C_5	C_5^2	C_5^3	C_5^4	$\epsilon = e^{2\pi i/5}$
A	1	1	1	1	1	T_z
E_1	$\left\{\begin{matrix}1\\1\end{matrix}\right.$	$\begin{matrix}\epsilon\\\epsilon^*\end{matrix}$	$\begin{matrix}\epsilon^2\\\epsilon^{2*}\end{matrix}$	$\begin{matrix}\epsilon^{2*}\\\epsilon^2\end{matrix}$	$\left.\begin{matrix}\epsilon^*\\\epsilon\end{matrix}\right\}$	(T_x, T_y)
E_2	$\left\{\begin{matrix}1\\1\end{matrix}\right.$	$\begin{matrix}\epsilon^2\\\epsilon^{2*}\end{matrix}$	$\begin{matrix}\epsilon^*\\\epsilon\end{matrix}$	$\begin{matrix}\epsilon\\\epsilon^*\end{matrix}$	$\left.\begin{matrix}\epsilon^{2*}\\\epsilon^2\end{matrix}\right\}$	

C_6	E	C_6	C_3	C_2	C_3^2	C_6^5	$\epsilon = e^{2\pi i/6}$
A	1	1	1	1	1	1	T_z
B	1	-1	1	-1	1	-1	
E_1	$\left\{\begin{matrix}1\\1\end{matrix}\right.$	$\begin{matrix}\epsilon\\\epsilon^*\end{matrix}$	$\begin{matrix}-\epsilon^*\\-\epsilon\end{matrix}$	$\begin{matrix}-1\\-1\end{matrix}$	$\begin{matrix}-\epsilon\\-\epsilon^*\end{matrix}$	$\left.\begin{matrix}\epsilon^*\\\epsilon\end{matrix}\right\}$	(T_x, T_y)
E_2	$\left\{\begin{matrix}1\\1\end{matrix}\right.$	$\begin{matrix}-\epsilon^*\\-\epsilon\end{matrix}$	$\begin{matrix}-\epsilon\\-\epsilon^*\end{matrix}$	$\begin{matrix}1\\1\end{matrix}$	$\begin{matrix}-\epsilon^*\\-\epsilon\end{matrix}$	$\left.\begin{matrix}-\epsilon\\-\epsilon^*\end{matrix}\right\}$	

TABLE 7–5 Character Tables of the
Dihedral Groups D_p
$(p = 2, 3, 4, 5, 6)$

$D_2 \equiv V$	E	$C_2(z)$	$C_2(y)$	$C_2(x)$	
A	1	1	1	1	
B_1	1	1	-1	-1	T_z
B_2	1	-1	1	-1	T_y
B_3	1	-1	-1	1	T_x

D_3	E	$2C_3$	$3C_2$	
A_1	1	1	1	
A_2	1	1	-1	T_z
E	2	-1	0	(T_x, T_y)

D_4	E	$2C_4$	$C_4^2 = C_2$	$2C_2'$	$2C_2''$	
A_1	1	1	1	1	1	
A_2	1	1	1	-1	-1	T_z
B_1	1	-1	1	1	-1	
B_2	1	-1	1	-1	1	
E	2	0	-2	0	0	(T_x, T_y)

D_5	E	$2C_5$	$2C_5^2$	$5C_2$	
A_1	1	1	1	1	
A_2	1	1	1	-1	T_z
E_1	2	$2\cos 72°$	$2\cos 144°$	0	(T_x, Ty)
E_2	2	$2\cos 144°$	$2\cos 72°$	0	

D_6	E	$2C_6$	$2C_3$	C_2	$3C_2'$	$3C_2''$	
A_1	1	1	1	1	1	1	
A_2	1	1	1	1	-1	-1	T_z
B_1	1	-1	1	-1	1	-1	
B_2	1	-1	1	-1	-1	1	
E_1	2	1	-1	-2	0	0	(T_x, T_y)
E_2	2	-1	-1	2	0	0	

TABLE 7–6 Character Tables of the Groups
C_{pv} $(p = 2, 3, 4, 5, 6)$

C_{2v}	E	C_2	$\sigma_{v(zx)}$	$\sigma_{v(yz)}$	
A_1	1	1	1	1	T_z
A_2	1	1	-1	-1	
B_1	1	-1	1	-1	T_x
B_2	1	-1	-1	1	T_y

C_{3v}	E	$2C_3$	$3\sigma_v$	
A_1	1	1	1	T_z
A_2	1	1	-1	
E	2	-1	0	(T_x, T_y)

C_{4v}	E	$2C_4$	C_2	$2\sigma_v$	$2\sigma_d$	
A_1	1	1	1	1	1	T_z
A_2	1	1	1	-1	-1	
B_1	1	-1	1	1	-1	
B_2	1	-1	1	-1	1	
E	2	0	-2	0	0	(T_x, T_y)

C_{5v}	E	$2C_5$	$2C_5^2$	$5\sigma_v$	
A_1	1	1	1	1	T_z
A_2	1	1	1	-1	
E_1	2	2 cos 72°	2 cos 144°	0	(T_x, T_y)
E_2	2	2 cos 144°	2 cos 72°	0	

C_{6v}	E	$2C_6$	$2C_3$	C_2	$3\sigma_v$	$3\sigma_d$	
A_1	1	1	1	1	1	1	T_z
A_2	1	1	1	1	-1	-1	
B_1	1	-1	1	-1	1	-1	
B_2	1	-1	1	-1	-1	1	
E_1	2	1	-1	-2	0	0	(T_x, T_y)
E_2	2	-1	-1	2	0	0	

TABLE 7–7 Character Tables of the Groups
C_{ph} $(p = 2, 3, 4, 5, 6)$

C_{2h}	E	C_2	i	σ_h	
A_g	1	1	1	1	
B_g	1	-1	1	-1	
A_u	1	1	-1	-1	T_z
B_u	1	-1	-1	1	T_x, T_y

C_{3h}	E	C_3	C_3^2	σ_h	S_3	S_3^5	$\epsilon = e^{2\pi i/3}$
A'	1	1	1	1	1	1	
E'	$\begin{cases}1\\1\end{cases}$	$\begin{matrix}\epsilon\\\epsilon*\end{matrix}$	$\begin{matrix}\epsilon*\\\epsilon\end{matrix}$	$\begin{matrix}1\\1\end{matrix}$	$\begin{matrix}\epsilon\\\epsilon*\end{matrix}$	$\left.\begin{matrix}\epsilon*\\\epsilon\end{matrix}\right\}$	(T_x, T_y)
A''	1	1	1	-1	-1	-1	T_z
E''	$\begin{cases}1\\1\end{cases}$	$\begin{matrix}\epsilon\\\epsilon*\end{matrix}$	$\begin{matrix}\epsilon*\\\epsilon\end{matrix}$	$\begin{matrix}-1\\-1\end{matrix}$	$\begin{matrix}-\epsilon\\-\epsilon*\end{matrix}$	$\left.\begin{matrix}-\epsilon*\\-\epsilon\end{matrix}\right\}$	

C_{4h}	E	C_4	C_2	C_4^3	i	S_4^3	σ_h	S_4	
A_g	1	1	1	1	1	1	1	1	
B_g	1	-1	1	-1	1	-1	1	-1	
E_g	$\begin{cases}1\\1\end{cases}$	$\begin{matrix}i\\-i\end{matrix}$	$\begin{matrix}-1\\-1\end{matrix}$	$\begin{matrix}-i\\i\end{matrix}$	$\begin{matrix}1\\1\end{matrix}$	$\begin{matrix}i\\-i\end{matrix}$	$\begin{matrix}-1\\-1\end{matrix}$	$\left.\begin{matrix}-i\\i\end{matrix}\right\}$	
A_u	1	1	1	1	-1	-1	-1	-1	
B_u	1	-1	1	-1	-1	1	-1	1	T_z
E_u	$\begin{cases}1\\1\end{cases}$	$\begin{matrix}i\\-i\end{matrix}$	$\begin{matrix}-1\\-1\end{matrix}$	$\begin{matrix}-i\\i\end{matrix}$	$\begin{matrix}-1\\-1\end{matrix}$	$\begin{matrix}-i\\i\end{matrix}$	$\begin{matrix}1\\1\end{matrix}$	$\left.\begin{matrix}i\\-i\end{matrix}\right\}$	(T_x, T_y)

C_{5h}	E	C_5	C_5^2	C_5^3	C_5^4	σ_h	S_5	S_5^7	S_5^3	S_5^9	$\epsilon = e^{2\pi i/5}$
A'	1	1	1	1	1	1	1	1	1	1	
E_1'	$\begin{cases}1\\1\end{cases}$	$\begin{matrix}\epsilon\\\epsilon*\end{matrix}$	$\begin{matrix}\epsilon^2\\\epsilon^{2}*\end{matrix}$	$\begin{matrix}\epsilon^{2}*\\\epsilon^2\end{matrix}$	$\begin{matrix}\epsilon*\\\epsilon\end{matrix}$	$\begin{matrix}1\\1\end{matrix}$	$\begin{matrix}\epsilon\\\epsilon*\end{matrix}$	$\begin{matrix}\epsilon^2\\\epsilon^{2}*\end{matrix}$	$\begin{matrix}\epsilon^{2}*\\\epsilon^2\end{matrix}$	$\left.\begin{matrix}\epsilon*\\\epsilon\end{matrix}\right\}$	(T_x, T_y)
E_2'	$\begin{cases}1\\1\end{cases}$	$\begin{matrix}\epsilon^2\\\epsilon^{2}*\end{matrix}$	$\begin{matrix}\epsilon*\\\epsilon\end{matrix}$	$\begin{matrix}\epsilon\\\epsilon*\end{matrix}$	$\begin{matrix}\epsilon^{2}*\\\epsilon^2\end{matrix}$	$\begin{matrix}1\\1\end{matrix}$	$\begin{matrix}\epsilon^2\\\epsilon^{2}*\end{matrix}$	$\begin{matrix}\epsilon*\\\epsilon\end{matrix}$	$\begin{matrix}\epsilon\\\epsilon*\end{matrix}$	$\left.\begin{matrix}\epsilon^{2}*\\\epsilon^2\end{matrix}\right\}$	
A''	1	1	1	1	1	-1	-1	-1	-1	-1	T_z
E_1''	$\begin{cases}1\\1\end{cases}$	$\begin{matrix}\epsilon\\\epsilon*\end{matrix}$	$\begin{matrix}\epsilon^2\\\epsilon^{2}*\end{matrix}$	$\begin{matrix}\epsilon^{2}*\\\epsilon^2\end{matrix}$	$\begin{matrix}\epsilon*\\\epsilon\end{matrix}$	$\begin{matrix}-1\\-1\end{matrix}$	$\begin{matrix}-\epsilon\\-\epsilon*\end{matrix}$	$\begin{matrix}-\epsilon^2\\-\epsilon^{2}*\end{matrix}$	$\begin{matrix}-\epsilon^{2}*\\-\epsilon^2\end{matrix}$	$\left.\begin{matrix}-\epsilon*\\-\epsilon\end{matrix}\right\}$	
E_2''	$\begin{cases}1\\1\end{cases}$	$\begin{matrix}\epsilon^2\\\epsilon^{2}*\end{matrix}$	$\begin{matrix}\epsilon*\\\epsilon\end{matrix}$	$\begin{matrix}\epsilon\\\epsilon*\end{matrix}$	$\begin{matrix}\epsilon^{2}*\\\epsilon^2\end{matrix}$	$\begin{matrix}-1\\-1\end{matrix}$	$\begin{matrix}-\epsilon^2\\-\epsilon^{2}*\end{matrix}$	$\begin{matrix}-\epsilon*\\-\epsilon\end{matrix}$	$\begin{matrix}-\epsilon\\-\epsilon*\end{matrix}$	$\left.\begin{matrix}-\epsilon^{2}*\\-\epsilon^2\end{matrix}\right\}$	

C_{6h}	E	C_6	C_3	C_2	C_3^2	C_6^5	i	S_3^5	S_6^5	σ_h	S_6	S_3	$\epsilon = e^{2\pi i/6}$
A_g	1	1	1	1	1	1	1	1	1	1	1	1	
B_g	1	-1	1	-1	1	-1	1	-1	1	-1	1	-1	
E_{1g}	$\begin{cases}1\\1\end{cases}$	$\begin{matrix}\epsilon\\\epsilon*\end{matrix}$	$\begin{matrix}-\epsilon*\\-\epsilon\end{matrix}$	$\begin{matrix}-1\\-1\end{matrix}$	$\begin{matrix}-\epsilon\\-\epsilon*\end{matrix}$	$\begin{matrix}\epsilon*\\\epsilon\end{matrix}$	$\begin{matrix}1\\1\end{matrix}$	$\begin{matrix}\epsilon\\\epsilon*\end{matrix}$	$\begin{matrix}-\epsilon*\\-\epsilon\end{matrix}$	$\begin{matrix}-1\\-1\end{matrix}$	$\begin{matrix}-\epsilon\\-\epsilon*\end{matrix}$	$\left.\begin{matrix}\epsilon*\\\epsilon\end{matrix}\right\}$	
E_{2g}	$\begin{cases}1\\1\end{cases}$	$\begin{matrix}-\epsilon*\\-\epsilon\end{matrix}$	$\begin{matrix}-\epsilon\\-\epsilon*\end{matrix}$	$\begin{matrix}1\\1\end{matrix}$	$\begin{matrix}-\epsilon*\\-\epsilon\end{matrix}$	$\begin{matrix}-\epsilon\\-\epsilon*\end{matrix}$	$\begin{matrix}1\\1\end{matrix}$	$\begin{matrix}-\epsilon*\\-\epsilon\end{matrix}$	$\begin{matrix}-\epsilon\\-\epsilon*\end{matrix}$	$\begin{matrix}1\\1\end{matrix}$	$\begin{matrix}-\epsilon*\\-\epsilon\end{matrix}$	$\left.\begin{matrix}-\epsilon\\-\epsilon*\end{matrix}\right\}$	
A_u	1	1	1	1	1	1	-1	-1	-1	-1	-1	-1	T_z
B_u	1	-1	1	-1	1	-1	-1	1	-1	1	-1	1	
E_{1u}	$\begin{cases}1\\1\end{cases}$	$\begin{matrix}\epsilon\\\epsilon*\end{matrix}$	$\begin{matrix}-\epsilon*\\-\epsilon\end{matrix}$	$\begin{matrix}-1\\-1\end{matrix}$	$\begin{matrix}-\epsilon\\-\epsilon*\end{matrix}$	$\begin{matrix}\epsilon*\\\epsilon\end{matrix}$	$\begin{matrix}-1\\-1\end{matrix}$	$\begin{matrix}-\epsilon\\-\epsilon*\end{matrix}$	$\begin{matrix}\epsilon*\\\epsilon\end{matrix}$	$\begin{matrix}1\\1\end{matrix}$	$\begin{matrix}\epsilon\\\epsilon*\end{matrix}$	$\left.\begin{matrix}-\epsilon*\\-\epsilon\end{matrix}\right\}$	(T_x, T_y)
E_{2u}	$\begin{cases}1\\1\end{cases}$	$\begin{matrix}-\epsilon*\\-\epsilon\end{matrix}$	$\begin{matrix}-\epsilon\\-\epsilon*\end{matrix}$	$\begin{matrix}1\\1\end{matrix}$	$\begin{matrix}-\epsilon*\\-\epsilon\end{matrix}$	$\begin{matrix}-\epsilon\\-\epsilon*\end{matrix}$	$\begin{matrix}-1\\-1\end{matrix}$	$\begin{matrix}\epsilon*\\\epsilon\end{matrix}$	$\begin{matrix}\epsilon\\\epsilon*\end{matrix}$	$\begin{matrix}-1\\-1\end{matrix}$	$\begin{matrix}\epsilon*\\\epsilon\end{matrix}$	$\left.\begin{matrix}\epsilon\\\epsilon*\end{matrix}\right\}$	

TABLE 7–8   Tables of Characters of the Groups
D_{ph} ($p = 2, 3, 4, 5, 6$)

$D_{2h} \equiv V_h$	E	$C_2(z)$	$C_2(y)$	$C_2(x)$	i	$\sigma(xy)$	$\sigma(zx)$	$\sigma(yz)$	
A_g	1	1	1	1	1	1	1	1	
B_{1g}	1	1	−1	−1	1	1	−1	−1	
B_{2g}	1	−1	1	−1	1	−1	1	−1	
B_{3g}	1	−1	−1	1	1	−1	−1	1	
A_u	1	1	1	1	−1	−1	−1	−1	
B_{1u}	1	1	−1	−1	−1	−1	1	1	T_z
B_{2u}	1	−1	1	−1	−1	1	−1	1	T_y
B_{3u}	1	−1	−1	1	−1	1	1	−1	T_x

D_{3h}	E	$2C_3$	$3C_2$	σ_h	$2S_3$	$3\sigma_v$	
A_1'	1	1	1	1	1	1	
A_2'	1	1	−1	1	1	−1	
E'	2	−1	0	2	−1	0	(T_x, T_y)
A_1''	1	1	1	−1	−1	−1	
A_2''	1	1	−1	−1	−1	1	T_z
E''	2	−1	0	−2	1	0	

D_{4h}	E	$2C_4$	C_2	$2C_2'$	$2C_2''$	i	$2S_4$	σ_h	$2\sigma_v$	$2\sigma_d$	
A_{1g}	1	1	1	1	1	1	1	1	1	1	
A_{2g}	1	1	1	−1	−1	1	1	1	−1	−1	
B_{1g}	1	−1	1	1	−1	1	−1	1	1	−1	
B_{2g}	1	−1	1	−1	1	1	−1	1	−1	1	
E_g	2	0	−2	0	0	2	0	−2	0	0	
A_{1u}	1	1	1	1	1	−1	−1	−1	−1	−1	
A_{2u}	1	1	1	−1	−1	−1	−1	−1	1	1	T_z
B_{1u}	1	−1	1	1	−1	−1	1	−1	−1	1	
B_{2u}	1	−1	1	−1	1	−1	1	−1	1	−1	
E_u	2	0	−2	0	0	−2	0	2	0	0	(T_x, T_y)

D_{5h}	E	$2C_5$	$2C_5^2$	$5C_2$	σ_h	$2S_5$	$2S_5^3$	$5\sigma_v$	
A_1'	1	1	1	1	1	1	1	1	
A_2'	1	1	1	−1	1	1	1	−1	
E_1'	2	2 cos 72°	2 cos 144°	0	2	2 cos 72°	2 cos 144°	0	(T_x, T_y)
E_2'	2	2 cos 144°	2 cos 72°	0	2	2 cos 144°	2 cos 72°	0	
A_1''	1	1	1	1	−1	−1	−1	−1	
A_2''	1	1	1	−1	−1	−1	−1	1	T_z
E_1''	2	2 cos 72°	2 cos 144°	0	−2	−2 cos 72°	−2 cos 144°	0	
E_2''	2	2 cos 144°	2 cos 72°	0	−2	−2 cos 144°	−2 cos 72°	0	

D_{6h}	E	$2C_6$	$2C_3$	C_2	$3C_2'$	$3C_2''$	i	$2S_3$	$2S_6$	σ_h	$3\sigma_d$	$3\sigma_v$	
A_{1g}	1	1	1	1	1	1	1	1	1	1	1	1	
A_{2g}	1	1	1	1	-1	-1	1	1	1	1	-1	-1	
B_{1g}	1	-1	1	-1	1	-1	1	-1	1	-1	1	-1	
B_{2g}	1	-1	1	-1	-1	1	1	-1	1	-1	-1	1	
E_{1g}	2	1	-1	-2	0	0	2	1	-1	-2	0	0	
E_{2g}	2	-1	-1	2	0	0	2	-1	-1	2	0	0	
A_{1u}	1	1	1	1	1	1	-1	-1	-1	-1	-1	-1	
A_{2u}	1	1	1	1	-1	-1	-1	-1	-1	-1	1	1	T_z
B_{1u}	1	-1	1	-1	1	-1	-1	1	-1	1	-1	1	
B_{2u}	1	-1	1	-1	-1	1	-1	1	-1	1	1	-1	
E_{1u}	2	1	-1	-2	0	0	-2	-1	1	2	0	0	(T_x, T_y)
E_{2u}	2	-1	-1	2	0	0	-2	1	1	-2	0	0	

TABLE 7-9 Character Tables of the Groups
D_{pd} $(p = 2, 3, 4, 5, 6)$

$D_{2d} \equiv V_d$	E	$2S_4$	C_2	$2C_2'$	$2\sigma_d$	
A_1	1	1	1	1	1	
A_2	1	1	1	-1	-1	
B_1	1	-1	1	1	-1	
B_2	1	-1	1	-1	1	T_z
E	2	0	-2	0	0	(T_x, T_y)

D_{3d}	E	$2C_3$	$3C_2$	i	$2S_6$	$3\sigma_d$	
A_{1g}	1	1	1	1	1	1	
A_{2g}	1	1	-1	1	1	-1	
E_g	2	-1	0	2	-1	0	
A_{1u}	1	1	1	-1	-1	-1	
A_{2u}	1	1	-1	-1	-1	1	T_z
E_u	2	-1	0	-2	1	0	(T_x, T_y)

D_{4d}	E	$2S_8$	$2C_4$	$2S_8^3$	C_2	$4C_2'$	$4\sigma_d$	
A_1	1	1	1	1	1	1	1	
A_2	1	1	1	1	1	-1	-1	
B_1	1	-1	1	-1	1	1	-1	
B_2	1	-1	1	-1	1	-1	1	T_z
E_1	2	$\sqrt{2}$	0	$-\sqrt{2}$	-2	0	0	(T_x, T_y)
E_2	2	0	-2	0	2	0	0	
E_3	2	$-\sqrt{2}$	0	$\sqrt{2}$	-2	0	0	

D_{5d}	E	$2C_5$	$2C_5^2$	$5C_2$	i	$2S_{10}^3$	$2S_{10}$	$5\sigma_d$	
A_{1g}	1	1	1	1	1	1	1	1	
A_{2g}	1	1	1	-1	1	1	1	-1	
E_{1g}	2	$2\cos 72°$	$2\cos 144°$	0	2	$2\cos 72°$	$2\cos 144°$	0	
E_{2g}	2	$2\cos 144°$	$2\cos 72°$	0	2	$2\cos 144°$	$2\cos 72°$	0	
A_{1u}	1	1	1	1	-1	-1	-1	-1	
A_{2u}	1	1	1	-1	-1	-1	-1	1	T_z
E_{1u}	2	$2\cos 72°$	$2\cos 144°$	0	-2	$-2\cos 72°$	$-2\cos 144°$	0	(T_x, T_y)
E_{2u}	2	$2\cos 144°$	$2\cos 72°$	0	-2	$-2\cos 144°$	$-2\cos 72°$	0	

D_{6d}	E	$2S_{12}$	$2C_6$	$2S_4$	$2C_3$	$2S_{12}^5$	C_2	$6C_2'$	$6\sigma_d$	
A_1	1	1	1	1	1	1	1	1	1	
A_2	1	1	1	1	1	1	1	-1	-1	
B_1	1	-1	1	-1	1	-1	1	1	-1	
B_2	1	-1	1	-1	1	-1	1	-1	1	T_z
E_1	2	$\sqrt{3}$	1	0	-1	$-\sqrt{3}$	-2	0	0	(T_x, T_y)
E_2	2	1	-1	-2	-1	1	2	0	0	
E_3	2	0	-2	0	2	0	-2	0	0	
E_4	2	-1	-1	2	-1	-1	2	0	0	
E_5	2	$-\sqrt{3}$	1	0	-1	$\sqrt{3}$	-2	0	0	

TABLE 7–10 Character Tables of the
Groups S_p ($p = 4, 6, 8$)

S_4	E	S_4	C_2	S_4^3	
A	1	1	1	1	
B	1	-1	1	-1	T_z
E	$\begin{cases}1\\1\end{cases}$	$\begin{matrix}i\\-i\end{matrix}$	$\begin{matrix}-1\\-1\end{matrix}$	$\begin{matrix}-i\\i\end{matrix}$	(T_x, T_y)

S_6	E	C_3	C_3^2	i	S_6^5	S_6	$\epsilon = e^{2\pi i/3}$
A_g	1	1	1	1	1	1	
E_g	$\begin{cases}1\\1\end{cases}$	$\begin{matrix}\epsilon\\\epsilon^*\end{matrix}$	$\begin{matrix}\epsilon^*\\\epsilon\end{matrix}$	$\begin{matrix}1\\1\end{matrix}$	$\begin{matrix}\epsilon\\\epsilon^*\end{matrix}$	$\begin{matrix}\epsilon^*\\\epsilon\end{matrix}$	
A_u	1	1	1	-1	-1	-1	T_z
E_u	$\begin{cases}1\\1\end{cases}$	$\begin{matrix}\epsilon\\\epsilon^*\end{matrix}$	$\begin{matrix}\epsilon^*\\\epsilon\end{matrix}$	$\begin{matrix}-1\\-1\end{matrix}$	$\begin{matrix}-\epsilon\\-\epsilon^*\end{matrix}$	$\begin{matrix}-\epsilon^*\\-\epsilon\end{matrix}$	(T_x, T_y)

S_8	E	S_8	C_4	S_8^3	C_2	S_8^5	C_4^3	S_8^7	$\epsilon = e^{2\pi i/8}$
A	1	1	1	1	1	1	1	1	
B	1	-1	1	-1	1	-1	1	-1	T_z
E_1	$\begin{cases}1\\1\end{cases}$	$\begin{matrix}\epsilon\\\epsilon^*\end{matrix}$	$\begin{matrix}i\\-i\end{matrix}$	$\begin{matrix}-\epsilon^*\\-\epsilon\end{matrix}$	$\begin{matrix}-1\\-1\end{matrix}$	$\begin{matrix}-\epsilon\\-\epsilon^*\end{matrix}$	$\begin{matrix}-i\\i\end{matrix}$	$\begin{matrix}\epsilon^*\\\epsilon\end{matrix}$	(T_x, T_y)
E_2	$\begin{cases}1\\1\end{cases}$	$\begin{matrix}i\\-i\end{matrix}$	$\begin{matrix}-1\\-1\end{matrix}$	$\begin{matrix}-i\\i\end{matrix}$	$\begin{matrix}1\\1\end{matrix}$	$\begin{matrix}i\\-i\end{matrix}$	$\begin{matrix}-1\\-1\end{matrix}$	$\begin{matrix}-i\\i\end{matrix}$	
E_3	$\begin{cases}1\\1\end{cases}$	$\begin{matrix}-\epsilon^*\\-\epsilon\end{matrix}$	$\begin{matrix}-i\\i\end{matrix}$	$\begin{matrix}\epsilon\\\epsilon^*\end{matrix}$	$\begin{matrix}-1\\-1\end{matrix}$	$\begin{matrix}\epsilon^*\\\epsilon\end{matrix}$	$\begin{matrix}i\\-i\end{matrix}$	$\begin{matrix}-\epsilon\\-\epsilon^*\end{matrix}$	

TABLE 7–11 Character Tables of the Cubic Groups
$T, T_h, T_d, O, O_h, I, I_h$

T	E	$4C_3$	$4C_3^2$	$3C_2$	$\epsilon = e^{2\pi i/3}$
A	1	1	1	1	
E	$\begin{cases}1\\1\end{cases}$	$\begin{matrix}\epsilon\\\epsilon^*\end{matrix}$	$\begin{matrix}\epsilon^*\\\epsilon\end{matrix}$	$\begin{matrix}1\\1\end{matrix}$	
F	3	0	0	-1	T

$T_h = T \times i$; T in F_u.

T_d	E	$8C_3$	$3C_2$	$6S_4$	$6\sigma_d$	
0	E	$8C_3$	$3C_2$	$6C_4$	$6C'_2$	
A_1	1	1	1	1	1	
A_2	1	1	1	-1	-1	
E	2	-1	2	0	0	
F_1	3	0	-1	1	-1	T in 0
F_2	3	0	-1	-1	1	T in T_d

$0_h = 0 \times i$; T in F_{1u}.

I	E	$12C_5$	$12C_5^2$	$20C_3$	$15C_2$	
A	1	1	1	1	1	
F_1	3	$\dfrac{1+\sqrt{5}}{2}$	$\dfrac{1-\sqrt{5}}{2}$	0	-1	T
F_2	3	$\dfrac{1-\sqrt{5}}{2}$	$\dfrac{1+\sqrt{5}}{2}$	0	-1	
G	4	-1	-1	1	0	
H	5	0	0	-1	0	

$I_h = I \times i$; T in F_{1u}.

TABLE 7–12 Character Tables of the Groups $C_{\infty v}$ and $D_{\infty h}$ for Linear Molecules

$C_{\infty v}$	E	$2C_\infty^\phi$	$\ldots$	$\infty\sigma_v$	
$A_1 \equiv \Sigma^+$	1	1	$\ldots$	1	T_z
$A_2 \equiv \Sigma^-$	1	1	$\ldots$	-1	
$E_1 \equiv \Pi$	2	$2\cos\ \phi$	$\ldots$	0	(T_x, T_y)
$E_2 \equiv \Delta$	2	$2\cos 2\phi$	$\ldots$	0	
$E_3 \equiv \Phi$	2	$2\cos 3\phi$	$\ldots$	0	
$\ldots$	$\ldots$	$\ldots$	$\ldots$	$\ldots$	

$D^{\infty h}$	E	$2C_\infty^\phi$	$\ldots$	$\infty\sigma_v$	i	$2S_\infty^\phi$	$\ldots$	∞C_2	
$A_{1g} \equiv \Sigma_g^+$	1	1	$\ldots$	1	1	1	$\ldots$	1	
$A_{2g} \equiv \Sigma_g^-$	1	1	$\ldots$	-1	1	1	$\ldots$	-1	
$E_{1g} \equiv \Pi_g$	2	$2\cos\ \phi$	$\ldots$	0	2	$-2\cos\ \phi$	$\ldots$	0	
$E_{2g} \equiv \Delta_g$	2	$2\cos 2\phi$	$\ldots$	0	2	$2\cos 2\phi$	$\ldots$	0	
$\ldots$	$\ldots$	$\ldots$	$\ldots$	$\ldots$	$\ldots$	$\ldots$	$\ldots$	$\ldots$	
$A_{1u} \equiv \Sigma_u^+$	1	1	$\ldots$	1	-1	-1	$\ldots$	-1	T_z
$A_{2u} \equiv \Sigma_u^-$	1	1	$\ldots$	-1	-1	-1	$\ldots$	1	
$E_{1u} \equiv \Pi_u$	2	$2\cos\ \phi$	$\ldots$	0	$-2'$	$2\cos\ \phi$	$\ldots$	0	(T_x, T_y)
$E_{2u} \equiv \Delta_u$	2	$2\cos 2\phi$	$\ldots$	0	-2	$-2\cos 2\phi$	$\ldots$	0	
$\ldots$	$\ldots$	$\ldots$	$\ldots$	$\ldots$	$\ldots$	$\ldots$	$\ldots$	$\ldots$	

In the case of groups where there is a horizontal plane of symmetry one prime is given to the A, B, E, or F if the character is $+1$ for a reflection at this plane, two primes if it is -1. If there is a center of symmetry, the indices g and u are used according to whether we have $+1$ or -1 with respect to inversion.

Besides these symbols the coordinates $x, y,$ or z (or $T_x, T_y, T_z,$ where T stands for translation), representing the direction of the electric vector, are found in the row corresponding to their transformation properties. Instead of (x, y) the complex symbol $x \pm iy$ is also often used, meaning that any vector in the xy plane transforms according to the corresponding representation. In complete tables the components of rotation usually indicated by R_x, R_y, R_z and $x^2, y^2, z^2, xy, xz, yz$ are also given. Both are needed for the discussion of vibrational problems, the latter for interpreting Raman spectra.

Many of the groups are isomorphic having the same character table. Some groups can be derived from another by the addition of only one new element. For example, $C_{4h} = C_4 \times i$ (direct product). Group C_{4h} has twice as many classes (and irreducible representations) as C_4. The product of i with any element of C_4 must be an element of the new group. Each representation of C_4 will occur in C_{4h} with g and u. The new classes have the same characters as in C_4 in g representations and their negatives in u representations. (see the corresponding tables of characters, Tables 7–4 and 7–7.)

Other such relations are:

$$C_{3h} = C_3 \times \sigma_h; \quad C_{6h} = C_6 \times i; \quad D_{2h} \equiv V_h = D_2 \times i$$
$$D_{3d} = D_3 \times i; \quad D_{4h} = D_4 \times i; \quad D_{6h} = D_6 \times i; \quad \ldots ,$$

The cyclic groups require some special remarks. These have only one symmetry element, a p-fold axis, but the operation might be applied $(p-1)$ times *before* reaching identity, and after each rotation by $2\pi/p$ the molecule is transformed into itself. Thus, we have groups whose elements are

$$E, C_p, C_p^2, C_p^3, \ldots, C_p^{p-1}$$

C_p^p is equal to E, naturally.

Cyclic groups are Abelian, i. e., if X and A are any of the elements of the group, $X^{-1}AX = A$, and every element is a class by itself. Since all successive rotations are already considered, no rotation in the opposite sense can lead to any new situation. (The reciprocal of C_p^1 is C_p^{p-1}, etc.) Then, the law

$$l_1^2 + l_2^2 + \ldots + l_h^2 = h$$

tells us that all irreducible representations must be one-dimensional. (If a given l_i were 2, for example, three other l_i should be zero to keep the sum equal to h, but of course an l_i cannot be zero, and h in this case is also the number of classes or irreducible representations since the group is Abelian.) This does not mean, however, that they must all consist of a number of $+1$ or -1. Indeed, the following one-dimensional representation can be immediately given:

$$E \quad C_p^1 \quad C_p^2 \quad C_p^3 \quad \ldots \quad C_p^{p-1}$$
$$1 \equiv e^0 \quad e^{2\pi i/p} \quad e^{4\pi i/p} \quad e^{6\pi i/p} \quad \ldots \quad e^{(p-1)2\pi i/p}$$

It is seen that

$$C_p^1 C_p^2 = C_p^3 \quad \text{and also} \quad e^{2\pi i/p} e^{4\pi i/p} = e^{6\pi i/p}$$

and so forth. The representation being one-dimensional, its components are at the same time characters. If we call one of them ϵ^m with $\epsilon = e^{2\pi i/p}$ and $m = 0, 1, 2, \ldots, (p-1)$, then the set of exponentials ϵ^{2m} is also an irreducible representation. (However, if the maximum value of $2m$ is greater than p it will be identical with a representation already obtained. Only integers can be considered, since otherwise after p rotations by $2\pi/p$ (a complete turn), we would not obtain identity.)
Moivre's formula

$$\epsilon^m = e^{2\pi i m/p} = \cos\frac{2\pi m}{p} + i \sin\frac{2\pi m}{p}$$
$$\epsilon^{m*} = e^{-2\pi i m/p} = \cos\frac{2\pi m}{p} - i \sin\frac{2\pi m}{p}$$

often makes it possible to obtain the characters in simpler form. For group C_4, for example, with $p = 4$ and symmetry elements E, C_4, $C_4^2 = C_2$, and C_4^3 and $m = 0, 1, 2, 3$, we have, in this order,

$$1 \quad i \quad -1 \quad -i$$

It is important that in replacing every character by its complex conjugate we again have an irreducible representation:

$$1 \quad -i \quad -1 \quad i$$

This is generally so. These two one-dimensional representations are usually considered together and, in practice, they can be treated as one degenerate representation. They are indicated by E as a two-dimensional representation. Two wave functions corresponding to such a pair would have the same energy, but this is only accidental degeneracy. They would not transform into a linear combination of the two functions under symmetry operations.

Two other irreducible representations of group C_4 are

$$1 \quad 1 \quad 1 \quad 1$$
$$1 \quad -1 \quad 1 \quad -1$$

Putting ϵ^{2m} into the exponentials would give the same as the second of these, as is easily seen.

For $C_3, C_5,$ and C_6 the conditions are not quite so simple and it is preferable to keep ϵ in the character tables ($\epsilon = e^{2\pi i/p}$, where

$p = 3, 5,$ and 6 for the three groups, respectively). With some use of the Moivre formula, the tables become understandable. It has to be remembered, too, that with these complex characters the orthogonality relation is

$$\sum_R \chi_j(R)^* \chi_i(R) = h \delta_{ij} \quad \text{and} \quad a_i = \frac{1}{h} \sum_R \chi^*(R) \chi_i(R)$$

The infinite groups $C_{\infty v}$ and $D_{\infty h}$ also deserve some special comment. It is not surprising to find $2 \cos \phi$ among the characters instead of just a number, since in this case ϕ has no fixed value. Characters like $2 \cos k\phi$, where k is an integer, enter into other irreducible representations. Nonintegers are not acceptable since we would not then obtain the same with $\phi = 2\pi$ and $\phi = 0$.

A slight difficulty arises if we try to use the formula

$$a_i = \frac{1}{h} \sum_R \chi(R) \chi_i(R)$$

to determine how many times a certain irreducible representation occurs in a reducible one. In the above formula the summation has to be replaced by integration giving

$$a_i = \frac{1}{h} \int \chi(R) \chi_i(R) \, d\phi$$

For example, for group $D_{\infty h}$ we have actually an infinite number of elements for $C_\infty, \sigma_v, S_\infty,$ and C_2. For each of these four we can integrate from 0 to 2π and count them as 2π elements in h. In doing so E and i have to be omitted, since E is one of the C_∞ ($\phi = 0$) and i is one of the S_∞ ($\phi = 0$) and they are already covered by the integration. When two $\cos k\phi$ should be multiplied by one other we may use the formula

$$\cos k_1 \phi \cos k_2 \phi = \tfrac{1}{2} [\cos (k_1 + k_2)\phi + \cos (k_1 - k_2)\phi]$$

In the character tables of groups $C_{\infty v}$ and $D_{\infty h}$ two different notations are used. One is based on angular momenta, the other on symmetry. The relation between the two is found in the following way.

We take the z axis in the direction of the internuclear axis of the linear molecule. Then the position of each electron can be characterized by the three cylindrical coordinates $z_i, \rho_i, \phi_i,$ where ρ_i is the distance from the axis and ϕ_i the azimuthal angle. If ϕ_1 refers to the first electron, the relative azimuth of another electron i with respect to the first one is equal to

$$\phi_i' = \phi_i - \phi_1$$

Now we can set up the Schrödinger equation in terms of $z_i, \rho_i,$ and ϕ_i'.

Changing ϕ_1 then means simply a rotation of the whole electron cloud around the internuclear axis, leaving the Schrödinger equation unchanged. If ψ_e is the electronic eigenfunction of the molecule then $\psi_e^* \psi_e$ must remain unchanged too, since it measures the electronic charge distribution. Wigner and Witmer [80][6] have shown that for this to be true the electronic wave function must have the following form:

$$\psi_e = X e^{+i\Lambda\phi_1} \qquad \text{or} \qquad \psi_e = \bar{X} e^{-i\Lambda\phi_1}$$

where X or $\bar{X}$ depend on all the coordinates except ϕ_1, and $\bar{X}$ differs from X inasmuch as all the ϕ_i' are replaced by their negatives (The product of the exponentials in $\psi_e^* \psi_e$ is then constant.)

The angular momentum is the eigenvalue of operator

$$\frac{h}{2\pi i} \frac{\partial}{\partial \phi_1}$$

which gives with the above functions

$$\frac{h}{2\pi} \Lambda \psi_e \qquad \text{and} \qquad -\frac{h}{2\pi} \Lambda \psi_e$$

The quantum number Λ is thus seen to measure the angular momentum.

For Σ terms $\Lambda = 0$ and there is only one solution. Then the state is nondegenerate and transforms like a one-dimensional representation. The character for C_∞ must be $+1$ since the wave function does not depend on ϕ_1. Therefore, Σ states belong to A representations. Σ^+ and Σ^- will have character $+1$ or -1, respectively, for a reflection at any plane containing the nuclei (σ_v).

For $\Pi, \Delta, \ldots$ terms $\Lambda = 1, 2, \ldots$. These states belong to two-dimensional representations. $\Lambda = +1$ and -1. etc., represent the rotation of the electronic cloud with respect to the internuclear axis in one sense or the opposite sense.

Operation C_∞ now means to multiply the first function by $e^{i\Lambda\phi}$ and the second one by $e^{-i\Lambda\phi}$. If we think of the two wave functions as forming a column vector we see immediately that this change can be achieved by a matrix whose character is $e^{i\Lambda\phi} + e^{-i\Lambda\phi} = 2\cos\Lambda\phi$:

$$\begin{pmatrix} X e^{i\Lambda(\phi_1+\phi)} \\ \bar{X} e^{-i\Lambda(\phi_1+\phi)} \end{pmatrix} = \begin{pmatrix} e^{i\Lambda\phi} & 0 \\ 0 & e^{-i\Lambda\phi} \end{pmatrix} \begin{pmatrix} X e^{i\Lambda\phi_1} \\ \bar{X} e^{-i\Lambda\phi_1} \end{pmatrix}$$

Operation σ_v transforms the one wave function into the other and the character is 0.

If the molecule has a center of symmetry ($D_{\infty h}$), indices g and u are introduced.

[6] See [76], pp. 213 and 217.

7-10. GENERAL REFERENCES ON GROUP THEORY

E. Wigner, *Gruppentheorie und ihre Anwendung auf die Quanten-mechanik der Atomspektren* (Braunschweig: Vieweg, 1931); English edition: *Group Theory and its Application to the Quantum Mechanics of Atomic Spectra* (New York: Academic Press, 1959).

A. Speiser, *Theorie der Gruppen von Endlicher Ordnung* (Berlin: Springer, 1927).

W. Burnside, *The Theory of Groups* (New York: Cambridge University Press, 1927).

B. L. Van der Waerden, *Die Gruppentheoretische Methode in der Quantenmechanik* (Berlin: Springer, 1932).

S. Bhagavantam and T. Venkatarayudu, *Theory of Groups and its Applications to Physical problems* (2nd ed.; Waltair, India: Andhra University, 1951).

B. Higman, *Applied Group-Theoretic and Matrix Methods* (Fair Lawn, N. J.: Oxford University Press, Inc., 1955).

V. Heine, *Group Theory in Quantum Mechanics* (London: Pergamon Press, 1960).

F. D. Murnaghan, *The Theory of Group Representations* (Baltimore: The Johns Hopkins Press, 1938).

H. Weyl, *The Classical Groups* (Princeton, N. J.: Princeton University Press, 1939).

D. E. Littlewood, *The Theory of Group Characters* (New York: Oxford University Press, 1940).

R. S. Mulliken, *Phys. Rev.* **43**, 279 (1933). (Electronic spectra of polyatomic molecules.)

G. Placzek, Handbuch der Radiologie, Vol. 6., No. 2. (1934), p. 293 (Raman and infrared spectra.)

F. Seitz, *Z. Kristallographie*, A88, 433 (1934). (Crystallographic groups.)

L. Tisza, *Z. Physik*, **82**, 48 (1933). (Symmetry point groups; overtones of vibrations, degenerate cases.)

J. E. Rosenthal and G. M. Murphy, *Rev. Mod. Phys.*, 8, 317 (1936). (Vibrations of polyatomic molecules.)

H. Sponer and E. Teller, *Rev. Mod. Phys.*, **13**, 75 (1941). (Electronic spectra of polyatomic molecules.)

8

The Calculation of Spectral Quantities by the Molecular Orbital Method

8-1. *CIS* AND *TRANS*-BUTADIENE (LCAO MO APPROXIMATION)

Cis-butadiene was used as our model for an LCAO MO calculation in the Hückel approximation in Chapter 3, so we need not repeat it now; we may turn our attention immediately to the evaluation of spectral quantities. This work was originally done by Mulliken in 1939 and much of this chapter is inspired by one of his publications [92].

We shall assume that both *cis*- and *trans*-butadiene are coplanar and that all the carbon atoms have trigonal hybridization with 120° between the axes of the σ orbitals and one π orbital per carbon.

Cis-butadiene belongs to symmetry point group C_{2v} and *trans*-butadiene to C_{2h}. In Fig. 8-1, the assumed coordinate axes are given. The z axis, following the adopted convention, lies in the direction of C_2, i.e., in the plane of the molecule for *cis*-butadiene but perpendicular to it for *trans*-butadiene. σ_v corresponds to the plane of the molecule for the *cis*-isomer.

Tables 8-1 and 8-2 give the characters for the two groups.

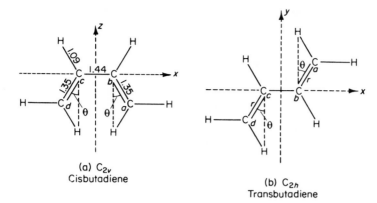

(a) C_{2v}
Cisbutadiene

(b) C_{2h}
Transbutadiene

Fig. 8-1

TABLE 8–1

C_{2v}		E	C_2	σ_v	σ_v'
Γ_1	A_1; z	1	1	1	1
Γ_2	A_2	1	1	-1	-1
Γ_3	B_1; x	1	-1	1	-1
Γ_4	B_2; y	1	-1	-1	1
Γ		4	0	-4	0

TABLE 8–2

C_{2h}		E	C_2	σ_h	i
Γ_1'	A_g	1	1	1	1
Γ_2'	A_u; z	1	1	-1	-1
Γ_3'	B_g	1	-1	-1	1
Γ_4'	B_u; x,y	1	-1	1	-1
Γ'		4	0	-4	0

In the last row there are the characters of the reducible representation based on and obtained by carrying out the operations of the group on the four π-electronic atomic orbitals $\psi_a, \psi_b, \psi_c, \psi_d$ (see p. 163).

For example, for σ_v in the case of *cis*-butadiene we have

$$\begin{pmatrix} -\psi_a \\ -\psi_b \\ -\psi_c \\ -\psi_d \end{pmatrix} = \begin{pmatrix} -1 & 0 & 0 & 0 \\ 0 & -1 & 0 & 0 \\ 0 & 0 & -1 & 0 \\ 0 & 0 & 0 & -1 \end{pmatrix} \begin{pmatrix} \psi_a \\ \psi_b \\ \psi_c \\ \psi_d \end{pmatrix} \text{ and } \chi = -4$$

with the antisymmetry of the π orbitals for a reflection at their nodal plane (here σ_v) taken into account.

The next question is: to which irreducible representations belong the molecular orbitals ϕ_i? The formula

$$a_i = \frac{1}{h} \sum_R \chi(R) \chi_i(R)$$

enables us to determine the number of times any given irreducible representation (Γ_i) occurs in the reducible one (Γ).

We obtain for *cis*-butadiene

$$\Gamma_1 \quad A_1 \quad a_1 = \tfrac{1}{4}(4 \times 1 + 0 \times 1 - 4 \times 1 + 0 \times 1) = 0$$
$$\Gamma_2 \quad A_2 \quad a_2 = \tfrac{1}{4}(4 \times 1 + 0 \times 1 + 4 \times 1 - 0 \times 1) = 2$$
$$\Gamma_3 \quad B_1 \quad a_3 = \tfrac{1}{4}(4 \times 1 - 0 \times 1 - 4 \times 1 - 0 \times 1) = 0$$
$$\Gamma_4 \quad B_2 \quad a_4 = \tfrac{1}{4}(4 \times 1 - 0 \times 1 + 4 \times 1 + 0 \times 1) = 2$$

and for trans-butadiene

$$\Gamma_1' \quad A_g \quad a_1 = 0$$
$$\Gamma_2' \quad A_u \quad a_2 = 2$$
$$\Gamma_3' \quad B_g \quad a_3 = 2$$
$$\Gamma_4' \quad B_u \quad a_4 = 0$$

Now, we know that any molecular wave function, hence any of the ϕ_i, must transform like one of the irreducible representations of the corresponding symmetry point group. Since, on the other hand, the ϕ_i are built from the AO $\psi_a, \psi_b, \psi_c, \psi_d$ on which our reducible representations are based, we have the result that in the case of *cis*-butadiene two molecular orbitals transform like A_2 and two like B_2, and in the case of *trans*-butadiene two transform like A_u and two like B_g. (Actually the characteristic antisymmetry of the π-atomic orbitals is what restricts us to the representations having -1 as the character for σ_v and σ_h for *cis*- and *trans*-butadiene, respectively.)

We have already obtained the molecular orbitals as linear combinations of atomic orbitals in Chapter 3. They are

$$\phi_1 = 0.3717\psi_a + 0.6015\psi_b + 0.6015\psi_c + 0.3717\psi_d$$
$$\phi_2 = 0.6015\psi_a + 0.3717\psi_b - 0.3717\psi_c - 0.6015\psi_d$$
$$\phi_3 = 0.6015\psi_a - 0.3717\psi_b - 0.3717\psi_c + 0.6015\psi_d$$
$$\phi_4 = 0.3717\psi_a - 0.6015\psi_b + 0.6015\psi_c - 0.3717\psi_d$$

$$(8\text{-}1)$$

They apply to *cis*- as well as *trans*-butadiene since we have neglected interactions between nonneighbors.

It is easy to assign these MO to the available irreducible representations in looking at the signs in (8-1):

	cis	*trans*
ϕ_1	B_2	A_u
ϕ_2	A_2	B_g
ϕ_3	B_2	A_u
ϕ_4	A_2	B_g

For example, ϕ_3 (*cis*) conserves its sign for σ'_v but changes it for σ_v and C_2 because of the antisymmetry of the π orbitals in the plane of the molecule; therefore it belongs to B_2.

Through a knowledge of group theory, however, the ϕ_i may be obtained more easily. In this simple case it reduces to the use of σ'_v, whose matrix of transformation (and character) can be only $+1$ or -1, implying that either $C_1 = C_4$ and $C_2 = C_3$; or $C_1 = -C_4$ and $C_2 = -C_3$. This was used in Sec. 3-4 to reduce the order of the secular equation.

In the LCAO MO approximation the electrons are placed into the available MO in order of increasing energy. In the ground state ϕ_1 and ϕ_2 are doubly occupied while ϕ_3 and ϕ_4 are empty. The schemes in Fig. 8-2 represent the ground state and the excited states obtained by the lifting of *one* electron to a higher orbital.

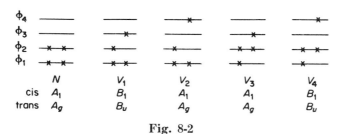

Fig. 8-2

The symmetry of the total wave function, which is a product of the occupied MO (taking twice the doubly occupied ones), is obtained by forming the direct product of the four irreducible representations to which the individual ϕ_i belong. In doing this one does not care about doubly occupied orbitals since these always give A_1 (*cis*) or A_g (*trans*). Table 8-3 shows all possible direct products. From these tables we obtain immediately the symmetries of

TABLE 8-3

	cis					trans			
	A_1	A_2	B_1	B_2		A_g	A_u	B_g	B_u
A_1	A_1	A_2	B_1	B_2	A_g	A_g	A_u	B_g	B_u
A_2	A_2	A_1	B_2	B_1	A_u	A_u	A_g	B_u	B_g
B_1	B_1	B_2	A_1	A_2	B_g	B_g	B_u	A_g	A_u
B_2	B_2	B_1	A_2	A_1	B_u	B_u	B_g	A_u	A_g

the five states shown in Fig. 8-2.

We are now ready to derive the selection rules for transitions between these states. We shall consider those from the ground state to the other states.

Cis

$V_1 \leftarrow N$	$B_1 \leftarrow A_1$	x axis polarized
$V_2 \leftarrow N$	$A_1 \leftarrow A_1$	z axis polarized
$V_3 \leftarrow N$	$A_1 \leftarrow A_1$	z axis polarized
$V_4 \leftarrow N$	$B_1 \leftarrow A_1$	x axis polarized

Trans

$V_1 \leftarrow N$	$B_u \leftarrow A_g$	allowed for x and y
$V_2 \leftarrow N$	$A_g \leftarrow A_g$	forbidden
$V_3 \leftarrow N$	$A_g \leftarrow A_g$	forbidden
$V_4 \leftarrow N$	$B_u \leftarrow A_g$	allowed for x and y

For *cis*-butadiene all four transitions are allowed; two of them are polarized according to the z axis and two according to the x axis. No transition is allowed with a polarization perpendicular to the plane of the molecule.

For *trans*-butadiene two transitions are allowed and two are forbidden. The allowed ones may be polarized according to any direction in the plane of the molecule (xy plane). $A_g \longleftrightarrow A_g$ transitions are forbidden because none of the coordinates x, y or z transforms like A_g and hence the integral in the expression of the transition moment could not be totally symmetrical (see Chapter 7). (Note that the two forbidden transitions are forbidden by the Laporte rule as well, $g \longleftrightarrow g$.)

Thus, there is a striking difference between the two isomers which should make it possible to infer from the spectrum the presence of the one or the other.

The excitation energies can be easily computed in terms of the resonance integral β, in units of which the energies of the orbitals were obtained in Chapter 3. We had (for one electron in each case):

$$
\begin{aligned}
\phi_1 \quad & E_1 = 1.618\beta + \alpha \\
\phi_2 \quad & E_2 = 0.618\beta + \alpha \\
\phi_3 \quad & E_3 = -0.618\beta + \alpha \\
\phi_4 \quad & E_4 = -1.618\beta + \alpha
\end{aligned}
\tag{8-2}
$$

In obtaining these values, however, we neglected overlap integrals. This affects the energies a great deal, and we have to introduce overlap for even a qualitive interpretation of the spectra. Wheland [30] has shown that this can be done by using a simple formula without making a wholly new calculation. Wheland has improved the Hückel approximation inasmuch as he takes account of overlap integrals (S) between adjacent orbitals, but he still neglects resonance and overlap integrals between nonclose neighbors.

Using the same notation as in Chapter 3, the secular determinant for butadiene in the LCAO MO approximation is

$$(\alpha_1 - E)c_1 + (\beta_{12} - ES_{12})c_2 + (\beta_{13} - ES_{13})c_3 + (\beta_{14} - ES_{14})c_4 = 0$$
$$(\beta_{12} - ES_{12})c_1 + (\alpha_2 - E)c_2 + (\beta_{23} - ES_{23})c_3 + (\beta_{24} - ES_{24})c_4 = 0$$
$$(\beta_{13} - ES_{13})c_1 + (\beta_{23} - ES_{23})c_2 + (\alpha_3 - E)c_3 + (\beta_{34} - ES_{34})c_4 = 0$$
$$(\beta_{14} - ES_{14})c_1 + (\beta_{24} - ES_{24})c_2 + (\beta_{34} - ES_{34})c_3 + (\alpha_4 - E)c_4 = 0$$

$$(8\text{-}3)$$

Wheland assumes that

1. $\alpha_1 = \alpha_2 = \alpha_3 = \alpha_4 = \alpha$;
2. overlap integrals between π orbitals of adjacent carbon atoms are all equal to S and all other overlap integrals are equal to zero;
3. resonance integrals between π orbitals of adjacent carbon atoms are all equal to β and all other resonance integrals are equal to zero.

Then we have

$$(\alpha - E)c_1 + (\beta - ES)c_2 = 0$$
$$(\beta - ES)c_1 + (\alpha - E)c_2 + (\beta - ES)c_3 = 0$$
$$(\beta - ES)c_2 + (\alpha - E)c_3 + (\beta - ES)c_4 = 0$$
$$(\beta - ES)c_3 + (\alpha - E)c_4 = 0$$

$$(8\text{-}4)$$

Dividing throughout by $(\beta - ES)$ and putting

$$y = \frac{\alpha - E}{\beta - ES} \tag{8-5}$$

the secular determinant becomes

$$c_1 y + c_2 = 0$$
$$c_1 + c_2 y + c_3 = 0$$
$$c_2 + c_3 y + c_4 = 0$$
$$c_3 + c_4 y = 0$$

$$(8\text{-}6)$$

This is exactly what we had in the Hückel approximation and we do not need to make a new calculation for obtaining the possible values of y. However, y now has a different meaning. (It was $(\alpha - E)/\beta$ in the Hückel approximation.) In order to express the energy in units taking overlap into account Wheland defined a new resonance integral γ the following way:

$$\gamma = \beta - S\alpha \qquad \text{or} \qquad \beta = \gamma + S\alpha \tag{8-7}$$

Substituting the latter expression into

$$E = \frac{\alpha - y\beta}{1 - yS} \tag{8-8}$$

which is obtained from (8-5), we have

$$E = \frac{\alpha - y\gamma - yS\alpha}{1 - yS}$$

or

$$E = \frac{\alpha(1 - yS)}{1 - yS} - \frac{y\gamma}{1 - yS}$$

and

$$E = \alpha - \frac{y}{1 - yS}\gamma = \alpha + m\gamma \tag{8-9}$$

if

$$m = -\frac{y}{1 - yS} \tag{8-10}$$

Thus we obtain the energies with their resonance part in units of γ, which is a resonance integral taking overlap into account in using the last expression for m.

If, for example, $y = +1$, then taking $S = 0.25$ we obtain

$$m = -\frac{1}{1 - 0.25 \times 1} = -1.33$$

For $y = -1$,

$$m = -\frac{-1}{1 + 0.25 \times 1} = 0.80$$

It is worth noting that a similar formula applies even if interactions between nonneighbors are included if only β and S are assumed to be proportional, so that if for two atoms r and s

$$\beta_{rs} = \eta_{rs}\beta_0$$

where β_0 is one of the β_{rs} chosen as unit and η_{rs} is a constant, then also

$$S_{rs} = \eta_{rs}S_0$$

Then a nondiagonal element in the secular determinant becomes

$$\beta_{rs} - ES_{rs} = \eta_{rs}(\beta_0 - ES_0)$$

and

$$\gamma_{rs} = \beta_{rs} - S_{rs}\alpha = \eta_{rs}(\beta_0 - S_0\alpha) = \eta_{rs}\gamma_0$$

Dividing throughout by $\beta_0 - ES_0$,

$$y = \frac{\alpha - E}{\beta_0 - ES_0}$$

and by the above argument

$$E = \alpha + m\gamma_0 \tag{8-11}$$

This is valid as long as all the α are equal.

The coefficients c_i are (before normalization) the same whether overlap is taken into account or not, since these do not depend on the definition of y. When we normalize the MO, however,

$$\sum_r c_r^2 + 2 \sum_{r<s} \sum c_r c_s S_{rs} = 1 \qquad (8\text{-}12)$$

and we cannot neglect the terms under the double sum any more. In Wheland's approximation, where nonneighbor interactions are neglected, we can write for the electronic charge densities

$$q_r = \sum [c_r^2 + \sum_{r'} c_r c_{r'} S_{rr'}] \qquad (8\text{-}13)$$

where the summation is taken over all occupied orbitals, doubly occupied orbitals are counted twice, and r' is an atom adjacent to r. This means that if we divide the terms $c_r c_{r'} S_{rr'}$ equally between r and r' we obtain the same charges as in the Hückel approximation. This is still true if nonneighbor interactions are included, i.e., r' is any atom except r, but the whole procedure clearly loses much of its meaning. If the aim is an approximate idea of the electronic charge distribution in the molecule it is better to think of it with the c_r^2 terms located at the nuclei and the $c_r c_{r'} S_{rr'}$ terms at the bond between r and r'.[1] (see McWeeny [93], Payette and Sandorfy [94]).

The inclusion of overlap in the molecular orbital methods causes serious problems which were discussed by Coulson and Chirgwin [95] and by Löwdin [96], who used orthogonal *atomic* orbitals. These latter found wide application in quantum chemistry (see Chapter 9.).

We return now to the butadiene molecule. The energies of the orbitals are, from Wheland's formula (with $S = 0.25$),

	in β units	in γ units
E_1:	$1.618\beta + \alpha$	$1.152\gamma + \alpha$
E_2:	$0.618\beta + \alpha$	$0.535\gamma + \alpha$
E_3:	$-0.618\beta + \alpha$	$-0.731\gamma + \alpha$
E_4:	$-1.618\beta + \alpha$	$-2.717\gamma + \alpha$

It is seen that as a consequence of the inclusion of overlap the energies are "compressed" for $m > 0$ and "expanded" for $m < 0$. (Let us remember that $\alpha, \beta,$ and γ are negative quantities and thus the stablest levels are the most negative ones, as they should be.) This changes the whole picture and shows the importance of overlap integrals.

The excitation energies for transition $V_1 \leftarrow N$ are

$$(0.535\gamma + \alpha) - (-0.731\gamma + \alpha) = 1.266\gamma$$

and

$$\begin{array}{ll} V_1 \leftarrow N & 1.266\gamma \\ V_2 \leftarrow N & 3.252\gamma \\ V_3 \leftarrow N & 1.883\gamma \\ V_4 \leftarrow N & 3.869\gamma \end{array}$$

[1] Cf. "population analysis." See R. S. Mulliken, J. Chem. Phys. *23*, 1833, 1841, 2338, 2343 (1955).

Now we need the numerical value of γ. It is seldom computed theoretically. In fact, because of the many approximations it involves, it is preferable to conserve the empirical character of the method. An adequate choice of the parameter might compensate for some of its inadequacies.

β (or γ) can be easily related to bond energies following a suggestion by Lennard-Jones [97]. As we saw in Chapter 3, for one carbon-carbon double bond the contribution to the energy of the molecule of the two π electrons is

$$2(\alpha + \beta)$$

Thus 2β *approximately* represents the energy of the π bond or the difference between the energy of a double bond and a single bond. There is thus a possibility of relating β or γ to the heat of hydrogenation. (See the discussion of the similar problem in the valence-bond treatment of benzene, p. 236.)

There are many difficulties involved which we do not discuss here.

Another way of estimating β and γ is by comparison with the observed spectrum. Smakula [98] measured the ultraviolet spectrum of butadiene and found the maximum of the first band at 2170 Å. The other bands lie in the far ultraviolet.

2170 Å is equal to about $46,080 \, \text{cm}^{-1} \cong 5.7 \, \text{ev} \cong 131 \, \text{kcal/mole}$. If we assign this band to the $V_1 \leftarrow N$ transition,

$$1.266\gamma = 131 \, \text{kcal/mole}$$

and $$\gamma \cong 103 \, \text{kcal/mole} \cong 4.47 \, \text{ev} \cong 36,050 \, \text{cm}^{-1}$$

($1 \, \text{ev} = 23.06 \, \text{kcal/mole} = 8066 \, \text{cm}^{-1}$).

This value of γ could be used for computing the wavelengths of the other bands, but unfortunately lack of experimental data precludes further comparisons between theory and experiment. (But see the next chapters on benzene and the acenes.)

The β or γ obtained from the spectrum are not expected to give the same values as those obtained from thermodynamic data, since in the simple MO method we cannot distinguish the related singlet and triplet states and actually obtain energies corresponding to their mean.

The value of γ varies from one family of compounds to another. The whole procedure is somewhat frustrating, but even so, much more insight can be gained about spectra by using this method than one might think at first sight.

Our next task is to compute the transition moments. For transition $V_1 \leftarrow N$ of *cis*-butadiene the transition moment lies in the direction of the x axis and is equal to

$$Q_{V_1 \leftarrow N} = \int \frac{1}{\sqrt{2}} [\phi_2(1)\overline{\phi_2(2)} - \phi_2(2)\overline{\phi_2(1)}][x(1) + x(2)]$$

$$\frac{1}{2}[\phi_2(1)\overline{\phi_3(2)} - \phi_2(2)\overline{\phi_3(1)} - \overline{\phi_2(1)}\phi_3(2) + \overline{\phi_2(2)}\phi_3(1)] \qquad (8\text{-}14)$$

We remember that

$$(M_x)_{mn} = eQ_{mn}$$

(See Chapter 5, p. 98).

In (8-14) all possible permutations of the electrons are taken into account; naturally they are equally acceptable. We did not need to do this so far in the simple molecular orbital method, but we shall have to do it right from the beginning in the higher approximations of the MO method (Chapters 10-12) as we did in the valence-bond method. The signs in (8-14) are chosen in such a way that the wave functions describe singlet states.

Strictly speaking, it is the total wave functions of states N and V, and not just ϕ_2 and ϕ_3 which should enter this expression. It is readily seen, however, that integration over the wave functions of the electrons, which remain in closed shells and are not involved in the transition would merely give unity, since the wave functions are normalized.

The factors of normalization in (8-14) take into account the fact that the N state can be represented by only one Slater function, but we need two for the excited state where we have simply occupied orbitals with the spins free. The bars mean β spin.

Because of the orthogonality of the spin functions the same electrons must have the same spin left and right of the operator, or else the corresponding term is zero. Furthermore, because of the orthogonality of the molecular orbitals (ϕ_i), the electron not affected by the operator $x(1)$ or $x(2)$ must be in the same ϕ_i left and right of the operator, or again the term is zero. If we take all this into account we see that only four of the sixteen terms remain. With $x(1)$ we have eight terms:

$$\int \phi_2(1)\overline{\phi_2(2)}\, x(1)\, \phi_2(1)\overline{\phi_3(2)}\, d\tau_1 = 0$$

$$-\int \phi_2(1)\overline{\phi_2(2)}\, x(1)\, \overline{\phi_2(1)}\phi_3(2)\, d\tau_1 = 0$$

$$-\int \phi_2(1)\overline{\phi_2(2)}\, x(1)\, \phi_2(2)\overline{\phi_3(1)}\, d\tau_1 = 0$$

$$\int \phi_2(1)\overline{\phi_2(2)}\, x(1)\, \overline{\phi_2(2)}\phi_3(1)\, d\tau_1 \neq 0$$

$$-\int \phi_2(2)\overline{\phi_2(1)}\, x(1)\, \phi_2(1)\overline{\phi_3(2)}\, d\tau_1 = 0$$

$$\int \phi_2(2)\overline{\phi_2(1)}\, x(1)\, \phi_2(2)\overline{\phi_3(1)}\, d\tau_1 \neq 0$$

$$\int \phi_2(2)\,\overline{\phi_2(1)}\,x(1)\,\overline{\phi_3(1)}\,\phi_3(2)\,d\tau_1 = 0$$

$$-\int \phi_2(2)\,\overline{\phi_3(1)}\,x(1)\,\overline{\phi_2(2)}\,\phi_3(1)\,d\tau_1 = 0$$

With $x(2)$ we have, of course, eight other terms, two of which remain. Finally,

$$Q = \frac{4}{2\sqrt{2}}\int \phi_2 x \phi_3\,dx = \sqrt{2}\int \phi_2 x \phi_3\,dx$$

The presence of $\sqrt{2}$ is due to the presence of $x(1)$ and $x(2)$, i.e., to the fact that any of the two electrons can make the jump. (With only one electron the factor would be $1/\sqrt{2}$.) Now we can substitute for ϕ_2 and ϕ_3 their linear combinations in terms of atomic orbitals. We had in the Hückel approximation

$$\phi_2 = 0.6015(\psi_a - \psi_d) + 0.3717(\psi_b - \psi_c)$$
$$\phi_3 = 0.6015(\psi_a + \psi_d) - 0.3717(\psi_b + \psi_c)$$

(8-15)

This gives the approximate result:

$$Q = \sqrt{2}\,[0.362(x_a - x_d) - 0.138(x_b - x_c)] \qquad (8\text{-}16)$$

Carrying through the summation we encounter terms like

$$\int \psi_a x \psi_a\,dx = \int \psi_a x_a \psi_a\,dx = x_a \qquad (8\text{-}17)$$

and terms like

$$\int \psi_a x \psi_b\,dx = \int \psi_a \frac{x_a + x_b}{2}\psi_b\,dx = \frac{x_a + x_b}{2}S_{ab} \qquad (8\text{-}18)$$

Here x_a and x_b are the x coordinates of nuclei a and b, and it might appear strange at first sight that we identify the coordinates of the electron with the coordinates of the nuclei. However, the mean value for an integral like $\int \psi_a x \psi_a\,dx$ in the field of core a is actually $\int \psi_a x_a \psi_a\,dx$ since for any dx at a given distance x from nucleus a there is a similar element dx at the same distance x in the opposite direction, where the value of ψ_a is the same. (Think of the boundary surface of a π electron.) Since x_a is a constant, we can put it before the integral sign.

For the mixed terms the mean value is clearly as given above, if only the two atoms are identical. These terms are smaller since they are multiplied by the overlap integral. Many of them cancel out; the remaining ones were neglected.

Numerically with $\theta = 30°$, the C_a-C_b distance equal to 1.35Å and the C_b-C_c distance to 1.44Å (this is a little too short but we preferred to keep the data as they were in Mulliken's paper of 1939), we obtain with the center of coordinates at the midpoint of the central C—C bond (Fig. 8-1):

$$cis \quad \begin{cases} x_a = 0.72 + 1.35 \sin 30° = 1.395\,\text{Å} \\ x_b = 0.72\,\text{Å} \\ z_a = 1.35 \cos 30° = 1.169\,\text{Å} \\ z_b = 0 \end{cases}$$

$$trans \quad \begin{cases} x_a = 1.395\,\text{Å} \\ x_b = 0.72\,\text{Å} \\ y_a = 1.169\,\text{Å} \\ y_b = 0 \end{cases}$$

With these values, using the coefficients in (8–15) and taking into account the signs of the coordinates, we obtain the scheme shown in Table 8–4.

TABLE 8–4

	With Conjugation		Without Conjugation	
	Q^2 *cis*	Q^2 *trans*	Q^2 *cis*	Q^2 *trans*
$V_1 \leftarrow N$	1.316	2.746	0.224	0.898
$V_2 \leftarrow N$	0.547	0	0.674	0
$V_3 \leftarrow N$	0.547	0	0.674	0
$V_4 \leftarrow N$	0.037	0.246	0.224	0.898
Total	2.447	2.992	1.796	1.796

Since $D \equiv Q^2$ and Q^2 was given in Å^2 we obtain for the oscillator strength f, using $f = 1.085 \times 10^{-5} \omega D^2$ with $\lambda = 2100\,\text{Å}$ for both compounds:

$$f_{cis} = 0.68; \qquad f_{trans} = 1.42$$

These values are about four times as high as the observed ones. This discrepancy is quite general with the LCAO method and is probably linked to the overemphasis of polar structures (see Chapter 10–5). The factor varies from about 1/3 to 1/5 for different molecules.

In Table 8–4 the columns under "without conjugation" were obtained by Mulliken [99] by putting the resonance integral between the two central atoms, $\beta_{bc} = 0$. This cuts the molecule into two halves, each containing one insulated double bond. Then we have to take 1.34 Å and 1.54 Å for the C—C distances in the double bonds and single bond, respectively. All the coefficients in the ϕ_i are equal to $\pm (0.5)$ and all four transitions coincide. This way interesting conclusions may be drawn concerning the effect of conjugation on the electronic spectrum.

The total intensity of the four transitions increases, and more so for the *trans* isomer than for the *cis* isomer. The most conspicuous effect is a pronounced bathochromic shift of the first band (1.266γ against 2.13γ for ethylene (2β or $0.80\gamma + 1.33\gamma = 2.13\gamma$)) and a great increase of its intensity. For nonconjugated butadiene the total intensity of the four transitions is simply twice the intensity of the only transition of ethylene in this approximation. (For ethylene: $Q_x = \sqrt{2}\,[0.5 \times 2 \times 0.67] = 0.948$ and $Q_x^2 = 0.898$.) For conjugated butadiene (Table 8-4) the relative intensities of the four bands are very different and the first band is highly favored, especially for the *trans* isomer.

Available experimental results [100] indicate that under normal circumstances 1,3-butadiene and most of its derivatives exist predominantly in the *trans* form.

Lennard-Jones [101] made a refined LCAO MO calculation on butadiene taking into account the variation of β with the internuclear distance. His results gave a somewhat better fit with experiment. Transition moments are especially sensitive to small changes in the values of the coefficients in the ϕ_i.

8-2. POLYENES

Hausser, Kuhn, and Smakula [98, 102, 103] measured the ultraviolet absorption spectra of a number of compounds containing polyenic chains. Some of these, like carotenoides, have an important place in nature. Vitamin A is a derivative of decapentene with five conjugated double bonds.

In the spectra of all these compounds the first band system is the most prominent and is followed toward shorter waves by much weaker band systems. The first band is gradually displaced toward longer waves and its intensity increases when the number (n) of conjugated double bonds increases, but the shift is less for high values of n. From the eighth band on, the first band is in the visible and the compounds are colored.

	$\lambda(\text{Å})$	$\omega(\text{cm}^{-1})$
Butadiene [98]	2170	46,080
Hexatriene [104]	2510	39,750
Octatetraene [105]	3040	32,900

Mulliken was the first to apply the simple LCAO MO method to these molecules. He found that the first band corresponds to the $V_1 \leftarrow N$ band of butadiene and considered its shifting and its increase in intensity at the expense of the rest of the spectra a manifestation of conjugation.

We given in Table 8-5 the energies of the orbitals and the LCAO coefficients for hexatriene, which the reader might want to use in exercises.

TABLE 8-5 Hexatriene [106–108]

β	Energy γ $(S = 0.25)$	c_1	c_2	c_3	c_4	c_5	c_6
1.80194	1.24230	0.23192	0.41791	0.52112	+	+	+
1.24698	0.95063	0.41791	0.52112	0.23192	−	−	−
0.44504	0.40048	0.52112	0.23192	−0.41791	−	+	+
−0.44504	−0.50075	0.52112	−0.23192	−0.41791	+	+	−
−1.24698	−1.81180	0.41791	−0.52112	0.23192	+	−	+
−1.80194	−3.27915	0.23192	−0.41791	0.52112	−	+	−

The excitation energy for the first transition is seen to be 0.901γ, well below the 1.266γ of butadiene.

Mulliken [99] worked out in detail the case of octatetraene (four double bonds) and β-carotene (eleven double bonds).

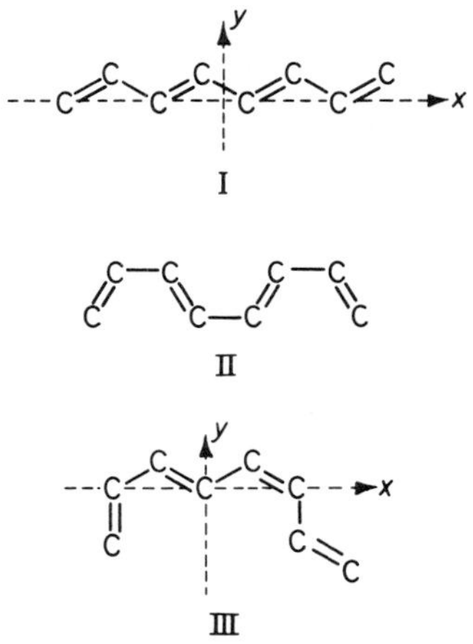

Fig. 8-3

For all these molecules several stereoisomers can be imagined. Three of them are given in Fig. 8–3 for octatetraene. Isomer I is "all *trans*" similar to *trans*-butadiene. II and III are partly *cis* but the "all *cis*" form seems to be impossible because of the repulsion between the hydrogens. Naturally, the computed intensities are highly dependent upon the shape of the molecule. For I $Q^2 = 9.40$ for the $V_1 \leftarrow N$ transition; for III it is 5.63. This transition is allowed with y or x but the latter is highly favored.

One obtains

$$Q_y^2 = 0.24 \quad \text{and} \quad Q_x^2 = 9.16 \quad \text{for I}$$

and

$$Q_y^2 = 0.17 \quad \text{and} \quad Q_x^2 = 5.46 \quad \text{for III}$$

In this way the $V_1 \leftarrow N$ transition is approximately polarized in the direction of the long (x) axis of the molecule; it is strongest if the molecule has its most extended form (all *trans*). As in the case of butadiene calculated intensities are about four times as high as the observed ones.

The theory interprets well the red shift with increasesing n in the series of the polyenes (1.266γ for butadiene, 0.901γ for hexatriene, 0.699γ for octatetraene), as well as the increase of intensity of the first band which accompanies it.

The all-*trans* form is predominant for most polyenes at room temperature but sometimes *cis* forms do occur. Zechmeister *et al.* [109, 110] studied a number of isomers of carotenoides and used the "*cis*-peaks" to identify the latter. These correspond to transitions allowed for the *cis* but forbidden for the *trans* form.

Calculations for the longer chains would be tedious, but Coulson and Coulson and Moffitt deduced closed formulas from which the energies and the coefficients can be obtained immediately [111, 112].

8-3. BENZENE

Benzene belongs to symmetry point group D_{6h}, having the characters given in Table 8-6.

TABLE 8-6

D_{6h}		E	$2C_6$	$2C_3$	C_2	$3C_2'$	$3C_2''$	i	$2S_3$	$2S_6$	σ_h	$3\sigma_d$	$3\sigma_v$	
Γ_1	A_{1g}	1	1	1	1	1	1	1	1	1	1	1	1	
Γ_2	A_{2g}	1	1	1	1	-1	-1	1	1	1	1	-1	-1	
Γ_3	B_{1g}	1	-1	1	-1	1	-1	1	-1	1	-1	1	-1	
Γ_4	B_{2g}	1	-1	1	-1	-1	1	1	-1	1	-1	-1	1	
Γ_5	E_{1g}	2	1	-1	-2	0	0	2	1	-1	-2	0	0	
Γ_6	E_{2g}	2	-1	-1	2	0	0	2	-1	-1	2	0	0	
Γ_7	A_{1u}	1	1	1	1	1	1	-1	-1	-1	-1	-1	-1	
Γ_8	A_{2u}	1	1	1	1	-1	-1	-1	-1	-1	-1	1	1	T_z
Γ_9	B_{1u}	1	-1	1	-1	1	-1	-1	1	-1	1	-1	1	
Γ_{10}	B_{2u}	1	-1	1	-1	-1	1	-1	1	-1	1	1	-1	
Γ_{11}	E_{1u}	2	1	-1	-2	0	0	-2	-1	1	2	0	0	(T_x, T_y)
Γ_{12}	E_{2u}	2	-1	-1	2	0	0	-2	1	1	-2	0	0	
Γ_{MO}		6	0	0	0	-2	0	0	0	0	-6	0	2	
Γ_{VB}		5	0	2	3	1	3	3	2	0	5	3	1	
Γ_{VB}'		12	0	0	0	0	0	0	0	0	12	0	0	

The group contains 24 elements divided into 12 classes. The coefficient of the symbols in the first row indicates the number of elements belonging to a given class. $C_2, C_3,$ and C_6 are rotations around the main axis, which is perpendicular to the plane of the benzene molecule at its center, by $180°, 120°,$ and $60°,$ respectively.

This axis is at the same time a three- and six-fold rotation-reflection axis (S_3 and S_6). The three C_2' are rotations with respect to the two-fold axes which lie in the molecular plane passing through a pair of para-carbons. The three C_2'' indicate rotations around the two-fold axis which bisect two opposite C—C bonds. σ_h is a reflection in the plane of the molecule, the three σ_v and the three σ_d are reflections at planes perpendicular to σ_h, the former containing an axis passing through two para-carbon atoms and the latter bisecting C—C bonds.

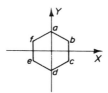

Fig. 8-4

Γ_{MO} is a reducible representation based on the six atomic orbitals. Its characters can be obtained rapidly if it is realized that only those atoms (AO's) contribute to the character of a given operation which remain at their places during that operation. (They could not be on the diagonal otherwise.) Thus E has the character 6; C_2, C_3, and C_6 have character 0; C_2 has -2 (because it goes through two carbons and because we have π orbitals); C_2'' has 0; for the inversion we have 0 since $i = C_2 \times \sigma_h$ where C_2 changes the positions of all the nuclei and σ_h does not restore them; σ_h has. -6; the S_3 and S_6 have 0; the σ_v have 2 and the σ_d zero. Now we can use the relation

$$a_i = \frac{1}{h} \sum_R \chi_i(R)\chi(R)$$

to determine the number of molecular orbitals that belong to any particular irreducible representation. It is important to remember that every member under the sum occurs as many times as there are elements in a given class.

For Γ_1 we obtain

$$a_1 = \frac{1}{24}[1 \times 1 \times 6 - 3 \times 1 \times 2 - 1 \times 1 \times 6 + 3 \times 1 \times 2] = 0$$

Similarly for the other irreducible representations we obtain that

$$a_2 = 0, \qquad a_3 = 0, \qquad a_4 = 1$$
$$a_5 = 1, \qquad a_6 = 0, \qquad a_7 = 0$$
$$a_8 = 1, \qquad a_9 = 0, \qquad a_{10} = 0$$
$$a_{11} = 0, \qquad a_{12} = 1$$

Thus

$$\Gamma_{MO} = \Gamma_4 + \Gamma_5 + \Gamma_8 + \Gamma_{12}$$

or

$$\Gamma_{MO} = B_{2g} + E_{1g} + A_{2u} + E_{2u}$$

where E_{1g} and E_{2u} represent, naturally, a degenerate pair of wave functions each.

If the six π AO are indicated by $a, b, c, d, e,$ and f the secular equation can be written

$$
\begin{aligned}
0 &= C_a y + C_b + C_f \\
0 &= C_a + C_b y + C_c \\
0 &= C_b + C_c y + C_d \\
0 &= C_c + C_d y + C_e \\
0 &= C_d + C_e y + C_f \\
0 &= C_e + C_f y + C_a
\end{aligned}
\qquad (8\text{-}19)
$$

It could be solved by the conventional method. However, symmetry considerations permit us to simplify the problem a great deal.

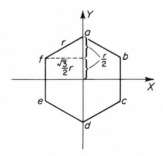

Fig. 8-5

For an A_{2u} state we must have, because of the $+1$ character of the three σ_v and the three σ_d,

$$c_a = c_b = c_c = c_d = c_e = c_f$$

Hence from any of the six equations

$$0 = cy + 2c \qquad \text{and} \qquad y = -2$$

Normalization makes all the coefficients equal to $1/\sqrt{6}$ and

$$\phi_1 = \frac{1}{\sqrt{6}} \left(\psi_a + \psi_b + \psi_c + \psi_d + \psi_e + \psi_f \right) \qquad (8\text{-}20)$$

For a B_{2g} state the character for the σ_v is $+1$ but for the σ_d it is -1. It is easily seen that then the signs of the $c_a, \ldots$ must alternate.

$$c_a = c_c = c_e = -c_b = -c_d = -c_f$$

From any of the equations

$$0 = cy - 2c \qquad \text{and} \qquad y = +2$$

The coefficients are $1/\sqrt{6}$ and $-1/\sqrt{6}$ alternating, and

$$\phi_6 = \frac{1}{\sqrt{6}} (\psi_a - \psi_b + \psi_c - \psi_d + \psi_e - \psi_f) \qquad (8\text{-}21)$$

Instead of using the secular equation, since the orbitals are perfectly determined we can compute the energy directly from

$$E_i = \int \phi_i H \phi_i \, d\tau$$

In the usual approximation, neglecting interactions between non-neighbors and with $\alpha = \int \psi_a H \psi_a \, d\tau$ and $\beta = \int \psi_a H \psi_b \, d\tau$, we obtain, substituting the linear combination of ϕ_1,

$$E_1 = \alpha + 2\beta$$

In the same way ϕ_6 yields

$$E_6 = \alpha - 2\beta$$

(The signs of the y are the opposite of those of 2β. See Sec. 3-2.)

Thus, we have found two of the roots of the secular equation. The remaining wave functions must be degenerate transforming like E_{1g} or E_{2u} and, therefore, we expect to find two double roots corresponding to them. The two degenerate wave functions cannot be found by simple inspection. Group theory, however, offers a general method whereby this type of problem can always be solved.

If for a moment we return to the A_{2u} and B_{1g} states of benzene we see that the related linear combinations could have been obtained the following way. We execute all the operations of the group on one of the AO from which the MO are built, say ψ_a; each time we multiply the result by the character and sum for all operations:

$$\sum_R \chi_i(R) R \psi_a \qquad (8\text{-}22)$$

It will be sufficient to use the characters of group D_6 which correspond to the upper left quarter of the character table of group $D_{6h}(D_6 = D_6 \times i)$. Since this is a π-electronic problem only the representations with -1 for σ_h are acceptable, and using the characters of D_{6h} instead of D_6 would simply multiply everything by two (Table 8-7). For A_{2u}

TABLE 8–7

D_6	E	$2C_6$	$2C_3$	C_2	$3C_2'$	$3C_2''$	
A_1	1	1	1	1	1	1	
A_2	1	1	1	1	−1	−1	T_z
B_1	1	−1	1	−1	1	−1	
B_2	1	−1	1	−1	−1	1	
E_1	2	1	−1	−2	0	0	(T_x, T_y)
E_2	2	−1	−1	2	0	0	
Γ_{MO}	6	0	0	0	−2	0	
Γ_{VB}	5	0	2	3	1	3	
Γ_{VB}'	12	0	0	0	0	0	

$$\phi_1 = \frac{1}{\sqrt{N}}[(1 \times \psi_a) + (1 \times \psi_b) + (1 \times \psi_f) + (1 \times \psi_c) + (1 \times \psi_e)$$
$$+ (1 \times \psi_d) - (-1 \times \psi_a) - (-1 \times \psi_c) - (-1 \times \psi_e)$$
$$- (-1 \times \psi_b) - (-1 \times \psi_d) - (-1 \times \psi_f)]$$
$$= \frac{2}{\sqrt{N}} (\psi_a + \psi_b + \psi_c + \psi_d + \psi_e + \psi_f)$$

or after normalization (neglecting overlap integrals)

$$\phi_1 = \frac{1}{\sqrt{6}} (\psi_a + \psi_b + \psi_c + \psi_d + \psi_e + \psi_f) \qquad (8\text{-}20)$$

Operating on any of the other AO would yield the same result in this case.

The same procedure with the characters of B_{2g} yields

$$\phi_6 = \frac{1}{\sqrt{N}} [(1 \times \psi_a) - (1 \times \psi_b) - (1 \times \psi_f) + (1 \times \psi_c) + (1 \times \psi_e)$$
$$- (1 \times \psi_d) - (-1 \times \psi_a) - (-1 \times \psi_c) - (-1 \times \psi_e)$$
$$- (1 \times \psi_b) - (1 \times \psi_d) - (1 \times \psi_f)]$$
$$= \frac{2}{\sqrt{N}} (\psi_a - \psi_b + \psi_c - \psi_d + \psi_e - \psi_f)$$

and after normalization

$$\phi_6 = \frac{1}{\sqrt{6}} (\psi_a - \psi_b + \psi_c - \psi_d + \psi_e - \psi_f) \qquad (8\text{-}21)$$

The justification for this so-called "basis function generating machine" is somewhat complicated and will not be given here. It may be found in Wigner's *Group Theory* [113, Chap. 12] or in Eyring, Walter, and Kimball's *Quantum Chemistry* [40, p. 188] or in Tinkham's *Atoms, Molecules and Solids* [114, p. 71]. A different and perhaps easier demonstration may be found in Daudel, Lefebvre, and Moser's *Quantum Chemistry* [19, p. 338]. The problem is to construct a function which transforms like a given irreducible representation and the method is quite plausible for one-dimensional representations where the matrices are identical with their own characters. (If, for example, ψ_a transforms into ψ_f under a given operation, then ψ_f must clearly be in the wave function with the adequate sign.) It is of a general validity, however, and may be applied to degenerate representations as well.

Operations belonging to the same class generally transform an AO into different AO and have to be taken separately.

We now evaluate the linear combinations corresponding to E_{1g}.

$$\phi_2' = \frac{1}{\sqrt{N}} [(2 \times \psi_a) + (1 \times \psi_b) + (1 \times \psi_f) - (1 \times \psi_c) - (1 \times \psi_e)$$
$$- (2 \times \psi_d)]$$
$$= \frac{1}{\sqrt{12}} (2\psi_a + \psi_b - \psi_c - 2\psi_d - \psi_e + \psi_f) \qquad (8\text{-}23)$$

If we apply the same procedure to ψ_b we have a different result:

$$\phi_3' = \frac{1}{\sqrt{N}} [(2 \times \psi_b) + (1 \times \psi_c) + (1 \times \psi_a) - (1 \times \psi_d) - (1 \times \psi_f)$$
$$- (2 \times \psi_e)]$$
$$= \frac{1}{\sqrt{12}} (\psi_a + 2\psi_b + \psi_c - \psi_d - 2\psi_e - \psi_f) \qquad (8\text{-}24)$$

Operating upon ψ_c we obtain

$$\frac{1}{\sqrt{12}} (-\psi_a + \psi_b + 2\psi_c + \psi_d - \psi_e - 2\psi_f)$$

but this is immediately seen to be the difference of the two former. Only two linearly independent functions are obtained. The others are either identical with one of them or are linear combinations of them. (The linear independence of the functions must always be ascertained.)

Functions ϕ_2' and ϕ_3' are not orthogonal, but we can use instead of them their sum and difference combinations, obtaining (after renormalization, if necessary)

$$\phi_2 = \frac{1}{\sqrt{4}} (\psi_a + \psi_b - \psi_d - \psi_e) \qquad (8\text{-}25)$$

$$\phi_3 = \frac{1}{\sqrt{12}} (\psi_a - \psi_b - 2\psi_c - \psi_d + \psi_e + 2\psi_f) \qquad (8\text{-}26)$$

The energy can be computed from

$$E_2 = \int \phi_2 H \phi_2 \, d\tau$$

by substituting the corresponding linear combination. Neglecting nonneighbor interactions we obtain

$$E_2 = \alpha + \beta$$

Similarly with ϕ_3 we have

$$E_3 = \int \phi_3 H \phi_3 \, d\tau = \alpha + \beta$$

showing that ϕ_2 and ϕ_3 form a degenerate pair. We still have to compute the E_{2u} orbitals. Proceeding the same way as for E_{1g} we obtain

$$\phi_4' = \frac{1}{\sqrt{12}} (2\psi_a - \psi_b - \psi_c + 2\psi_d - \psi_e - \psi_f)$$

$$\phi_5' = \frac{1}{\sqrt{12}} (-\psi_a + 2\psi_b - \psi_c - \psi_d + 2\psi_e - \psi_f)$$

or, taking the sum and difference for having an orthogonal pair,

$$\phi_4 = \frac{1}{\sqrt{4}} (\psi_a - \psi_b + \psi_d - \psi_e) \qquad (8\text{-}27)$$

$$\phi_5 = \frac{1}{\sqrt{12}} (\psi_a + \psi_b - 2\psi_c + \psi_d + \psi_e - 2\psi_f) \qquad (8\text{-}28)$$

Then,

$$E_4 = \int \phi_4 H \phi_4 \, d\tau = \alpha - \beta$$

and

$$E_5 = \int \phi_5 H \phi_5 \, d\tau = \alpha - \beta$$

Thus we were able to obtain all the π-molecular orbitals by symmetry considerations only, without even solving the secular equation. However, this cannot always be done. The circumstance that made it possible in the case of benzene was that we had only one (or no) orbital for each irreducible representation. In the case of butadiene, for example, which was treated in the last chapter, there are two orbitals having A_2 and B_2 symmetry, and the coefficients are not all determined by symmetry. The method used in this chapter would yield with the characters of A_2 in the case of cis-butadiene, omitting factors of normalization, either

$$\psi_a - \psi_d \qquad \text{or} \qquad \psi_b - \psi_c$$

since ψ_a always transforms into ψ_a or ψ_d, and ψ_b always transforms into ψ_b or ψ_c. The c_b/c_a ratio is, therefore, not determined by symmetry. However, symmetry enables us to say that

$$c_a = -c_d \qquad \text{and} \qquad c_b = -c_c$$

reducing the order of the secular determinant as seen in the last chapter. (See the next chapter for a more elaborate example.)

In the ground state the orbitals of lowest energy, ϕ_1 and (ϕ_2, ϕ_3), will be fully occupied. Now, the total wave function in this approximation is a simple product of the ϕ_i. On the other hand, the wave

function of every closed shell must be totally symmetrical and, therefore, the symmetry of the ground state is A_{1g} with configuration
$(\phi_1)^2(\phi_2, \phi_3)^4$. (See p. 131 and [19], p. 447.)

We now turn our attention to the excited states. The following
may be imagined by exciting only one electron:

$$(\phi_1)^2 (\phi_{2,3})^3 (\phi_{4,5}) \qquad B_{1u}, B_{2u}, E_{1u}$$

$$(\phi_1)^2 (\phi_{2,3})^3 (\phi_6) \qquad E_{2g}$$

$$(\phi_1) (\phi_{2,3})^4 (\phi_{4,5}) \qquad E_{2g}$$

$$(\phi_1) (\phi_{2,3})^4 (\phi_6) \qquad B_{1u}$$

All of them could be either singlet or triplet, since the simple LCAO
method cannot separate states of different multiplicity belonging to
the same configuration.

The transitions of lowest energy can be expected to be

$$N(\phi_1)^2(\phi_{2,3})^4 \rightarrow V(\phi_1)^2(\phi_{2,3})^3(\phi_{4,5})$$

The excited state's symmetry is given by the direct product

$$E_{1g} \times E_{2u} = B_{1u} + B_{2u} + E_{1u}$$

These states would have the same energy only in this approximation. In a higher approximation, where interaction between the electrons is taken into account, they would (and in reality they do)
split, yielding three excited levels of different energy.

It is seen from the character table that z transforms like A_{2u} and
x and y like E_{1u}. Hence we have the following selection rules for
transitions from the ground state:

$$B_{1u} \leftarrow A_{1g} \qquad \text{forbidden}$$

$$B_{2u} \leftarrow A_{1g} \qquad \text{forbidden}$$

$$E_{1u} \leftarrow A_{1g} \qquad \text{allowed with } (x, y)$$

For the latter the direct product corresponding to the transition
moment $A_{1g} \times E_{1u} \times E_{1u}$ gives first a reducible representation with
characters $4, 4, 1, 1, 0, 0$, which by inspection is seen to decompose
into $A_{1g} + A_{2g} + E_{2g}$. It contains the totally symmetrical representation, making the transition an allowed one.

The following pseudo-wave functions can be written [115] for
configuration $(\phi_1)^2 (\phi_{2,3})^3 (\phi_{4,5})$:

$$\Psi_1 = \phi_1(1) \phi_1(2) \phi_2(3) \phi_2(4) \phi_3(5) \phi_4(6)$$

$$\Psi_2 = \phi_1(1) \phi_1(2) \phi_2(3) \phi_3(4) \phi_3(5) \phi_5(6)$$

$$\Psi_3 = \phi_1(1) \phi_1(2) \phi_2(3) \phi_2(4) \phi_3(5) \phi_5(6)$$

$$\Psi_4 = \phi_1(1) \phi_1(2) \phi_2(3) \phi_3(4) \phi_3(5) \phi_4(6)$$

They all have the same energy and may be combined to give wave functions of the right symmetry such as:

$$B_{1u}: \qquad \frac{1}{\sqrt{2}}(\Psi_3 + \Psi_4)$$

$$B_{2u}: \qquad \frac{1}{\sqrt{2}}(\Psi_1 - \Psi_2)$$

$$E_{1u}: \qquad \frac{1}{\sqrt{2}}(\Psi_1 + \Psi_2) \text{ and } \frac{1}{\sqrt{2}}(\Psi_3 - \Psi_4)$$

This may be checked if we take the simply occupied ϕ_i in each case, substitute for them their linear combinations in terms of atomic orbitals, $[(8\text{-}20)\text{-}(8\text{-}28)]$, carry through the multiplications and then apply all the symmetry operations of group D_6. For example, with $\psi_a = a, \psi_b = b, \ldots,$

$$\Psi_1 - \Psi_2 = -4ab + 4af + 4bc - 4cd + 4de - 4ef$$

and it can be easily seen, using the character table, that this expression transforms like B_{2u}.

We are now able to calculate the transition moments for transitions from the ground state to any of the three states having the wave functions above (see Fig. 8-5).

$B_{2u} \leftarrow A_{1g}:$

$$Q_x = \int \Psi_0 (x_1 + x_2) \frac{1}{\sqrt{2}} (\Psi_1 - \Psi_2) \, d\tau$$

$$= \int \phi_3 x \phi_4 \, d\tau - \int \phi_2 x \phi_5 \, d\tau$$

$$\int \phi_3 x \phi_4 \, d\tau = \frac{1}{\sqrt{12}} \frac{1}{\sqrt{4}} \int (a - b - 2c - d + e + 2f) x (a - b + d - e) d\tau$$

$$= \frac{1}{2\sqrt{12}} [x_b - x_e] = \frac{\sqrt{3}}{2\sqrt{12}} r$$

and

$$\int \phi_2 x \phi_5 \, d\tau = \frac{1}{\sqrt{12}} \frac{1}{\sqrt{4}} \int (a + b - d - e) x (a + b - 2c + d + e - 2f) d\tau$$

$$= \frac{1}{2\sqrt{12}} [x_b - x_e] = \frac{\sqrt{3}}{2\sqrt{12}} r$$

Hence

$$Q_x = \int \phi_3 x \phi_4 d\tau - \int \phi_2 x \phi_5 d\tau = 0$$

(Cross terms were neglected.) Similarly for this transition

$$Q_y = 0$$

in accordance with the selection rules.

$B_{1u} \leftarrow A_{1g}:$

$$Q_x = \int \Psi_0 (x_1 + x_2) \frac{1}{\sqrt{2}} (\Psi_3 + \Psi_4) \, d\tau$$

$$= \int \phi_3 x \phi_5 \, d\tau + \int \phi_2 x \phi_4 \, d\tau = \frac{\sqrt{6}}{4} r - \frac{\sqrt{6}}{4} r = 0$$

Also $Q_y = 0$.

$E_{1u} \leftarrow A_{1g}$: This is the allowed transition. We have to compute

$$\int \Psi_0 (q_1 + q_2) \frac{1}{\sqrt{2}} (\Psi_1 + \Psi_2) \, d\tau$$

and

$$\int \Psi_0 (q_1 + q_2) \frac{1}{\sqrt{2}} (\Psi_3 - \Psi_4) \, d\tau, \qquad q = x \text{ or } y$$

Then, adding together the four parts, we obtain that

$$Q^2 = Q_x^2 + Q_y^2 = 2r^2$$

where the degeneracy of the excited state is already taken into account, since both functions were considered. With $r = 1.39 \, \text{Å}$ one obtains

$$D \equiv Q^2 = 3.86 \, \text{Å}^2$$

Taking for the wavelength $\lambda = 1830 \, \text{Å}$ the oscillator strength becomes

$$f = 1.085 \times 10^{-5} \times \frac{1 \times 3.86}{1830 \times 10^{-8}} = 2.29$$

As usual in this approximation this value is three or four times as high as the observed one.

In the absorption spectrum of benzene there are three well-known band systems corresponding to singlet-singlet transitions. The weak band system centered at about $2550 \, \text{Å}$ has been assigned by Sklar [116] to the forbidden $^1B_{2u} \leftarrow {}^1A_{1g}$ transition. According to Sklar its appearance is due to the diminishing of the molecular symmetry by a non-totally symmetrical vibration, now known to be the E_{2g} vibration, which is at $606 \, \text{cm}^{-1}$ in the ground state and at $521 \, \text{cm}^{-1}$ in the excited state. We shall come back to this interesting idea in Chapter 9. The second, stronger band system (about $2050 \, \text{Å}$) may then be assigned to the $^1B_{1u} \leftarrow {}^1A_{1g}$ transition, and the strong band system at about $1830 \, \text{cm}^{-1}$ to the allowed $^1E_{1u} \leftarrow {}^1A_{1g}$ transition, which is polarized in the plane of the benzene molecule.

The assignment of the $^1B_{2u} \leftarrow {}^1A_{1g}$ band may be considered as one of the best-established assignments in molecular spectroscopy. There is still some uncertainty concerning the second band system [117]. However, we are not going to discuss this problem further at this stage (see Chapters 9 and 15).

8-4 THE ACENES

The straight condensed-ring aromatic molecules naphthalene, anthracene, naphthacene, and pentacene have played a very important role in the evolution of our ideas about the π-electronic spectra of conjugated organic molecules. Their treatment by the Hückel approximation of the LCAO MO method is due to Coulson [118]. (However, Davydov had studied naphthalene earlier [119].)

These molecules are coplanar and belong to symmetry pointgroup D_{2h}. All the irreducible representations of this group are one-dimensional (Table 8-8).

TABLE 8-8 The character table of group D_{2h}

$D_{2h} \equiv V_h$	E	$C_2(z)$	$C_2(y)$	$C_2(x)$	i	$\sigma(xy)$	$\sigma(zx)$	$\sigma(yz)$
A_g	1	1	1	1	1	1	1	1
B_{1g}	1	1	-1	-1	1	1	-1	-1
B_{2g}	1	-1	1	-1	1	-1	1	-1
B_{3g}	1	-1	-1	1	1	-1	-1	1
A_u	1	1	1	1	-1	-1	-1	-1
$B_{1u, z}$	1	1	-1	-1	-1	-1	1	1
$B_{2u, y}$	1	-1	1	-1	-1	1	-1	1
$B_{3u, x}$	1	-1	-1	1	-1	1	1	-1
Γ	10	0	-2	0	0	-10	0	2

We shall work out the problem related to the naphthalene molecule. (Fig. 8-6). The z axis is perpendicular to the plane of the molecule.

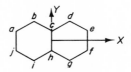

Fig. 8-6

The characters of the reducible representation (Γ) corresponding to the ten π-atomic orbitals are obtained when we execute the related symmetry operations and count the carbon atoms, which remain at their places. Each such atom contributes -1 if the π-AO is upside down after the operation, $+1$ otherwise.

We first use the rule

$$a_i = \frac{1}{h} \sum \chi(R)\chi_i(R)$$

to find the number of MO belonging to each irreducible representation ($h = 8$). The result is

$$\Gamma = 2B_{2g} + 3B_{3g} + 2A_u + 3B_{1u} \tag{8-29}$$

Knowing this, we can simplify the secular equation. It is, in the usual Hückel approximation

$$
\begin{aligned}
0 &= c_a y + c_b + c_j \\
0 &= c_b y + c_a + c_c \\
0 &= c_c y + c_b + c_d + c_h \\
0 &= c_d y + c_c + c_e \\
0 &= c_e y + c_d + c_f \\
0 &= c_f y + c_e + c_g \\
0 &= c_g y + c_f + c_h \\
0 &= c_h y + c_g + c_i + c_c \\
0 &= c_i y + c_h + c_j \\
0 &= c_j y + c_i + c_a
\end{aligned}
\tag{8-30}
$$

The general basis forming method described on p. 199 gives for B_{2g}, operating on ψ_a and taking into account the antisymmetry of the π-AO with respect to the plane of the molecule

$$\frac{1}{\sqrt{N}} (\psi_a - \psi_f - \psi_e + \psi_j)$$

or

$$c_a = c_j = -c_e = -c_f \tag{8-31}$$

Operating on ψ_b yields

$$\frac{1}{\sqrt{N}} (\psi_b - \psi_d - \psi_g + \psi_i)$$

or

$$c_b = c_i = -c_d = -c_g \tag{8-32}$$

and operating on ψ_c yields

$$\frac{1}{\sqrt{N}} (\psi_c - \psi_h - \psi_c + \psi_h - \psi_h + \psi_c + \psi_h - \psi_c)$$

i.e.,

$$c_c = c_h = 0 \tag{8-33}$$

This latter result is due to the antisymmetry with respect to $\sigma(yz)$, which passes through c and h and requires that c_c and c_h change sign and at the same time remain unchanged. The ratio c_a/c_b is not determined by symmetry since ψ_a and ψ_b never transform into each other, and this is so for any two coefficients that do not belong to the same set [(8-31) or (8-32)].

The use of relations (8-31) through (8-33) reduces the secular equation to a system of only two equations with two unkowns:

$$0 = c_a y + c_b + c_a, \qquad 0 = c_b y + c_a \tag{8-34}$$

or

$$0 = y + \frac{c_b}{c_a} + 1, \qquad 0 = \frac{c_b}{c_a} y + 1$$

Hence

$$\frac{c_b}{c_a} = -(y + 1)$$

and

$$0 = -y^2 - y + 1, \qquad 0 = y^2 + y - 1$$

The roots of this equation are -1.6180 and $+0.6180$. These roots are familiar from the treatment of butadiene and appear because $c_c = c_h = 0$ actually reduces the naphthalene molecule to two butadienes. The coefficients are easily obtained for each of these roots from the reduced secular equation and the condition of normalization, which is

$$4c_a^2 + 4c_b^2 + 2c_c^2 = 1$$

(But $c_c = 0$ for B_{2g} symmetry.)

By similar procedures B_{3g} and B_{1u} each yield one system of three equations and A_u one system of two equations.

Actually it is not necessary to use here the full power of group theory; it is sufficient to look at the characters of $\sigma(zx)$ and $\sigma(yz)$, the two symmetry planes perpendicular to the plane of the molecule. Anyway, we have four cases:

1. B_{1u} $[\sigma(zx): +1; \sigma(yz): +1]$

$$c_a = c_e = c_f = c_j$$
$$c_b = c_d = c_g = c_i$$
$$c_c = c_h$$

2. B_{2g} $[\sigma(zx): +1; \sigma(yz): -1]$

$$c_a = c_j = -c_e = -c_f$$
$$c_b = c_i = -c_d = -c_g$$
$$c_c = c_h = 0$$

3. B_{3g} $[\sigma(zx): -1; \sigma(yz): +1]$

$$c_a = -c_j = c_e = -c_f$$
$$c_b = -c_i = c_d \overset{+}{=} -c_g$$
$$c_c = -c_h$$

4. A_u $[\sigma(zx): -1; \sigma(yz): -1]$

$$c_a = -c_e = c_f = -c_j$$
$$c_b = -c_d = c_g = -c_i$$
$$c_c = -c_h = 0$$

Thus instead of solving a system of ten equations, we have to solve two systems of three and two systems of two equations. This is a great simplification. Table 8-9 summarizes the results. The signs

TABLE 8-9

Energy		ϕ_i	Symmetry	c_a	c_b	c_c
β	$\gamma\ (S = 0.25)$					
2.30278	1.46144	ϕ_1	$B_{1u}(P_1)$	0.23070	0.30055	0.46140
1.61803	1.15203	ϕ_2	$B_{2g}(Q_1)$	0.42533	0.26287	0
1.30278	0.98271	ϕ_3	$B_{3g}(R_1)$	0.17352	0.39958	0.34705
1.00000	0.80000	ϕ_4	$B_{1u}(P_2)$	0.40825	0	-0.40825
0.61803	0.53532	ϕ_5	$A_u(S_1)$	0.26286	0.42533	0
-0.61803	-0.73097	ϕ_6	$B_{2g}(Q_2)$	0.26286	-0.42533	0
-1.00000	-1.33333	ϕ_7	$B_{3g}(R_2)$	0.40825	0	-0.40825
-1.30278	-1.93203	ϕ_8	$B_{1u}(P_3)$	0.17352	-0.39958	0.34705
-1.61803	-2.71713	ϕ_9	$A_u(S_2)$	0.42533	-0.26287	0
-2.30278	-5.42718	ϕ_{10}	$B_{3g}(R_3)$	0.23070	-0.30055	0.46140

of the other coefficients may be derived from the relations given on p. 208. In the "symmetry" column the P, Q, R, S notation was introduced by Coulson for the sake of simplification. Figure 8-7,

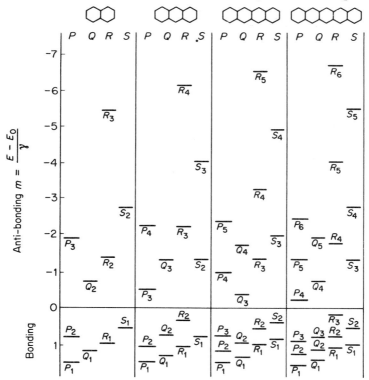

Fig. 8-7

taken from Coulson's paper [118], gives the energies of the orbitals for naphthalene, anthracene, naphthacene, and pentacene in γ units using the same symbols.[1]

In order to obtain the selection rules we need the direct products of representations corresponding to pairs of orbitals. They are easily derived from the table of characters (Table 8–10).

TABLE 8–10

		P B_{1u}	Q B_{2g}	R B_{3g}	S A_u
P	B_{1u}	A_g	B_{3u}	B_{2u}	B_{1g}
Q	B_{2g}	B_{3u}	A_g	B_{1g}	B_{2u}
R	B_{3g}	B_{2u}	B_{1g}	A_g	B_{3u}
S	A_u	B_{1g}	B_{2u}	B_{3u}	A_g

Doubly filled orbitals again give A_g. Hence the symmetry of the ground state is A_g. The first excited state is obtained by a transition from ϕ_5 to ϕ_6 This gives $A_u \times B_{2g} = B_{2u}$. Thus, the first transition is $B_{2u} \leftarrow A_g$. The direct product $A_g \times B_{2u} = B_{2u}$ gives y polarization. According to this result the first transition would be polarized according to the *short* axis of the naphthalene molecule. This is contrary to experiment. Only naphthalene shows this discrepancy, however. Similar calculation as above gives $B_{2u} \leftarrow A_g$ for the first band of anthracene, naphthacene, and pentacene with y polarization as well, in agreement with experiment. The simple Hückel approximation of the LCAO MO method is not able to interpret the reversal of the order of the two lowest-frequency band systems, which is the phenomenon encountered here. It will be discussed in Chapters 14 and 15.

Table 8–11, taken from Coulson, gives LCAO data for the first five transitions of naphthalene.

TABLE 8–11

	Description		Excitation energy	Polarization
$V_1 \leftarrow N$	$\phi_6 \leftarrow \phi_5;$	$B_{2u} \leftarrow A_g$	1.267γ	y
$V_2 \leftarrow N$	$\phi_6 \leftarrow \phi_4;$	$B_{3u} \leftarrow A_g$	1.532γ	x
$V_3 \leftarrow N$	$\phi_6 \leftarrow \phi_3;$	$B_{1g} \leftarrow A_g$	1.715γ	forbidden
$V_4 \leftarrow N$	$\phi_7 \leftarrow \phi_5;$	$B_{3u} \leftarrow A_g$	1.868γ	x
$V_5 \leftarrow N$	$\phi_6 \leftarrow \phi_2;$	$A_g \leftarrow A_g$	1.884γ	forbidden

The first excitation energy for anthracene is 0.836γ, the second one 1.261γ.

In view of the approximate character of the method one should

[1] Fig. 8–7 is reproduced with the permission of The Institute of Physics and The Physical Society of London.

not try to push comparisons too far. It can be said, however, that the results interpret very well the pronounced shift of the first bands toward longer waves when the number of benzene rings increases in the acene series.

To fit the first band of anthracene (about 26,000 cm^{-1} or 3900 Å), γ should be about 3.8 ev or 31,000 cm^{-1}. The shift is about 4500 cm^{-1} from anthracene to naphthacene and 3500 cm^{-1} from naphthacene to pentacene (or about 1000 Å in each case). We should not forget, however, that the LCAO method really gives the mean between singlet and triplet states of the same symmetry and, therefore, γ actually has a lower value. The assignment of the bands in the spectra of the acenes will be treated in more detail in Chapters 14 and 15.

The calculation of the transition moments is quite similar to that in the case of butadiene.

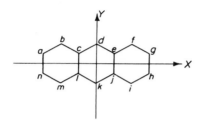

Fig. 8-8

We shall compute the transition moment for the first band of anthracene rather than for a band of naphthalene, since for the former the theory predicts the right polarization ($\phi_8 \leftarrow \phi_7$; $B_{2u} \leftarrow A_g$). (See Fig. 8-8.) Taking only three decimals we have [120]

$$\phi_7 = 0.220\psi_a + 0.311\psi_b - 0.091\psi_c - 0.440\psi_d - 0.091\psi_e$$
$$+ 0.311\psi_f + 0.220\psi_g - 0.220\psi_h - 0.311\psi_i + 0.091\psi_j$$
$$+ 0.440\psi_k + 0.091\psi_l - 0.311\psi_m - 0.220\psi_n$$
$$\phi_8 = 0.220\psi_a - 0.311\psi_b - 0.091\psi_c + 0.440\psi_d - 0.091\psi_e$$
$$- 0.311\psi_f + 0.220\psi_g + 0.220\psi_h - 0.311\psi_i - 0.091\psi_j$$
$$+ 0.440\psi_k - 0.091\psi_l - 0.311\psi_m + 0.220\psi_n$$

$$Q(V_1 \leftarrow N) = 2^{1/2} \int \psi_N y \psi_V \, d\tau = 2^{1/2} \int \phi_7 y \phi_8 \, d\tau$$
$$= 2^{1/2}[0.220^2 (y_a + y_g - y_h - y_n)$$
$$+ 0.311^2 (-y_b - y_f + y_i + y_m)$$
$$+ 0.091^2 (y_c + y_e - y_j - y_l) + 0.440^2 (-y_d + y_k)]$$

Using

$$y_a = y_g = -y_h = -y_n$$
$$y_b = y_f = -y_i = -y_m$$

$$y_c = y_e = -y_j = -y_l$$
$$y_d = -y_k$$

we have

$$Q(V_1 \leftarrow N) = 2^{1/2}[4 \times 0.220^2 y_a - 4 \times 0.311^2 y_b + 4 \times 0.091^2 y_c$$
$$- 2 \times 0.440^2 y_d]$$
$$= 2^{1/2}[0.194 y_a - 0.387 y_b + 0.032 y_c - 0.387 y_d] \qquad (8\text{-}35)$$

However, $y_a = y_c$ and $y_b = y_d$; hence, using $y_a = 0.70 \text{ Å}$ and $y_b = 1.40 \text{ Å}$, we obtain that

$$Q(V_1 \leftarrow N) = 2^{1/2}[0.226 \times 0.7 - 0.774 \times 1.4] = 1.310$$

and $D = 1.716 \text{ Å}^2$. With $\omega = 26{,}000 \text{ cm}^{-1}$,

$$f = 1.085 \times 10^{-5} \times 26{,}000 \times 1.716 = 0.48$$

The observed value is 0.09 [121]. Again we see that this method gives oscillator strengths much higher than experiment.

We mention for the benefit of the reader who would like to work out other examples that the energy levels for a great number of conjugated molecules are found in the book of A. and B. Pullman [28] and that the energies and coefficients of many of them are found in the dictionary published by Coulson and Daudel [29].

8-5 HETEROATOMIC MOLECULES IN THE SIMPLE MOLECULAR ORBITAL METHOD

So far we have treated only pure hydrocarbons. This treatment was characterized by the fact that the Coulomb integrals of all the carbons were taken as equal. This is actually an approximation, since the environment of different carbon atoms may be different. It a carbon atom is replaced by another atom it is inevitable that we assign to that atom a Coulomb integral different from that of a carbon atom.

After Hückel [122], Wheland and Pauling were the first to do this in a work on benzene derivatives [123]. They used $\alpha = 2\beta$ for nitrogen, and this value was later used by Coulson and Longuet-Higgins [124]. However, the resulting charge distribution leads to too-high values of the dipole moments for many molecules. The right choice of this parameter constitutes a difficult problem. Obviously, it varies from one molecule to the other even for the same heteroatom. One might try to find approximate values, however, for a given atom.

Mulliken [125, 126] suggested putting Coulomb integrals proportional to the electronegativities, and this approach was used by many people.

Electronegativity is a semiquantitative concept introduced by

Pauling [127]. It was linked to bond energies and the ionic character of bonds and was meant to represent the tendency of an atom to attract electrons. Later Mulliken [35] gave a more quantitative sense to this concept. According to him, the average of the first ionization potential, I_A, and the electron affinity, E_A, of an atom may be regarded as a measure of the electron-attracting power of the neutral atom and, therefore, of its electronegativity.

$$x_A = \tfrac{1}{2}(I_A + E_A)$$

where both I_A and E_A are to be taken with the positive sign and in the appropriate valence state. Then, Pauling's electronegativities are about equal to

$$x_A = \frac{I_A + E_A}{125}$$

if I_A and E_A are expressed in kcal/mole [32, p. 97]. Pauling gave a table of electronegativities for most of the elements of the periodic table. This was improved by Haissinsky [33], Bellugue and Daudel [34], and Gordy and Thomas [128]. Table 8–12 gives some values of x_A for the most commonly occurring elements [34].

TABLE 8–12

Atom	Valence	x_A
H	I	2.00
B	III	1.85
C	IV	2.50
N	III	3.15
O	II	3.60
F	I	4.15
Na	I	0.50
Mg	II	0.90
Al	III	1.25
Si	IV	1.65
P	III	1.85
S	II	2.45
Cl	I	3.10
Br	I	2.85
I	I	2.45

If $x_A > x_C$, A is a stronger attractor of electrons than carbon. The following relation between differences in electronegativities and differences in Coulomb integrals is reasonable to assume:

$$\alpha_A - \alpha_C = M(x_A - x_C)\beta_{CC} \qquad (8\text{-}36)$$

Laforgue [129] gave reasons to believe that M is approximately equal to 1.

In spite of all the good reasons that can be given, electronegativity is better considered as an empirical quantity. For more insight Pauling's *Nature of the Chemical Bond* [32, p. 97], Mulliken's paper [35, p. 198], Streitwieser's book [130, chap. 5], and a review by Pritchard and Skinner [131] are recommended.

Thus,

$$\alpha_A - \alpha_C = (x_A - x_C)\beta_{CC} \qquad (8\text{-}37)$$

where the supplement to the Coulomb integral of heteroatom A is expressed in units of the resonance integral β_{CC}. This choice of unit makes the calculations easier.

For a nitrogen atom, for example,

$$\alpha_N - \alpha_C = (3.15 - 2.50)\beta_{CC} = 0.65\,\beta_{CC}$$

Fig. 8-9

Taking as an example the pyridine molecule (Fig. 8–9), the diagonal term of the nitrogen atom in the secular equation is

$$\alpha + 0.65\beta$$

Then we have

$$
\begin{aligned}
0 &= c_a(\alpha + 0.65\beta - E) + c_b\beta + c_f\beta \\
0 &= c_b(\alpha - E) + c_a\beta + c_c\beta \\
0 &= c_c(\alpha - E) + c_b\beta + c_d\beta \\
0 &= c_d(\alpha - E) + c_c\beta + c_e\beta \\
0 &= c_e(\alpha - E) + c_d\beta + c_f\beta \\
0 &= c_f(\alpha - E) + c_e\beta + c_a\beta
\end{aligned}
\qquad (8\text{-}38)
$$

This may be simplified by dividing throughout by β and writing, as usual,

$$y = \frac{\alpha - E}{\beta}$$

We thus obtain

$$
\begin{aligned}
0 &= c_a(y + 0.65) + c_b + c_f \\
0 &= c_b y + c_a + c_c \\
0 &= c_c y + c_b + c_d \\
0 &= c_d y + c_c + c_e \\
0 &= c_e y + c_d + c_f \\
0 &= c_f y + c_e + c_a
\end{aligned}
\qquad (8\text{-}39)
$$

Group theory is of little help here since the D_{6h} symmetry of benzene was diminished to C_{2v} by replacing one carbon atom by a nitrogen atom. However, the plane passing through N and C_d perpendicular to the plane of the molecule makes it possible to reduce the secular equation, which is of the sixth degree, to one of the fourth and one of the second degree.

As a result of the greater electronegativity of nitrogen, positive charges appear at the *ortho* and *para* carbons.

We might take into account the increased electronegativity of the carbons linked to the nitrogen (or even of the *para* carbon, as Laforgue suggested [129]) by assigning them an increment to the Coulomb integral, which is usually taken as one-tenth or one-eighth of the supplement assigned to the nitrogen atom itself. (Some authors [132, 133] give significantly greater values to these parameters.)

As stated above, it is not easy to assign exact values to these parameters, and only qualitative conclusions should be drawn from results obtained by this procedure. It is reasonable, however, to look for "trends"; that is, vary these parameters gradually and observe the changes in charge distribution.

A series of such diagrams of charges and bond orders for pyridine type compounds (one carbon replaced by a heteroatom having one π electron, like carbon) were computed by Sandorfy [134] (Fig. 8-10).

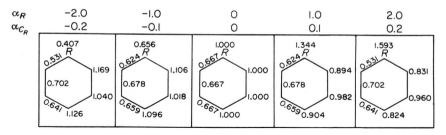

Fig. 8-10

Substituents can be treated similarly. Substituted benzene derivatives were treated extensively by Wheland and Pauling in 1935 [123].

The diagrams in Fig. 8-11 taken from a paper by the author refer to molecules like aniline or phenol where the substituent contributes two π electrons to the conjugated system [135]. It is often said that the substituent influences the benzene ring in two ways, by the mesomeric[2] and the inductive effect. The mesomeric effect is simply due to the addition of two more π electrons to the system, which alter the electronic charge distribution in the whole molecule. Its extent depends, in this approximation, on the difference between the Coulomb integral, α_R, associated with the substituent, R, and α_C for

---

[2] Also called the resonance effect or the conjugative effect.

a carbon atom. The closer α_R is to α_C the easier it is for the electrons of the substituent to penetrate into the benzene ring.

The inductive effect is due to the fact that the presence of the substituent modifies the potential field in the benzene ring, with the main result that the carbon linked to the substituent will have a somewhat modified electronegativity. This may be represented by a supplement to its Coulomb integral, generally taken as a fraction of α_R.

It is interesting to see what the charge distribution would be if only the mesomeric or only the inductive effect were present. The purely mesomeric effect is obtained if we give an extra Coulomb

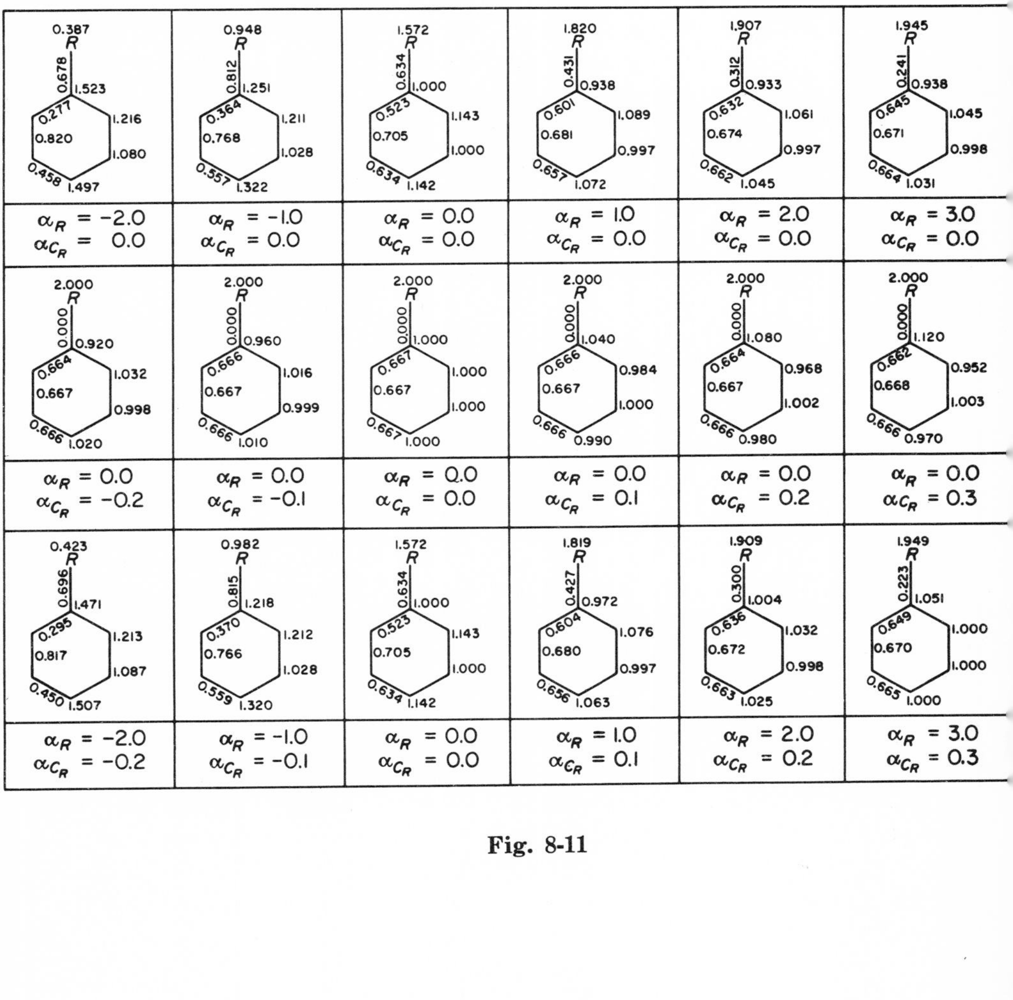

Row 1 (each hexagon, R substituent at top):

Position	Cell 1	Cell 2	Cell 3	Cell 4	Cell 5	Cell 6
top (R)	0.387	0.948	1.572	1.820	1.907	1.945
upper bond	0.678	0.812	0.634	0.431	0.312	0.241
top-right	1.523	1.251	1.000	0.938	0.933	0.938
upper-left	0.277	0.364	0.523	0.601	0.632	0.645
right	1.216	1.211	1.143	1.089	1.061	1.045
left	0.820	0.768	0.705	0.681	0.674	0.671
lower-right	1.080	1.028	1.000	0.997	0.997	0.998
lower-left	0.458	0.557	0.634	0.657	0.662	0.664
bottom	1.497	1.322	1.142	1.072	1.045	1.031
α_R	-2.0	-1.0	0.0	1.0	2.0	3.0
α_{C_R}	0.0	0.0	0.0	0.0	0.0	0.0

Row 2:

Position	Cell 1	Cell 2	Cell 3	Cell 4	Cell 5	Cell 6
top (R)	2.000	2.000	2.000	2.000	2.000	2.000
upper bond	0.000	0.000	0.000	0.000	0.000	0.000
top-right	0.920	0.960	1.000	1.040	1.080	1.120
upper-left	0.664	0.666	0.667	0.666	0.664	0.662
right	1.032	1.016	1.000	0.984	0.968	0.952
left	0.667	0.667	0.667	0.667	0.667	0.668
lower-right	0.998	0.999	1.000	1.000	1.002	1.003
lower-left	0.666	0.666	0.667	0.666	0.666	0.666
bottom	1.020	1.010	1.000	0.990	0.980	0.970
α_R	0.0	0.0	0.0	0.0	0.0	0.0
α_{C_R}	-0.2	-0.1	0.0	0.1	0.2	0.3

Row 3:

Position	Cell 1	Cell 2	Cell 3	Cell 4	Cell 5	Cell 6
top (R)	0.423	0.982	1.572	1.819	1.909	1.949
upper bond	0.696	0.815	0.634	0.427	0.300	0.223
top-right	1.471	1.218	1.000	0.972	1.004	1.051
upper-left	0.295	0.370	0.523	0.604	0.636	0.649
right	1.213	1.212	1.143	1.076	1.032	1.000
left	0.817	0.766	0.705	0.680	0.672	0.670
lower-right	1.087	1.028	1.000	0.997	0.998	1.000
lower-left	0.450	0.559	0.634	0.656	0.663	0.665
bottom	1.507	1.320	1.142	1.063	1.025	1.000
α_R	-2.0	-1.0	0.0	1.0	2.0	3.0
α_{C_R}	-0.2	-0.1	0.0	0.1	0.2	0.3

Fig. 8-11

integral to the substituent but none to the carbon linked to the substituent. The inductive effect is obtained if we put the resonance integral, β_{CR}, between these two atoms equal to zero and give an extra Coulomb integral to the carbon atom linked to the substituent.

Again we have given $(\alpha_R - \alpha_C)$ the successive values of -2, -1, 0, 1, 2, and 3 in β units and to $(\alpha_{c_R} - \alpha_C)$ one-tenth of these. If $(\alpha_R - \alpha_C) > 0$ the substituent is more electronegative than carbon.

In Fig. 8-11 the first row represents the pure mesomeric effect, the second row the pure inductive effect, and the third row the combined effect (charges and bond orders).

The diagrams of the third row for $\alpha_R = 1$, 2, and 3 are probably fairly close to aniline, phenol, and fluorobenzene. $\alpha_R = -1$ would be close to phenylphosphine.

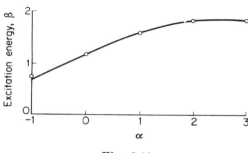

Fig. 8-12

The wavelengths in angstroms computed for the electronic transition of lowest frequency are given in Fig. 8-12 as functions of the parameter α_R. There is a systematic shift towards higher frequencies with increasing α_R and this is in agreement with experiment (see Chapter 15).

Similar work was carried out on the fulvene molecule by Cartier and Sandorfy [136].

Account should be taken of the fact that $\beta_{CC} \neq \beta_{CR}$. This could be done by the method of Lennard-Jones [97], who defined β as half of the difference between the energy of the respective double bond and single bond. ($E_{\pi,\,total} = 2\beta$ for ethylene). Bond energies or bond distances could be used as a basis for the β. Some refinements are described by Daudel, Lefebvre, and Moser [19, p. 70] and the subject will not be pursued here.

It is more difficult to introduce heteroatoms when overlap integrals are not neglected. We shall treat the example of the hypothetical radical

$$\diagup C{=}N{-}$$

with two π electrons.

The secular determinant for this system is

$$\begin{vmatrix} \alpha - E & \beta - ES \\ \beta - ES & \alpha - E + \delta\gamma \end{vmatrix} = 0 \qquad (8\text{-}40)$$

where the supplement δ is now expressed in units of $\gamma = \beta - S\alpha$.

In general we may write

$$\beta - ES = \beta - S\alpha + S(\alpha - E) = \gamma + S(\alpha - E) \qquad (8\text{-}41)$$

Then, if we divide throughout by γ we obtain

$$\begin{vmatrix} \dfrac{\alpha - E}{\gamma} & 1 + S\dfrac{\alpha - E}{\gamma} \\ 1 + S\dfrac{\alpha - E}{\gamma} & \dfrac{\alpha - E}{\gamma} + \delta \end{vmatrix} = 0 \qquad (8\text{-}42)$$

We can now apply a substitution proposed by Wheland [137]

$$\frac{\alpha - E}{\beta - S\alpha} = \frac{\alpha - E}{\gamma} = \frac{y}{1 - Sy} \qquad (8\text{-}43)$$

With this the determinant becomes

$$\begin{vmatrix} \dfrac{y}{1 - Sy} & 1 + S\dfrac{y}{1 - Sy} \\ 1 + S\dfrac{y}{1 - Sy} & \dfrac{y}{1 - Sy} + \delta \end{vmatrix} = 0 \qquad (8\text{-}44)$$

We multiply everywhere by $(1 - Sy)$ and obtain

$$\begin{vmatrix} y & 1 \\ 1 & y + \delta(1 - Sy) \end{vmatrix} = 0 \qquad (8\text{-}45)$$

For example, if $\delta = 1\gamma$ and $S = 0.25$ we have

$$\begin{vmatrix} y & 1 \\ 1 & (y + 1 - 0.25y) \end{vmatrix} = \begin{vmatrix} y & 1 \\ 1 & (\tfrac{3}{4}y + 1) \end{vmatrix}$$
$$= 3y^2 + 4y - 4 = 0$$

Hence, $y_1 = -2$ and $y_2 = \tfrac{2}{3}$; and from (8-43),

$$E_1 = \alpha_C + 1.33\gamma \qquad \text{and} \qquad E_2 = \alpha_C - 0.80\gamma$$

The condition of normalization is:

$$c_1^2 + c_2^2 + 2c_1c_2S = 1$$

For $y_1 = -2$, $c_1 = 0.4083$ and $c_2 = 0.8165$
For $y_2 = \tfrac{2}{3}$, $c_1 = 0.9486$ and $c_2 = -0.6324$

Had we neglected overlap integrals with $\alpha_N = 1\beta$ we would have obtained

$$\begin{vmatrix} y & 1 \\ 1 & y + 1 \end{vmatrix} = y^2 + y - 1 = 0$$

whence $y_1 = -1.618$ and $y_2 = 0.618$. With $c_1^2 + c_2^2 = 1$ we obtain for $y_1 = -1.618$

$$c_1 = 0.5257 \quad \text{and} \quad c_2 = 0.8506$$

and for $y_2 = 0.618$

$$c_1 = 0.8506 \quad \text{and} \quad c_2 = -0.5257$$

The diagram of charges, q_r, is, in the ground state, taking overlap into account,

$$\begin{array}{cc} 0.333 & 1.333 \\ C\!\!-\!\!\!\overset{0.333}{\rule{1.2cm}{0.4pt}}\!\!-\!\!N \end{array}$$

where the quantity we put on the bond is $2 \times 2c_1\, c_2 S$ (see McWeeny [93]).

Neglecting overlap,

$$\begin{array}{cc} 0.553 & 1.447 \\ C\!\!\rule{1.2cm}{0.4pt}\!\!N \end{array}$$

The energies are, respectively,

$$E_1 = \alpha_C + 1.33\gamma, \qquad E_1 = \alpha_C + 1.618\beta$$
$$E_2 = \alpha_C - 0.80\gamma, \qquad E_2 = \alpha_C - 0.618\beta$$

The excitation energies are 2.13γ or 2.236β, respectively.

It is seen that Wheland's formula (p. 188) does not apply here. This is connected to the fact that not all the α are equal. We have to include overlap from the beginning.

All these refinements are needed if we want to apply the simple LCAO MO method to the case of saturated hydrocarbons and their derivatives. Sandorfy and Daudel [138] proposed as a first approximation a method in which only the sp^3 hybrids linking together two carbons were considered. Sandorfy [139] tried a somewhat better approximation where the tetrahedral hybrids, which bind together two carbon atoms, were taken individually but the hybrids linked to the hydrogens were considered as forming a CH group orbital with the $1s$ orbital of the respective hydrogen atom. Yoshizumi [140] improved this method, which has been applied with success to the computation of ionization potentials by Fukui, Kato, and Yonezawa [141, 142]. Further work in this direction has been done by the latter authors and Morokuma [143, 144, 145] and by Del Re [146]. (see also p. 315.)

8-6 PERTURBATION METHODS USED IN CONNECTION WITH THE SIMPLE MOLECULAR ORBITAL METHOD

Perturbation methods have been used in connection with the simple LCAO MO method to treat the effect of a heteroatom or a substituent on a hydrocarbon. As an example we shall again turn to the butadiene molecule, where we shall replace carbon a by a heteroatom which is assumed to be more electronegative than carbon (Fig. 8-13). The LCAO MO method will be used in the Hückel approximation. We suppose that the essential effect of the heteroatom consists in modifying the Coulomb integral of atom a from α to $\alpha_a = \alpha + \alpha'$. For the value of α' we shall take $\alpha' = 1\beta$.

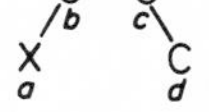

Fig. 8-13

According to first-order perturbation theory the perturbation modifies the energy of a state n by an amount equal to

$$E'_n = H'_n$$

We remember that in this approximation the total wave function of a given state is a simple product of the molecular orbitals taken once or twice, depending on the number of electrons they contain, and the energy is the sum of the energies of the same molecular orbitals. (see Fig. 8-14.)

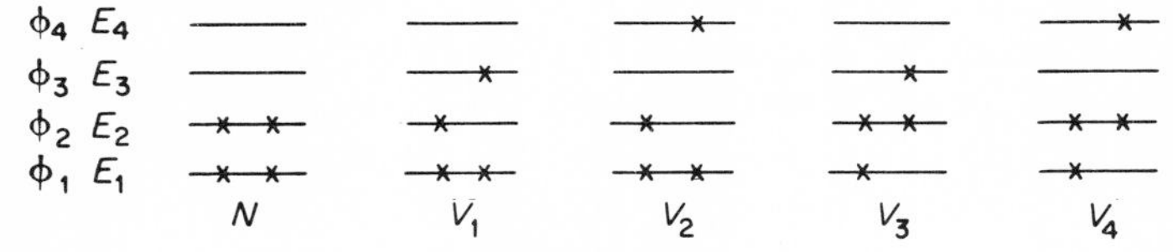

Fig. 8-14

Therefore if we compute the effect of the perturbation on the energies of the individual MO, the sum of these will represent the modification of the energy of the state as a whole. In order to compute transition energies it is sufficient, however, to do this for those MO between which the transition takes place.

Thus, for the first transition $V_1 \leftarrow N$ we need the perturbation on E_2 and E_3. For E_2 we have

$$\int \phi_2 H' \phi_2 \, d\tau = \int (0.6015\psi_a + 0.3717\psi_b - 0.3717\psi_c - 0.6015\psi_d)$$
$$\times H'(0.6015\psi_a + 0.3717\psi_b - 0.3717\psi_c - 0.6015\psi_d) \, d\tau \qquad (8\text{-}46)$$

Since we supposed that the perturbation affects only the Coulomb integral of atom a, all the terms will be taken equal to zero except

$$0.6015^2 \int \psi_a H' \psi_a \, d\tau = 0.362\alpha'$$

For E_3 we have similarly

$$\int \phi_3 H' \phi_3 \, d\tau = \int (0.6015\psi_a - 0.3717\psi_b - 0.3717\psi_c + 0.6015\psi_d)$$
$$\times H'(0.6015\psi_a - 0.3717\psi_b - 0.3717\psi_c + 0.6015\psi_d) \, d\tau \qquad (8\text{-}47)$$

which gives also $0.362\alpha'$ since the coefficients of ψ_a are the same in ϕ_2 and ϕ_3.

Hence, to the first order, the excitation energy of transition $V_1 \leftarrow N$ is not affected by the perturbation.

This is generally so for alternant hydrocarbons. In these there are no odd-numbered rings. Bathochromic or hypsochromic shifts are obtained, however, for nonalternant hydrocarbons (like fulvene or azulene) depending on the sign of α', i.e., whether the electronegativity of the heteroatom is greater or smaller than that of carbon, and on the sign of

$$c_{i,V_1}^2 - c_{i,N}^2$$

if the heteroatom replaces carbon i. The latter depends in turn on the position of i in the molecule. A very interesting study along these lines was made by Coulson [147].

In the present case, if we are interested in the transition energy of $V_2 \leftarrow N$, for example, we need the perturbation on E_4. This is

$$\int (0.3717\psi_a - 0.6015\psi_b + 0.6015\psi_c - 0.3717\psi_d)$$
$$\times H'(0.3717\psi_a - 0.6015\psi_b + 0.6015\psi_c - 0.3717\psi_d) \, d\tau \qquad (8\text{-}48)$$

It yields

$$0.3717^2 \int \psi_a H' \psi_a \, d\tau = 0.138\alpha'$$

Since α', like α, is a negative quantity, E_2 will be stabilized by $0.362\alpha'$ but E_4 only by $0.138\alpha'$, with the result that the two states will be further apart than in butadiene and the related band will undergo a hypsochromic shift.

A second-order perturbation calculation would be cumbersome and hardly justified in view of the rather approximate character of the LCAO MO method itself. This would require the use of formula (2-54) or the solution of secular determinant (2-41) with the appropriate approximations (see Sec. 2-4). The calculations are greatly facilitated by the symmetry of the unperturbed molecule since integrals like

$$H_{kn} \equiv \int \psi_k^0 H \psi_n^0 \, d\tau$$

vanish unless the two wave functions belong to the same irreducible representation. Concerning this type of calculation we refer the reader to Sec. 10–3.

Perturbation methods combined with the LCAO MO method were used by Coulson [148], Dewar [149], Dewar and Longuet-Higgins [150], Matsen [151], and Matsen, Robertson, and Chuoke [152, 153], among others.

9

The Calculation of Spectral
Quantities by
The Valence-Bond Method

9-1 BUTADIENE

Butadiene served as our sample for valence-bond calculations in Chapter 4. Taking into account the π electrons only and excluding polar structures, *cis*-butadiene can be represented by a canonical set consisting of only two structures (Fig. 9-1). As we have seen, the

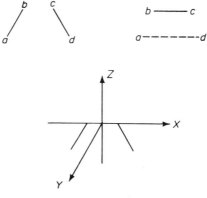

Fig. 9-1
223

wave function is of the form

$$\Psi = s_P \Psi_P + s_Q \Psi_Q \tag{9-1}$$

Two states are obtained; for the ground state

$$\begin{aligned} E_0 &= Q + 1.732\alpha \\ X_0 &= \sqrt{0.667}\,\Psi_P + \sqrt{0.089}\Psi_Q \\ &= 0.817\,\Psi_P + 0.299\,\Psi_Q \end{aligned} \tag{9-2}$$

and for the excited state

$$\begin{aligned} E_1 &\doteq Q - 1.732\alpha \\ X_1 &= \sqrt{0.667}\,\Psi_P - \sqrt{1.244}\,\Psi_Q \\ &= 0.817\Psi_P - 1.116\Psi_Q \end{aligned} \tag{9-3}$$

taking the d_{PQ} into account. To obtain the energy of excitation we need the numerical value of the exchange integral, α. We are going to adopt $\alpha = -1.92$ ev, the value derived by Sklar [116] from thermochemical data in the case of benzene. His reasoning will be outlined in the next section (p. 236). Then

$$\begin{aligned} E_1 - E_0 &= 3.464\alpha = -3.464 \times 1.92 \,\text{ev} = 6.651 \,\text{ev} \\ &\cong 53,650 \,\text{cm}^{-1} \cong 1865 \,\text{Å} \end{aligned}$$

This is a higher frequency than that of the first observed band of butadiene ($46,080 \,\text{cm}^{-1}$ or $2170 \,\text{Å}$). The method gives only one singlet-singlet transition, which is an obvious shortcoming. Inclusion of polar structures would improve the situation (Sec. 9-4).

In order to see whether this transition is allowed or forbidden we have to make use of the character table of group C_{2v}. σ_v is the plane of the molecule.

TABLE 9-1

		E	C_2	$\sigma_v(zx)$	$\sigma_v'(yz)$
Γ_1	A_1, z	1	1	1	1
Γ_2	A_2	1	1	-1	-1
Γ_3	B_1, x	1	-1	1	-1
Γ_4	B_2, y	1	-1	-1	1
Γ		2	2	2	2

The reducible representation (Γ) is now based on the two structure eigenfunctions, Ψ_P and Ψ_Q, since our molecular wave functions X_0 and X_1 are linear combinations of these. They play the same role as the atomic orbitals in the molecular orbital method. Their transformation properties are rather simple. They transform into themselves under any of the four operations of the group:

$$\begin{array}{c} E, C_2 \\ \sigma_v, \sigma_v' \end{array} \qquad \begin{pmatrix} P \\ Q \end{pmatrix} = \begin{pmatrix} 1 & 0 \\ 0 & 1 \end{pmatrix} \begin{pmatrix} P \\ Q \end{pmatrix}$$

The character of Γ is thus 2 for all operations. We have to add, however, a comment at this point. Although structures P and Q as represented pictorially remain obviously unchanged under any of the four operations, we have to remember that we need the transformation properties of the wave functions Ψ_P and Ψ_Q and not those of the pictures as they appear on the paper. Even though we see that a structure transforms into itself, the structure eigenfunction may change its sign. For other molecules a structure may transform into another structure, but then it does not contribute to the character.

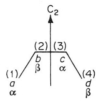

Fig. 9-2

Let us examine more closely the effect of operation C_2 on *cis*-butadiene (Fig. 9–2). The structure eigenfunction Ψ_P is a linear combination of four Slater determinants (Chapter 4, p. 57). The first term in the Slater determinant having the fully alternant spin-array $(\alpha\beta\alpha\beta)$ is transformed as follows:

$$\psi_a(1)\alpha(1)\psi_b(2)\beta(2)\psi_c(3)\alpha(3)\psi_d(4)\alpha(4)$$
$$\xrightarrow{C_2} \psi_d(4)\beta(4)\psi_c(3)\alpha(3)\psi_b(2)\beta(2)\psi_a(1)\alpha(1)$$

This reads: ψ_a with electron (1) having spin α is replaced by ψ_d with electron (4) having spin β, etc. To restore the original order of the spins we have to make two spin exchanges ($e' = 2$) and two electron exchanges ($e'' = 2$). Therefore, the sign of this term does not change under operation C_2. The other terms are equivalent to this one and will behave similarly. The same can be said about the terms in the other Slater determinants. In general, if under a given operation A transforms into B the sign of the transformation is given by

$$A \rightarrow (-1)^{e'+e''}B$$

This has been shown by Craig [154].

Now, for any alternant hydrocarbon there exists a fully alternant spin-array so that no two α or two β become close neighbors for singlet states, and it is easily seen that e' and e'' are always either both even or both odd, hence $(e' + e'')$ is always even and there is no change of sign. This is the case of open-chain polyenes and of aromatic hydrocarbons containing only hexagons.

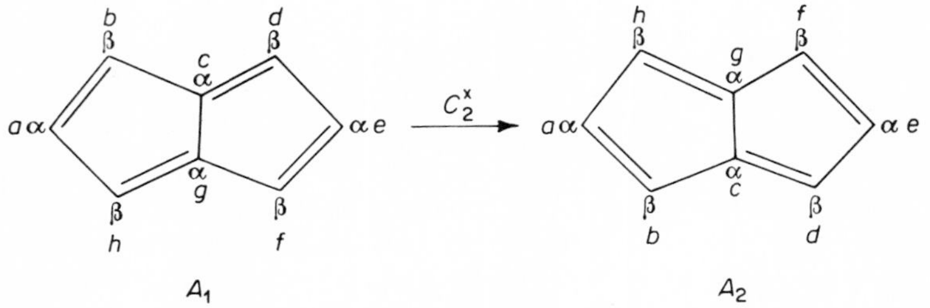

Fig. 9-3

This ceases to be true for nonalternant hydrocarbons such as pentalene, which was treated by Craig and Maccoll [155]. If the x axis is along the long axis of the molecule, under operation C_2^x structure A_1 transforms into A_2 (Fig. 9-3). It is seen that $e' = 3$ and $e'' = 0$ and $A_1 \xrightarrow{C_2^x} -A_2$.

Returning to butadiene we can now use the formula

$$a_i = \frac{1}{h} \sum_R \chi(R) \chi_i(R)$$

It obviously yields 2 for Γ_1 and 0 for the other irreducible representations. Thus, both X_0 and X_1 belong to the totally symmetrical representation (this may be seen by inspection once the wave functions are known) and the transition is allowed, polarized in the z direction.

For *trans*-butadiene the energies and eigenfunctions are the same, if we neglect interactions between noncontiguous AO. Using the character table of group C_{2h} (Table 9-2) and observing that again both structures remain unchanged under any of the operations of the group we again are lead to the conclusion that both eigenfunctions belong to the totally symmetrical representation.

TABLE 9-2

C_{2h}		E	C_2	i	σ_h
Γ_1'	A_g	1	1	1	1
Γ_2'	B_g	1	-1	1	-1
Γ_3'	A_u, z	1	1	-1	-1
Γ_4'	B_u, x, y	1	-1	-1	1

However, in this case no component of the electric vector transforms like Γ_1', and the transition is forbidden.

If we try to compute the transition moment for *cis*-butadiene we have to face a rather disconcerting fact. The integral to compute is

$$\int X_0 \sum_i e_i z_i X_1 \, d\tau$$

$$= \int (0.817 \Psi_P + 0.299 \Psi_Q) \sum_i e_i z_i (0.817 \Psi_P - 1.116 \Psi_Q) \, d\tau$$

$$= 0.667 \int \Psi_P \sum_i e_i z_i \Psi_P \, d\tau - 0.344 \int \Psi_Q \sum_i e_i z_i \Psi_Q \, d\tau$$

$$- 0.668 \int \Psi_P \sum_i e_i z_i \Psi_Q \, d\tau \qquad (9\text{-}4)$$

Ψ_P and Ψ_Q may be written down in terms of the appropriate Slater functions as it was done on p. 57.

$$\Psi_P = \frac{1}{\sqrt{4}} [(\alpha\beta\alpha\beta) - (\alpha\beta\beta\alpha) - (\beta\alpha\alpha\beta) + (\beta\alpha\beta\alpha)]$$

$$\Psi_Q = \frac{1}{\sqrt{4}} [(-\alpha\alpha\beta\beta) + (\beta\alpha\beta\alpha) + (\alpha\beta\alpha\beta) - (\beta\beta\alpha\alpha)]$$

Now, since the operator (the z_i in this case) is monoelectronic, only identical permutations can contribute nonzero terms to (9-4) and there will be as many for each of the three integrals as the two structure eigenfunctions therein contain Slater functions in common. This is four for the two first integrals and two for the last one. It is then seen that

$$0.667 - 0.334 - \frac{0.668}{2} = 0$$

and the transition moment, therefore, vanishes. (This argument disregards the lack of orthogonality of the atomic wave functions, but it is not necessary to do so.)

This is a rather disappointing feature of the valence-bond method. It is connected with the fact that one electron is assigned to each center in every structure eigenfunction and there is absolutely no change in charge distribution from which a transition moment could result. (The effective charge is always zero on all the carbon atoms.) This situation can be improved by the inclusion of polar structures, which will be discussed in Sec. 9-4. The valence-bond method in the homopolar approximation always yields zero transition moment.

Butadiene was studied by Kovner [156] in the valence-bond approximation. He also examined hexatriene and octatetraene. The excitation energies he obtained for the first transition are compared to the experimental values as follows:

	exp	calc
Butadiene	2170 Å	1900 Å
Hexatriene	2600	2570
Octatetraene	3020	3117

9-2 BENZENE

The first full-scale attack on benzene by the valence-bond method was made by Sklar in 1937 [116] and it constituted a major event in the history of molecular spectroscopy. We are going to treat this problem in some detail.

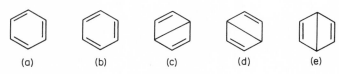

(a)   (b)   (c)   (d)   (e)

Fig. 9-4

Excluding polar structures, benzene can be represented by the five well-known structures shown in Fig. 9-4. The matrix components needed for setting up the secular equation may be obtained by Pauling's island method, which was described in Chapter 4,

$$H_{PQ} \equiv \int \Psi_P H \Psi_Q \, d\tau = \frac{1}{2^{n-i}} [Q + (f_1 - \tfrac{1}{2} f_2)\alpha] \tag{9-5}$$

f_3 in (4-85) being always zero for alternate hydrocarbons. Figure 9-5 gives the table of superpositions. [50] In this case $n = 3$, i is the number of islands, f_1 is the number of pairs of close neighbors belonging to the same island and f_2 the number of pairs of close neighbors belonging to different islands.

The secular equation is then

$$
\begin{aligned}
S_{Aj}(H_{AA} - E_j d_{AA}) + S_{Bj}(H_{AB} - E_j d_{AB}) + S_{Cj}(H_{AC} - E_j d_{AC}) \\
+ S_{Dj}(H_{AD} - E_j d_{AD}) + S_{Ej}(H_{AE} - E_j d_{AE}) = 0 \\
S_{Aj}(H_{BA} - E_j d_{BA}) + S_{Bj}(H_{BB} - E_j d_{BB}) + S_{Cj}(H_{BC} - E_j d_{BC}) \\
+ S_{Dj}(H_{BD} - E_j d_{BD}) + S_{Ej}(H_{BE} - E_j d_{BE}) = 0
\end{aligned}
\tag{9-6}
$$

....

Introducing the values of the H_{PQ}, setting the d_{PQ} equal to the coefficient of the respective Coulomb term, dividing everywhere by A, and making the substitution

$$X = \frac{Q - E_j}{A} \tag{9-7}$$

we obtain the following secular determinant:

$$
\begin{vmatrix}
X + \frac{3}{2} & \frac{1}{4}X + \frac{3}{2} & \frac{1}{2}X + \frac{3}{2} & \frac{1}{2}X + \frac{3}{2} & \frac{1}{2}X + \frac{3}{2} \\
\frac{1}{4}X + \frac{3}{2} & X + \frac{3}{2} & \frac{1}{2}X + \frac{3}{2} & \frac{1}{2}X + \frac{3}{2} & \frac{1}{2}X + \frac{3}{2} \\
\frac{1}{2}X + \frac{3}{2} & \frac{1}{2}X + \frac{3}{2} & X & \frac{1}{4}X + \frac{3}{2} & \frac{1}{4}X + \frac{3}{2} \\
\frac{1}{2}X + \frac{3}{2} & \frac{1}{2}X + \frac{3}{2} & \frac{1}{4}X + \frac{3}{2} & X & \frac{1}{4}X + \frac{3}{2} \\
\frac{1}{2}X + \frac{3}{2} & \frac{1}{2}X + \frac{3}{2} & \frac{1}{4}X + \frac{3}{2} & \frac{1}{4}X + \frac{3}{2} & X
\end{vmatrix} = 0 \tag{9-8}
$$

There are various ways of solving such a determinant for X. We could develop it according to minors or eliminate the s_{Pj} successively from the secular equation. In the case of benzene many simplifications would be possible. We prefer, however, to have recourse once again to symmetry considerations.

The character table of group D_{6h} was given in Table 8-5. Γ_{VB} is the reducible representation based on the five homopolar structures A, B, C, D, E.

To obtain its characters all we have to do is to see how the individual structures transform under the operations of group D_{6h}.

For the identity operation all five remain unchanged, so the character is 5. For C_2 (the axis being perpendicular to the plane of the molecule), $A \rightarrow B$, $B \rightarrow A$, $C \rightarrow C$, $D \rightarrow D$, $E \rightarrow E$, so the character is 3, since only those transforming into themselves contribute to the character. The sign of the transformation will always be positive for benzene for reasons given in the preceding section (p. 225). For C_3 we have $A \rightarrow A$, $B \rightarrow B$, $C \rightarrow E$, $D \rightarrow C$, $E \rightarrow D$, so the character is 2 and so forth.

Now we may use the formula

$$a_i = \frac{1}{h} \sum_R \chi(R)\chi_i(R)$$

to compute the number of times a given Γ_i occurs in Γ_{VB}. For Γ_1 we obtain

$$a_1 = \tfrac{1}{24}(1\cdot1\cdot5 + 1\cdot1\cdot3 + 2\cdot1\cdot2 + 2\cdot1\cdot0 + 3\cdot1\cdot1 + 3\cdot1\cdot3$$
$$+ 1\cdot1\cdot3 + 1\cdot1\cdot5 + 2\cdot1\cdot0 + 2\cdot1\cdot2 + 3\cdot1\cdot3 + 3\cdot1\cdot1) = 2$$

For Γ_2 we have

$$a_2 = \tfrac{1}{24}(1\cdot1\cdot5 + 1\cdot1\cdot3 + 2\cdot1\cdot2 + 2\cdot1\cdot0 - 3\cdot1\cdot1 - 3\cdot1\cdot3$$
$$+ 1\cdot1\cdot3 + 1\cdot1\cdot5 + 2\cdot1\cdot0 + 2\cdot1\cdot2 - 3\cdot1\cdot3 - 3\cdot1\cdot1) = 0$$

Similarly

$$a_3 = a_4 = a_6 = a_7 = a_8 = a_9 = a_{11} = a_{12} = 0$$

but $a_5 = a_{10} = 1$. Thus, we have

$$\Gamma = 2\Gamma_1 + \Gamma_{10} + \Gamma_6$$

or

$$\Gamma = 2A_{1g} + B_{2u} + E_{2g}$$

Thus, we have two A_{1g} states, one B_{2u} state, and one degenerate E_{2g} state. The next task is to find the corresponding linear combinations. We shall use the "basis forming machine" described in Chapter 8, p. 199. Forming the products

$$\sum_R \chi_i(R)RA$$

we obtain Table 9-3 (see also Fig. 9-5).

Table 9-3

Starting point		E	C_6	C_6'	C_3	C_3	C_2	$C_2'(ad)$	$C_2'(be)$	$C_2'(cf)$	$C_2''(a,b)$	$C_2''(b,c)$	$C_2''(c,d)$
A_{1g}	A	A	B	B	A	A	B	B	B	B	A	A	A
	C	C	D	E	E	D	C	C	E	D	D	C	E
B_{2u}	A	A	$-B$	$-B$	A	A	$-B$	$-B$	$-B$	$-B$	A	A	A
	C	C	$-D$	$-E$	E	D	$-C$	$-C$	$-E$	$-D$	D	C	E
E_{2g}	A	2A	$-B$	$-B$	$-A$	$-A$	2B	0	0	0	0	0	0
	C	2C	$-D$	$-E$	$-E$	$-D$	2C	0	0	0	0	0	0
	D	2D	$-E$	$-C$	$-C$	$-E$	2D	0	0	0	0	0	0
	E	2E	$-C$	$-D$	$-D$	$-C$	2E	0	0	0	0	0	0

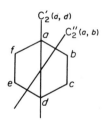

Fig. 9-5

The characters of group D_6 are used instead of D_{6h} since using the latter would merely multiply the results by 2 and this is taken care of by normalization (Table 8–7). Clearly, the Kekulé structures transform between themselves and the Dewar structures among themselves. As can be seen from Table 9–3, for the A_{1g} states, if we apply the operations to structure A we obtain $(1/\sqrt{N})(6\Psi_A + 6\Psi_B)$, giving $s_A = s_B$, and if we apply the operations to structure C we obtain $(1/\sqrt{N})(4\Psi_C + 4\Psi_D + 4\Psi_E)$, giving $s_C = s_D = s_E$. However, the s_A/s_C ratio and the other similar ratios are undetermined. So we go back to the secular equation and introduce there these relations among the coefficients. We find, from the first and third equations, for example,

$$s_A(X + \tfrac{3}{2} + \tfrac{1}{4}X + \tfrac{3}{2}) + 3s_C(\tfrac{1}{2}X + \tfrac{3}{2}) = 0$$
$$2s_A(\tfrac{1}{2}X + \tfrac{3}{2}) + s_C(X + \tfrac{1}{4}X + \tfrac{3}{2} + \tfrac{1}{4}X + \tfrac{3}{2}) = 0$$

After rearrangement we have

$$s_A(\tfrac{5}{4}X + 3) + s_C(\tfrac{3}{2}X + \tfrac{9}{2}) = 0$$
$$s_A(X + 3) + s_C(\tfrac{3}{2}X + 3) = 0 \tag{9-9}$$

Hence, the determinant is

$$\begin{vmatrix} \tfrac{5}{4}X + 3 & \tfrac{3}{2}X + \tfrac{9}{2} \\ X + 3 & \tfrac{3}{2}X + 3 \end{vmatrix} = X^2 - 2X - 12 = 0 \tag{9-10}$$

The roots of this equation are -2.61 and 4.61. Of these, since A is a negative quantity, -2.61 corresponds to the ground energy level, 4.61 to a highly excited state.

Thus so far we have, from $X = (Q - E_j)/A$,

$$A_{1g}: \quad E_0 = Q + 2.61A$$
$$A_{1g}: \quad E_4 = Q - 4.61A$$

The coefficients are obtained from the A_{1g} secular equation (9-9). If we normalize the eigenfunctions according to $2s_A^2 + 3s_C^2 = 1$, in other words if we neglect the d_{PQ} at normalization, we obtain for E_0:

$$s_A^2 = s_B^2 = 0.390 \quad \text{and} \quad s_C^2 = s_D^2 = s_E^2 = 0.073$$

Thus, the two Kekulé structures' total weight in the representation of the molecule in its ground state is 78 per cent and that of the three Dewar structures is 22 per cent. This is a well-known result. For E_4, according to the same procedure, the Kekulé structures still count for 53 per cent, the Dewar structures for 47 per cent. However, since the polar structures would certainly be very important in the excited states, these latter results have little meaning.

Let us now examine the B_{2u} state. According to Table 9-3 the right linear combination is

$$\frac{1}{\sqrt{N}}(\Psi_A - \Psi_B)$$

Applying the basis-forming machine to one of the Dewar structures yields no result. First, we have to normalize the wave function:

$$\frac{1}{N}\int (\Psi_A - \Psi_B)^2\, d\tau = \frac{1}{N}\left[\int \Psi_A^2\, d\tau + \int \Psi_B^2\, d\tau - 2\int \Psi_A\Psi_B\, d\tau\right]$$

$$= \frac{1}{N}\left(1 + 1 - 2 - \frac{1}{4}\right) = \frac{1}{N}\frac{3}{2} = 1$$

Hence, $N = \frac{3}{2}$. (We recall that $\int \Psi_A\Psi_B\, d\tau \equiv d_{AB}$) is taken to be the coefficient of H_{AB}.) (Fig. 9-6). Then the energy can be obtained directly as

$$E_1 = \frac{2}{3}\int (\Psi_A - \Psi_B)H(\Psi_A - \Psi_B)\, d\tau$$

$$= \frac{2}{3}[H_{AA} + H_{BB} - 2H_{AB}]$$

$$= \frac{2}{3}[2(Q + \frac{3}{2}A) - 2(\frac{1}{4}Q + \frac{3}{2}A)]$$

$$= Q$$

For this state $X = 0$ and each of the two Kekulé structures has 50 per cent of the weight and the Dewar structures zero.

There remains the degenerate state, E_{2g}. Starting with structure C we obtain

$$\frac{1}{\sqrt{N}}(2\Psi_C - \Psi_D - \Psi_E)$$

starting with structure D gives

$$\frac{1}{\sqrt{N}}(2\Psi_D - \Psi_C - \Psi_E)$$

and starting with E gives

$$\frac{1}{\sqrt{N}}(2\Psi_E - \Psi_C - \Psi_D)$$

but only two of them are linearly independent. Starting with A does not give any meaningful result (Table 9-3).

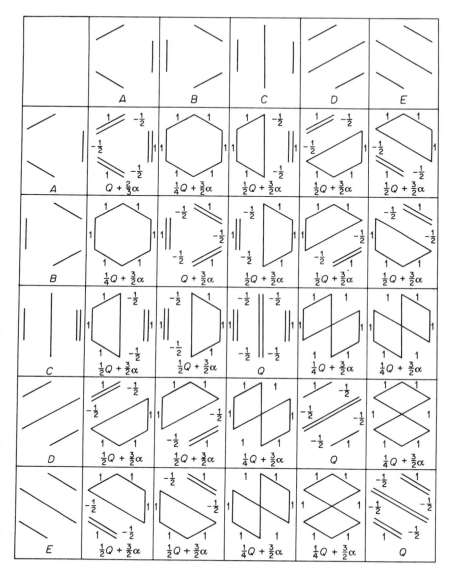

Fig. 9-6

First, we have to make sure that the two wave functions we choose are mutually orthogonal. They are not, but their sum and difference are:

$$\frac{1}{\sqrt{N}}(\Psi_C - \Psi_D), \qquad \frac{1}{\sqrt{N}}(\Psi_C + \Psi_D - 2\Psi_E)$$

In fact

$$d_{CC} - d_{CD} + d_{CD} - d_{DD} - 2d_{CE} + 2d_{DE} = 1 - \tfrac{1}{4} + \tfrac{1}{4} - 1 - \tfrac{1}{2} + \tfrac{1}{2} = 0$$

After normalization either of these functions gives the energy of the E_{2g} state. We obtain

$$\sqrt{\tfrac{2}{3}}\,(\Psi_C - \Psi_D) \qquad \text{and} \qquad \sqrt{\tfrac{2}{9}}\,(\Psi_C + \Psi_D - 2\Psi_E)$$

hence

$$
\begin{aligned}
E_{2,3} &= \tfrac{2}{3} \int (\Psi_C - \Psi_D) H (\Psi_C - \Psi_D) \, d\tau \\
&= \tfrac{2}{3}[H_{CC} - 2H_{CD} + H_{DD}] \\
&= \tfrac{2}{3}[Q - 2(\tfrac{1}{4}Q + \tfrac{3}{2}A) + Q] \\
&= \tfrac{2}{3}[\tfrac{3}{2}Q - 3A] = Q - 2A
\end{aligned}
$$

or

$$
\begin{aligned}
E_{2,3} &= \tfrac{2}{9} \int (\Psi_C + \Psi_D - 2\Psi_E) H (\Psi_C + \Psi_D - 2\Psi_E) \, d\tau \\
&= \tfrac{2}{9}[H_{CC} + H_{DD} - 4H_{EE} + 2H_{CD} - 4H_{CE} - 4H_{DE}] \\
&= \tfrac{2}{9}[Q + Q + 4Q + 2(\tfrac{1}{4}Q + \tfrac{3}{2}A) - 4(\tfrac{1}{4}Q + \tfrac{3}{2}A) - 4(\tfrac{1}{4}Q + \tfrac{3}{2}A)] \\
&= \tfrac{2}{9}[\tfrac{9}{2}Q - 9A] = Q - 2A
\end{aligned}
$$

The Kekulé structures do not contribute to this state. The coefficients of the others depend on the pair of functions chosen.

Finally, we have the following scheme of energies:

$$
\begin{aligned}
A_{1g}: \qquad & E_4 = Q - 4.61A \\
E_{2g}: \qquad & E_{2,3} = Q - 2A \\
B_{2u}: \qquad & E_1 = Q \\
A_{1g}: \qquad & E_0 = Q + 2.61A
\end{aligned}
$$

If we look at the character table of group D_{6h} we see that z belongs to A_{2u} and x and y to E_{1u}. Consequently *all* the transitions from the ground state are forbidden—a rather surprising result! ($A_{1g} \times E_{1u} \times E_{2g} = B_{1u} + B_{2u} + E_{1u}$ does not contain A_{1g}.)

The spectrum of benzene contains a weak band system centered at about $2550\,\text{Å}$ with $\epsilon_{max} \cong 220$. There follows a stronger band system at about $2050\,\text{Å}$ ($\epsilon_{max} \cong 7000$) and a very strong one at about $1830\,\text{Å}$ ($\epsilon_{max} \cong 47{,}000$).

Concerning the first band, we know today that Sklar's assignment of $^1B_{2u} \leftarrow {}^1A_{1g}$ was correct and it *is* a forbidden band. Sklar made the very successful suggestion that its appearance is due to a non-totally symmetrical vibration of benzene, which diminishes the symmetry of the molecule. (This possibility had been suggested previously by Herzberg and Teller [157].) This vibration is an E_{2g} vibration, which is at $606\,\text{cm}^{-1}$ in the ground state and $521\,\text{cm}^{-1}$ in the excited state. If Ψ_e is the electronic and Ψ_v the vibrational wave function, then the transition moment for an electronic-vibrational band is approximately [157]

$$\int \Psi_e' \Psi_v' M \Psi_e'' \Psi_v'' \, d\tau$$

and, since any vibration with vibrational quantum number $v = 0$ is totally symmetrical, the transition is of type

$$A_{1g} \times A_{1g} \rightarrow B_{2u} \times E_{2g} = E_{1u}$$

Since x and y transform according to E_{1u} we have

$$A_{1g} \times E_{1u} \times E_{1u} = A_{1g} + A_{2g} + E_{2g}$$

which contains A_{1g}; therefore, the transition is allowed.

The strongest bands in the vibrational fine structure of the 2550 Å benzene band system can be accounted for in the following way: the $0 \leftarrow 0$ band is missing; then there is a band at 521 cm^{-1} from the missing frequency corresponding to the purely electronic transition, followed by a series of bands corresponding to $n = 1, 2, \ldots$ quanta of a totally symmetrical vibration of 923 cm^{-1} of the excited state. In the ground state its frequency is at 992 cm^{-1} (in the infrared spectrum). In brief:

$$0 \leftarrow 0 + 521 \text{ cm}^{-1} + n(923) \text{ cm}^{-1}$$

In normal heptane solution the $0 \leftarrow 0$ band is inferred to be at 2690 Å (37,175 cm^{-1}). It appears in substituted benzene derivatives such as toluene where the six-fold symmetry is perturbed. (At the same time the whole spectrum is slightly shifted toward longer waves.)

The second band system of benzene is probably the forbidden transition $^1B_{1u} \leftarrow {}^1A_{1g}$ (but see [158, 159]) and the third one is $^1E_{1u} \leftarrow {}^1A_{1g}$. This latter transition is allowed since, as we have seen,

$$A_{1g} \times E_{1u} \times E_{1u} = A_{1g} + A_{2g} + E_{2g}$$

Thus, all these π electronic transitions are polarized in the plane of the molecule.

Sklar found an extremely weak band at 3400 Å, which he assigned to the first singlet-triplet transition of benzene. Craig, Hollas and King [160] have shown recently, however, that some of its intensity was due to impurities and that its intensity, is not higher than $f = 7 \times 10^{-12}$.

In the homopolar scheme that we have presented here there is no E_{1u} state. Since the obvious principal shortcoming of the method is the exclusion of polar structures, Sklar made an effort to include at least some of them. These were the twelve structures obtained by rotating and reflecting the structure shown in Fig. 9-7. The reducible

Fig. 9-7

representation $\Gamma_{VB'}$ corresponds to these twelve structures (see the character table on p. 196).

We shall not describe the details of this procedure, however, since a more refined method due to Craig [161] will be described in Sec. 9-4. We mention only that Sklar thereby found a polar state at $Q - 1.51A$ of E_{1u} symmetry to which he assigned the strong, allowed band of benzene at 1830 Å [116] (see Chapter 15).

For computing excitation energies we need the numerical value of the exchange integral A. The one most often used in the literature was the $A = -1.92$ ev obtained by Sklar through the following argument.

According to Kistiakowsky, Ruhoff, Smith, and Vaughan [162] the hydrogenation of benzene (C_6H_6) and 1, 3-cyclohexadiene (C_6H_8) to cyclohexane (C_6H_{12}) is accompanied by the following thermal changes:

$$C_6H_6 + 3H_2 \rightarrow C_6H_{12} + 49.802 \pm 0.150 \quad \text{kcal/mole}$$

$$C_6H_8 + 2H_2 \rightarrow C_6H_{12} + 55.367 \pm 0.100 \quad \text{kcal/mole}$$

$$C_6H_6 + H_2 \rightarrow C_6H_8 - 5.565 \pm 0.250 \quad \text{kcal/mole}$$

where the third row is obtained by subtracting the second from the first one. Let us suppose that B is equal to the hypothetical energy evolved on hydrogenation of a double bond in a molecule, which can be represented by only one structure. "Now the heat of hydrogenation of benzene to cyclohexadiene is smaller than B by an amount equal to the difference between the resonance energies of benzene and cyclohexadiene. Similarly the heat of hydrogenation of benzene to cyclohexane is smaller than $3B$ by the resonance energy of benzene, since cyclohexane has no resonance energy."

The energy of the ground state of benzene is $Q + 2.60A$. If benzene could be represented by only one Kekulé structure it would be $Q + 1.50A$. So the resonance energy of benzene is $1.10A$.

By a similar calculation one finds for cyclohexadiene (cf. butadiene) $Q + 1.732A$ and $Q + 1.50A$, yielding as resonance energy $0.232A$. Hence,

$$1.10 + 3B = 49.802 \text{ kcal/mole}$$

and

$$(1.10 - 0.232)A + B = -5570 \text{ kcal/mole}$$

giving

$$B = 32.872 \text{ kcal/mole}$$

and

$$A = -1.92 \text{ ev}$$

(With more exact values it would be -1.90, but -1.92 has been used by most authors.) Sklar's argument was afterwards criticized by Simonetta [163]. (see Section 9–4.)

9-3 NAPHTHALENE

Taking into account nonpolar structures only, the canonical set of naphthalene contains 42 structures that can be obtained from the formula

$$\frac{N!}{\left(\frac{N}{2}\right)!\left(\frac{N}{2}+1\right)!}$$

with $N = 10$, the number of π electrons (see p. 79).

In order to obtain the characters of the reducible representation based on the 42 structures we ought to examine the transformation properties of each one. This is somewhat tedious, although not prohibitive in this case. For larger molecules, however, the situation becomes rapidly worse. Anthracene, for example, has 429 structures. Therefore, a different method of finding the characters of the reducible representation will now be given. It is based on a theorem of Frobenius [164] related to symmetric groups (the elements of the symmetric group of order $n!$ are all the permutations of n numbers [113, Chap. 13]); and it was applied to naphthalene by German [165, 166]. We shall restrict ourselves to showing how to proceed.

The axes and numbering shown in Fig. 9–8 will be adopted. The z axis is perpendicular to the plane of the molecule. The character table of group D_{2h} is given in Table 9–4.

TABLE 9–4

		E	$C_2(z)$	$C_2(y)$	$C_2(x)$	i	$\sigma(xy)$	$\sigma(zx)$	$\sigma(yz)$
	Γ_1	A_g	1	1	1	1	1	1	1	1
	Γ_2	B_{1g}	1	1	-1	-1	1	1	-1	-1
	Γ_3	B_{2g}	1	-1	1	-1	1	-1	1	-1
	Γ_4	B_{3g}	1	-1	-1	1	1	-1	-1	1
	Γ_5	A_u	1	1	1	1	-1	-1	-1	-1
z	Γ_6	B_{1u}	1	1	-1	-1	-1	-1	1	1
y	Γ_7	B_{2u}	1	-1	1	-1	-1	1	-1	1
x	Γ_8	B_{3u}	1	-1	-1	1	-1	1	1	-1
	Γ		42	10	2	10	10	42	10	2

Let us consider a rotation around the y axis. Then 3 and 8 remain at their places but 1, 2, 9, and 10 will be replaced by 5, 4, 7, and 6 in the same order and vice versa. Now we take the following permutation:

$$\begin{pmatrix} 1 & 2 & 3 & 4 & 5 & 6 & 7 & 8 & 9 & 10 \\ 5 & 4 & 3 & 2 & 1 & 10 & 9 & 8 & 7 & 6 \end{pmatrix}$$

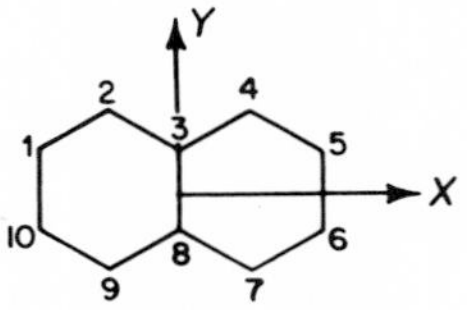

Fig. 9-8

This reads: 1 is replaced by 5, 2 by 4, 3 by 3, and so on. This permutation is equivalent to operation $C_2(y)$. Another way of writing the same permutation is

$$(3)\ (8)\ (1,5)\ (2,4)\ (6,10)\ (7,9)$$

which means that under the given permutation 3 and 8 remain at their places, 1 and 5 take each other's place, and so forth. In this way we can express the original permutation by a set of permutations of lower degrees, called *cycles*. Any permutation may be expressed as a product of two or more cycles, none of which has a letter in common. The numbers in a cycle may be rearranged, provided their proper sequence is retained. In the above example we have two cycles of degree 1 and four cycles of degree 2: $1^2 2^4$. Such an expression is called a *partition*.

In the same way we can find the permutation and the partition corresponding to any symmetry operation. The symmetric group of permutations will be isomorphic with the symmetry point group. Each partition corresponds to a class, but because of the possible permutations *within* the cycles the number of elements in a class will generally be higher for the symmetric group than for the symmetry point group.

The characters of a reducible representation of the symmetric group may be found according to Frobenius [164] from the following generating function:

$$(-1)^{N-\rho}(1-x)\prod_{i=1}^{\rho}(1+x^{\alpha_i})$$

In this expression N is the degree of the permutation, ρ is the number of cycles in it, and α_i is the number of elements in every cycle; the character will be the coefficient of x^k if $k = (N/2) - S$ with S being the quantum number of the total spin projection. Thus, for singlet states we have $k = N/2$. The characters of this reducible representation will be the same as those of the one based on the complete canonical set of valence-bond structures.

In our example, $N = 10$, $\rho = 2 + 4 = 6$, $k = \frac{1}{2}N = 5$, so that we have

$$(-1)^{10-6}(1-x)(1+x)^2(1+x^2)^4$$

where the coefficient of x^5 is equal to 2.

We may proceed the same way for any other operation of the group. For example, for the identity operation, E, we have

$$\begin{pmatrix} 1 & 2 & 3 & 4 & 5 & 6 & 7 & 8 & 9 & 10 \\ 1 & 2 & 3 & 4 & 5 & 6 & 7 & 8 & 9 & 10 \end{pmatrix}$$

$$= (1)\ (2)\ (3)\ (4)\ (5)\ (6)\ (7)\ (8)\ (9)\ (10)$$

with partition 1^{10}. In $(-1)^{10-10}(1-x)(1+x)^{10}$ the coefficient of x^5 is equal to 42, which is just the number of the canonical structures of naphthalene. The complete set of these characters is the Γ line of the character table on p. 237.

This method was applied by German [165, 166] to naphthalene and higher aromatic hydrocarbons.

Now that we have obtained the characters of the reducible representation, the formula

$$a_i = \frac{1}{h} \sum_R \chi(R)\chi_i(R)$$

gives us the number of states belonging to each of the irreducible representations of group D_{2h}. The result is

$$\Gamma = 16\Gamma_1 + 10\Gamma_2 + 6\Gamma_7 + 10\Gamma_8$$
$$= 16A_g + 10B_{1g} + 6B_{2u} + 10B_{3u}$$

Since x, y, and z transform like Γ_8, Γ_7, and Γ_6, respectively, transitions from Γ_1 to Γ_2 are forbidden but those from Γ_1 to Γ_7 are allowed, polarized according to the y (short) axis, and those from Γ_1 to Γ_8 are allowed, polarized according to the x (long) axis.

The next problem is to compute the energy levels. Group theory enabled us to reduce the original secular equation of degree 42 to one of 16, two of 10 and one of 6. It does not help in solving the four reduced secular equations.

The matrix elements may be easily found by use of the island method (see Chapter 4 and Sec. 9-2). Pauling and Wheland [167] were the first to carry out the calculations on naphthalene, and Sherman [168] greatly improved the approximation. In 1947 Blumenfeld [169] took up the problem again, taking into account all 42 nonpolar singlet structures.

The ground state is among the roots of the 16th-degree determinant and so is the first excited state. The energies of the first five states, as given by Blumenfeld, are the following:

$$E_4 = Q - 0.44A \qquad {}^1B_{2u}$$
$$E_3 = Q + 0.01A \qquad {}^1B_{1g}$$
$$E_2 = Q + 1.81A \qquad {}^1B_{3u}$$

$$E_1 = Q + 2.01A \qquad {}^1A_{1g}$$

$$E_0 = Q + 4.04A \qquad {}^1A_{1g}$$

According to this the first transition would be ${}^1A_{1g} \leftarrow {}^1A_{1g}$ and it would be forbidden. The first band system of naphthalene is actually weak, and attempts have been made [170] to interpret it as a forbidden band system. Today, however, we know that this is not so. A band may be weak though it is allowed, and this is the case of the first band system of naphthalene, which is located around 3100 A with $\epsilon_{max} \cong 220$. It is allowed and long-axis polarized. The second band system at about 2750 A with $\epsilon_{max} \cong 5000$ is short-axis polarized, and the third, very strong band system (about 2200 A and $\epsilon_{max} \cong 100,000$) is again long-axis polarized [171]. We shall have the opportunity to discuss the spectrum of naphthalene again (Chapters 14, 15).

Among the 42 homopolar, singlet structures of naphthalene three are of Kekulé type, 16 of them contain one, 19 contain two, and 4 contain three long bonds. Blumenfeld computed their weights for his three states of lowest energy; They are shown in Fig. 9-9, and will certainly interest the chemist. The numbers preceding the weight of

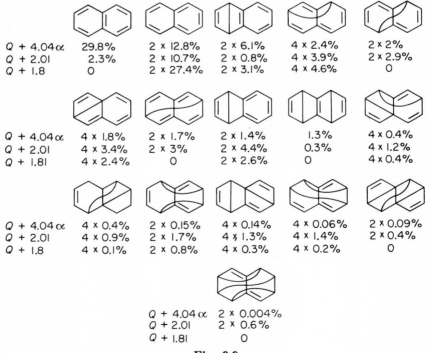

$Q + 4.04\alpha$ 29.8%	2 × 12.8%	2 × 6.1%	4 × 2.4%	2 × 2%
$Q + 2.01$ 2.3%	2 × 10.7%	2 × 0.8%	4 × 3.9%	2 × 2.9%
$Q + 1.8$ 0	2 × 27.4%	2 × 3.1%	4 × 4.6%	0

$Q + 4.04\alpha$ 4 × 1.8%	2 × 1.7%	2 × 1.4%	1.3%	4 × 0.4%
$Q + 2.01$ 4 × 3.4%	2 × 3%	2 × 4.4%	0.3%	4 × 1.2%
$Q + 1.81$ 4 × 2.4%	0	2 × 2.6%	0	4 × 0.4%

$Q + 4.04\alpha$ 4 × 0.4%	2 × 0.15%	4 × 0.14%	4 × 0.06%	2 × 0.09%
$Q + 2.01$ 4 × 0.9%	2 × 1.7%	4 × 1.3%	4 × 1.4%	2 × 0.4%
$Q + 1.8$ 4 × 0.1%	2 × 0.8%	4 × 0.3%	4 × 0.2%	0

$Q + 4.04\alpha$ 2 × 0.004%
$Q + 2.01$ 2 × 0.6%
$Q + 1.81$ 0

Fig. 9-9

the individual structures are the number of equivalent structures which go over to one another by symmetry operations.

Finally we give the decomposition of the reducible representation into its irreducible components for anthracene and naphthacene [169].

Anthracene: $\Gamma = 126\Gamma_1 + 106\Gamma_2 + 91\Gamma_7 + 106\Gamma_8$

Naphthacene: $\Gamma = 1282\Gamma_1 + 1212\Gamma_2 + 1156\Gamma_7 + 1212\Gamma_8$

9-4 INCLUSION OF POLAR STRUCTURES IN THE VALENCE-BOND METHOD

Representing molecules with a set of homopolar structures only may lead to fairly satisfactory results for the ground state, but the approximation will be certainly much worse for excited states in which polar (ionic) structures must play a considerably greater role. The impossiblity of obtaining nonzero transition moments is another grave shortcoming of the homopolar approximation.

As we have seen, Sklar made an attempt to include polar structures in his calculations on benzene. In 1950 Craig published a series of papers that went a long way toward the solution of the problem of including polar structures in the valence-bond method. We are going to present here an outline of his work [172, 173, 174].

Craig worked out in detail the examples of cyclobutadiene and benzene in the π electronic approximation. We prefer to apply his method to butadiene, our standard sample.

The first problem is the choice of a representative set of structures. The two well-known homopolar structures of butadiene are, omitting the σ bonds,

$$A:\ \overline{a\ \ b}\ \ \overline{c\ \ d} \qquad B:\ \overset{\frown}{a\ \ \overline{b\ \ c}\ \ d}$$

to which we add the following polar structures:

$$C:\ \overset{+}{a}\ \overset{-}{b}\ \overline{c\ \ d} \qquad D:\ \overset{-}{a}\ \overset{\frown}{\overset{+}{b}\ \ c}\ d$$

$$E:\ \overline{a\ \ b}\ \overset{+}{c}\ \overset{-}{d} \qquad F:\ \overline{a\ \ b}\ \overset{-}{c}\ \overset{+}{d}$$

The $(+)$ sign means that there are no π electrons on the corresponding atom, and the $(-)$ sign means that there are two of them. Naturally, there cannot be more than two electrons in a $2p_z$ orbital because of the Pauli principle.

Other possible structures are the following:

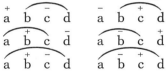

All these contain one pair of ionized atoms. Others contain two of them:

$$
\begin{array}{cccc}
\overset{+}{a} & \overset{-}{b} & \overset{+}{c} & \overset{-}{d} \\
\end{array}
\qquad
\begin{array}{cccc}
\overset{-}{a} & \overset{+}{b} & \overset{-}{c} & \overset{+}{d} \\
\end{array}
$$

$$
\begin{array}{cccc}
\overset{+}{a} & \overset{+}{b} & \overset{-}{c} & \overset{-}{d} \\
\end{array}
\qquad
\begin{array}{cccc}
\overset{-}{a} & \overset{-}{b} & \overset{+}{c} & \overset{+}{d} \\
\end{array}
$$

$$
\begin{array}{cccc}
\overset{+}{a} & \overset{-}{b} & \overset{-}{c} & \overset{+}{d} \\
\end{array}
\qquad
\begin{array}{cccc}
\overset{-}{a} & \overset{+}{b} & \overset{+}{c} & \overset{-}{d} \\
\end{array}
$$

Now, these latter must correspond to very high energies. This is because every pair of charges diminishes the number of covalent bonds by one and because the repulsion between the two electrons on the same atom is very great. Since terms like $\int \Psi_P H \Psi_Q \, d\tau$, where the two wave functions correspond to very different energies, are always small, such structures may be neglected safely. Structures containing one ionic bond *and* one long "bond" will be also neglected for similar reasons. So we will carry on with structures A to F.

It is important to make sure that these structures are linearly independent from one other. The canonical circle can still be used, taking into account the uncharged atoms only. Atoms marked with a $(+)$ sign have no π electrons at all and those having a $(-)$ sign have two π electrons with opposite spins, which are not available for coupling with other electrons.

Craig defines as "corresponding" structures those such as

$$
\underline{\qquad\qquad} \quad \text{and} \quad + - \underline{\qquad} \quad \text{or} \quad - + \underline{\qquad}
$$

because the polar bonds in the two last replace a covalent bond in the first one. Any polar structure corresponds to only one homopolar structure. It is advantageous to choose a set of polar structures whose corresponding nonpolar structures form a canonical set. Naturally, it is always possible to check upon the mutual independence of the structure eigenfunctions in comparing their expressions in terms of Slater functions (see below).

The eigenfunctions for structures A and B were given before (p. 57). They were

$$
\Psi_A = \frac{1}{\sqrt{4}} [\psi_I - \psi_{II} - \psi_{III} + \psi_{IV}] \tag{9-11}
$$

where the Slater function Ψ_I, for example, has the form:

$$
\Psi_I = \frac{1}{\sqrt{4!}}
\begin{vmatrix}
\psi_a(1)\alpha(1) & \psi_b(1)\beta(1) & \psi_c(1)\alpha(1) & \psi_d(1)\beta(1) \\
\psi_a(2)\alpha(2) & \psi_b(2)\beta(2) & \psi_c(2)\alpha(2) & \psi_d(2)\beta(2) \\
\psi_a(3)\alpha(3) & \psi_b(3)\beta(3) & \psi_c(3)\alpha(3) & \psi_d(3)\beta(3) \\
\psi_a(4)\alpha(4) & \psi_b(4)\beta(4) & \psi_c(4)\alpha(4) & \psi_d(4)\beta(4)
\end{vmatrix} \tag{9-12}
$$

or, in short notation,

$$
\Psi_I = \frac{1}{\sqrt{4!}} (\alpha\beta\alpha\beta) \tag{9-12}
$$

and

$$\Psi_A = \frac{1}{\sqrt{4}} \frac{1}{\sqrt{4!}} [(\alpha\beta\alpha\beta) - (\alpha\beta\beta\alpha) - (\beta\alpha\alpha\beta) + (\beta\alpha\beta\alpha)] \quad (9\text{-}13)$$

Similarly

$$\Psi_B = \frac{1}{\sqrt{4}} \frac{1}{\sqrt{4!}} [(\alpha\beta\alpha\beta) + (\beta\alpha\beta\alpha) - (\alpha\alpha\beta\beta) - (\beta\beta\alpha\alpha)] \quad (9\text{-}14)$$

Polar structure C will contain Slater functions such as

$$\psi^{\mathrm{I}} = \frac{1}{\sqrt{4!}} \begin{vmatrix} \psi_b(1)\alpha(1) & \psi_b(1)\beta(1) & \psi_c(1)\alpha(1) & \psi_d(1)\beta(1) \\ \psi_b(2)\alpha(2) & \psi_b(2)\beta(2) & \psi_c(2)\alpha(2) & \psi_d(2)\beta(2) \\ \psi_b(3)\alpha(3) & \psi_b(3)\beta(3) & \psi_c(3)\alpha(3) & \psi_d(3)\beta(3) \\ \psi_b(4)\alpha(4) & \psi_b(4)\beta(4) & \psi_c(4)\alpha(4) & \psi_d(4)\beta(4) \end{vmatrix}$$

$$= \frac{1}{\sqrt{4!}} (\widehat{\alpha\beta}\alpha\beta)(b) \qquad (9\text{-}15)$$

where in the short form the linked spins belong to electrons in the same $2p_z$ orbital, which is indicated by the letter in brackets. Since an exchange of these latter spins is meaningless we shall have only half as many Slater functions (2) as for the nonpolar structures.

$$\Psi_C = \frac{1}{\sqrt{2}} [\psi^{\mathrm{I}} - \psi^{\mathrm{II}}]$$

$$= \frac{1}{\sqrt{2}} \frac{1}{\sqrt{4!}} [(\widehat{\alpha\beta}\alpha\beta)(b) - (\widehat{\alpha\beta}\beta\alpha)(b)] \qquad (9\text{-}16)$$

It is advisable to keep the order of the atoms a, b, c, d in all the functions and make the upper link between noncontiguous atoms if such structures are considered. For example:

$$(\overset{+\;\overline{}\;-}{\widehat{\alpha\beta}\alpha\beta})(d)$$

Similarly,

$$\Psi_D = \frac{1}{\sqrt{2}} [\psi^{\mathrm{III}} - \psi^{\mathrm{IV}}] = \frac{1}{\sqrt{2}} \frac{1}{\sqrt{4!}} [(\widehat{\alpha\beta}\alpha\beta)(a) - (\widehat{\alpha\beta}\beta\alpha)(a)]$$

$$\Psi_E = \frac{1}{\sqrt{2}} [\psi^{\mathrm{V}} - \psi^{\mathrm{VI}}] = \frac{1}{\sqrt{2}} \frac{1}{\sqrt{4!}} [(\widehat{\alpha\beta\alpha}\beta)(d) - (\widehat{\beta\alpha\alpha}\beta)(d)]$$

$$\Psi_F = \frac{1}{\sqrt{2}} [\psi^{\mathrm{VII}} - \psi^{\mathrm{VIII}}] = \frac{1}{\sqrt{2}} \frac{1}{\sqrt{4!}} [(\widehat{\alpha\beta\alpha}\beta)(c) - (\widehat{\beta\alpha\alpha}\beta)(c)]$$

$$(9\text{-}17)$$

We shall need the transformation properties of the structure eigenfunctions. Polar structures, like nonpolar ones, transform into themselves or another structure under the various symmetry operations, with a sign that is the same as for the corresponding nonpolar structure, that is, $(-1)^{e'+e''}$ (see p. 225), since the number of interchanges necessary to restore the original order of spins and electrons can only change by an even number from a nonpolar to a corresponding polar structure. The formal proof was given by Craig [173, p. 396].

Now we turn again to the character table of group C_{2v} to which *cis*-butadiene belongs. The characters of the reducible representation based on the six structures A to F are obtained by first determining the transformation properties of each structure. These are given in Table 9–5.

TABLE 9–5

	E	C_2	σ_v	σ'_v
A	A	A	A	A
B	B	B	B	B
C	C	F	C	F
D	D	E	D	E
E	E	D	E	D
F	F	C	F	C

Only those which transform into themselves under a given operation contribute to the character. Thus, we have the results shown in Table 9–6.

TABLE 9–6

		E	C_2	$\sigma_v(zx)$	$\sigma'_v(zy)$
Γ_1	$A_1; z$	1	1	1	1
Γ_2	A_2	1	1	-1	-1
Γ_3	$B_1; x$	1	-1	1	-1
Γ_4	$B_2; y$	1	-1	-1	1
Γ		6	2	6	2

To break down the reducible representation into its irreducible components we make use of formula

$$a_i = \sum_R \chi(R)\chi_i(R)$$

and obtain:

$$\Gamma = 4\Gamma_1 + 2\Gamma_3 = 4A_1 + 2B_1$$

Applying the usual basis forming procedure (p. 199) we have, with the characters of Γ_1 and applying the operation to the various structures (Table 9–7):

TABLE 9–7

		E	C_2	σ_v	σ'_v
Γ_1	A	A	A	A	A
	B	B	B	B	B
	C	C	F	C	F
	D	D	E	D	E
	E	E	D	E	D
	F	F	C	F	C

This gives for the coefficients in the secular equation:

$$S_A, S_B, S_C = S_F, S_D = S_E$$

With the characters of Γ_3 we obtain (Table 9–8):

TABLE 9–8

		E	C_2	σ_v	σ'_v
Γ_3	A	A	$-A$	A	$-A$
	B	B	$-B$	B	$-A$
	C	C	$-F$	C	$-F$
	D	D	$-E$	D	$-E$
	E	E	$-D$	E	$-D$
	F	F	$-C$	F	$-C$

so that $S_A = 0$, $S_B = 0$, $S_C = -S_F$ and $S_D = -S_E$.

We now have to compute the matrix components forming the secular determinants. Only single exchange integrals between adjacent atoms will be considered, and the overlap integrals between atomic orbitals will be neglected. The matrix elements involving only non-polar structures have been computed before (p. 64).

$$H_{AA} \equiv \int \Psi_A H \Psi_A \, d\tau = Q + \tfrac{3}{2} A$$

$$H_{BB} \equiv \int \Psi_B H \Psi_B \, d\tau = Q \qquad\qquad (9\text{-}18)$$

$$H_{AB} \equiv \int \Psi_A H \Psi_B \, d\tau = \tfrac{1}{2} Q + \tfrac{3}{2} A$$

New integrals come in when terms involving the polar structures are considered.

$$H_{CC} \equiv \int \Psi_C H \Psi_C \, d\tau$$
$$= \tfrac{1}{2} [H^{\mathrm{I\,I}} - 2H^{\mathrm{I\,II}} + H^{\mathrm{II\,II}}] \qquad (9\text{-}19)$$

with

$$H^{\mathrm{I\,I}} \equiv \int \psi^{\mathrm{I}} H \psi^{\mathrm{I}} \, d\tau, \quad H^{\mathrm{I\,II}} \equiv \int \psi^{\mathrm{I}} H \psi^{\mathrm{II}} \, d\tau, \quad H^{\mathrm{II\,II}} \equiv \int \psi^{\mathrm{II}} H \psi^{\mathrm{II}} \, d\tau$$

where

$$\psi^{\mathrm{I}} = \frac{1}{\sqrt{4!}} \, (\widehat{\alpha\beta\alpha\beta}) \, (b)$$

and

$$\psi^{\mathrm{II}} = \frac{1}{\sqrt{4!}} \, (\widehat{\alpha\beta\beta\alpha}) \, (b)$$

We must remember that since the Hamiltonian does not affect spin, and the spin functions are orthogonal, only those terms can be different from zero in which the same electron has the same spin left and right of the operator. Furthermore, we neglect interactions between nonneighbors and overlap integrals and we only consider single exchange integrals.

The Hamiltonian has the form

$$H = (H(1) + H(2) + H(3) + H(4) \\ + H_{12} + H_{13} + H_{14} + H_{23} + H_{24} + H_{34})$$

where the $H(1), \ldots$ contain the kinetic energy operators $T(1), \ldots$ and the operators related to the part of the potential energy which represents the interaction of an electron with the core constituted by the nuclei and the electrons other than the π electrons and have the form $-Z_a e^2/r_{a_1}, \ldots$, and the $H_{12}, \ldots$, representing the repulsion between electrons (1) and (2), for example, have the form e^2/r_{12}.

Since all the part-Hamiltonians are either mono- or bielectronic and since for each one we have to integrate according to

$$d\tau = d\tau_1 \, d\tau_2 \, d\tau_3 \, d\tau_4$$

the $H(1), \ldots$ give nonzero contributions only if all electrons but one are assigned to the same atomic orbitals left and right of the operator, and the $H_{12}, \ldots$ if they differ in the assignments of no more than two electrons. This is, of course, linked to the neglect of overlap integrals, i.e., neglect of the nonorthogonality of the atomic orbitals.

First we compute the matrix component H_{cc} [Eq. (9-19)]. We obtain

$$H^{\mathrm{II}} = \frac{1}{4!} \int (\widehat{\alpha\beta\alpha\beta})\,(b)\,H(\widehat{\alpha\beta\alpha\beta})\,(b)\,d\tau \qquad (9\text{-}20)$$

It is sufficient to consider one of the permutations in $(\widehat{\alpha\beta\alpha\beta})$ and count its nonzero interactions with the 4! terms in $(\widehat{\alpha\beta\alpha\beta})$. The other permutations will give the same, and this is taken care of by taking away the factor 1/4!. Then the following terms will be different from zero:

$$Q' = \int b(1)\,\overline{b(2)}\,c(3)\,\overline{d(4)}\,Hb(1)\,\overline{b(2)}\,c(3)\,\overline{d(4)}\,d\tau_1 \, d\tau_2 \, d\tau_3 \, d\tau_4 \quad (9\text{-}21)$$

a Coulomb integral involving two identical polar structures; and

$$\zeta = \int b(1)\,\overline{b(2)}\,c(3)\,\overline{d(4)}\,Hb(3)\,\overline{b(2)}\,c(1)\,\overline{d(4)}\,d\tau_1 \, d\tau_2 \, d\tau_3 \, d\tau_4 \\ = \int b(1)\,c(3)\,Hb(3)\,c(1)\,d\tau_1 \, d\tau_3 \qquad\qquad (9\text{-}22)$$

an exchange integral, which has to be taken with the negative sign because we have made one permutation. Thus,

$$H^{\mathrm{II}} = Q' - \zeta$$

and, in the same way,

$$H^{\mathrm{III}} = Q' - \zeta$$

Furthermore,

$$H^{I\,II} = \frac{1}{4!} \int (\widehat{\alpha\beta\alpha\beta})\,(b)\,H(\widehat{\alpha\beta\beta\alpha})\,(b)\,d\tau = -A \qquad (9\text{-}23)$$

since we have to exchange the electrons on atoms c and d to have the spins matched, and we cannot make any other exchange since double exchanges are neglected. Finally the matrix component becomes

$$H_{CC} \equiv \int \Psi_C H \Psi_C \, d\tau$$
$$= \frac{1}{2}[Q' - \zeta + Q' - \zeta + 2A] = Q' - \zeta + A \qquad (9\text{-}24)$$

Next we compute H_{CD}:

$$H_{CD} \equiv \int \Psi_C H \Psi_D \, d\tau$$
$$= \frac{1}{2}\frac{1}{4!} \int [(\widehat{\alpha\beta\alpha\beta})\,(b) - (\widehat{\alpha\beta\beta\alpha})\,(b)]H[(\widehat{\alpha\beta\alpha\beta})\,(a) \qquad (9\text{-}25)$$
$$- (\widehat{\alpha\beta\beta\alpha})\,(a)]d\tau$$

The cross terms will make no contribution since they differ in the assignments of more than two electrons. The two others contribute integrals of the following type:

$$\int b(1)\,\overline{b(2)}\,c(3)\,\overline{d(4)}\,Ha(1)\,\overline{a(2)}\,c(3)\,\overline{d(4)}\,d\tau$$
$$= \int a(1)\,a(2)\,Hb(1)\,b(2)\,d\tau_1 d\tau_2 = \theta \qquad (9\text{-}26)$$

Thus, $H_{CD} = \theta$;

$$H_{CE} = \frac{1}{2}\frac{1}{4!} \int [(\widehat{\alpha\beta\alpha\beta})\,(b) - (\widehat{\alpha\beta\beta\alpha})\,(b)] \times$$
$$H[(\widehat{\alpha\beta\alpha\beta})\,(d) - (\widehat{\beta\alpha\alpha\beta})\,(d)]\,d\tau = 0 \qquad (9\text{-}27)$$

and

$$H_{CF} = \frac{1}{2}\frac{1}{4!} \int [(\widehat{\alpha\beta\alpha\beta})\,(b) - (\widehat{\alpha\beta\beta\alpha})\,(b)]H[(\widehat{\alpha\beta\alpha\beta})\,(c)$$
$$- (\widehat{\beta\alpha\alpha\beta})\,(c)]\,d\tau = 0 \qquad (9\text{-}28)$$

Like Craig, we only consider interactions between polar structures having the charges at the same atoms (same or opposite). By symmetry

$$H_{DE} = 0, \quad H_{DF} = 0, \quad H_{EF} = H_{CD} = \theta$$

The other diagonal polar matrix element is

$$H_{DD} = \frac{1}{2}\frac{1}{4!} \int [(\widehat{\alpha\beta\alpha\beta})\,(a) - (\widehat{\alpha\beta\beta\alpha})\,(a)]H[(\widehat{\alpha\beta\alpha\beta})\,(a) - (\widehat{\alpha\beta\beta\alpha}(a)]$$
$$= \frac{1}{2}[Q' + Q' + A + A] = Q' + A \qquad (9\text{-}29)$$

There is no ζ term because this would require an exchange between a and c or d, thus an exchange between nonadjacent atoms.

By symmetry,

$$H_{EE} = H_{DD} \quad \text{and} \quad H_{FF} = H_{CC}$$

Still other integrals come in if we consider the interaction between a polar and a nonpolar structure.

$$H_{AC} = \frac{1}{2\sqrt{2}} \frac{1}{4!} \int [(\alpha\beta\alpha\beta) - (\alpha\beta\beta\alpha) - (\beta\alpha\alpha\beta) + (\beta\alpha\beta\alpha)]H[(\widehat{\alpha\beta\alpha\beta})(b) - (\widehat{\alpha\beta\beta\alpha})(b)] d\tau \tag{9-30}$$

The nonzero terms will be of type

$$\int a(1)\overline{b(2)}c(3)\overline{d(4)}Hb(1)\overline{b(2)}c(3)\overline{d(4)}\, d\tau$$
$$= \int a(1)b(2)Hb(1)b(2)\, d\tau = \eta$$

It is seen immediately that there will be four terms like this, giving

$$H_{AC} = \sqrt{2}\,\eta \tag{9-31}$$

Also

$$H_{AC} = A_{AD} = H_{AE} = H_{AF}$$

$$H_{BC} = \frac{1}{2\sqrt{2}} \frac{1}{4!} \int [(\alpha\beta\alpha\beta) + (\beta\alpha\beta\alpha) - (\alpha\alpha\beta\beta) - (\beta\beta\alpha\alpha)]H[\widehat{\alpha\beta\alpha\beta})(b) - (\widehat{\alpha\beta\beta\alpha})(b)] d\tau \tag{9-32}$$

Only two terms remain, yielding

$$H_{BC} = \tfrac{1}{2}\sqrt{2}\,\eta \tag{9-33}$$

Also

$$H_{BC} = H_{BD} = H_{BE} = H_{BF}$$

[Notice that $(\widehat{\alpha\beta\alpha\beta})(b) = -(\widehat{\beta\alpha\alpha\beta})(b)$.] The $d_{PQ} = \int \Psi_P \Psi_Q\, d\tau$ will be put equal to the coefficient of the Coulomb term as in the nonpolar approximation.

Thus, we have all the elements needed to set up the secular determinant.

$$0 = s_A(Q - E + \tfrac{3}{2}A) + s_B(\tfrac{1}{2}Q - \tfrac{1}{2}E + \tfrac{3}{2}A)$$
$$+ s_C\sqrt{2}\,\eta + s_D\sqrt{2}\,\eta + s_E\sqrt{2}\,\eta + s_F\sqrt{2}\,\eta$$

$$0 = s_A(\tfrac{1}{2}Q - \tfrac{1}{2}E + \tfrac{3}{2}A) + s_B(Q - E)$$
$$+ s_C\tfrac{1}{2}\sqrt{2}\,\eta + s_D\tfrac{1}{2}\sqrt{2}\,\eta + s_E\tfrac{1}{2}\sqrt{2}\,\eta + s_F\tfrac{1}{2}\sqrt{2}\,\eta$$

$$0 = s_A\sqrt{2}\,\eta + s_B\tfrac{1}{2}\sqrt{2}\,\eta + s_C(Q' - E - \zeta + A)$$
$$+ s_D\theta + s_E\cdot 0 + s_F\cdot 0$$

$$0 = s_A\sqrt{2}\,\eta + s_B\tfrac{1}{2}\sqrt{2}\,\eta + s_C\theta + s_D(Q' - E + A)$$
$$+ s_E\cdot 0 + s_F\cdot 0 \tag{9-34}$$

$$0 = s_A\sqrt{2}\ \eta + s_B\tfrac{1}{2}\sqrt{2}\ \eta + s_C\cdot 0 + s_D\cdot 0 +$$
$$s_E(Q' - E + A) + s_F\theta$$
$$0 = s_A\sqrt{2}\ \eta + s_B\tfrac{1}{2}\sqrt{2}\ \eta + s_C\cdot 0 + s_D\cdot 0 +$$
$$s_E\theta + s_F(Q' - E - \zeta + A)$$

There are six parameters in these equations: Q, A, Q' ζ, θ, η. Now ζ and θ are really the same as A, except that ζ is used when one of the atoms involved is negatively charged and θ if both are negatively charged. They are of the type

$$\int a(1)b(2)\frac{e^2}{r_{12}}a(2)b(1)\,d\tau_1\,d\tau_2 = \int a(1)a(2)\frac{e^2}{r_{12}}b(1)b(2)\,d\tau_1\,d\tau_2$$

Simonetta [175], who continued Craig's work by including overlap integrals and interactions between charges on nonadjacent atoms, took them all to be equal, which amounts to supposing that all the atomic orbitals are the same in all three cases. This is probably a better approximation than introducing empirical values separately for each one.

Thus, we shall suppose that

$$\zeta = \theta = A$$

and use only A. Then we are left with three parameters: A, $\xi = Q' - Q$, and η.

Craig [172] made an attempt to compute these by using the simpler case of ethylene. Actually he adopted Sklar's value (-1.92 ev) for A and determined ξ, ζ, and η. However, Simonetta [175] criticized Sklar's value on the ground it does not take sufficient account of the ionic-covalent resonance energy of the insulated $C=C$ bond, which would lower it. Therefore, since we eliminated ζ we shall use Craig's method to determine A, ξ, and η.

The ethylene molecule as a two-π-electronic problem may be represented by the following three (singlet) structures:

$$\text{C=C} \qquad \overset{-}{\text{C}}-\overset{+}{\text{C}} \qquad \overset{+}{\text{C}}-\overset{-}{\text{C}}$$
$$\text{A} \qquad\qquad \text{B} \qquad\qquad \text{C}$$

$$H_{AA} = Q + A, \qquad H_{BB} = H_{CC} = Q' = Q + \xi$$
$$H_{AB} = H_{AC} = \sqrt{2}\ \eta \qquad H_{BC} = \theta = A$$

This gives the secular equation

$$0 = s_A(X + A) + s_B\sqrt{2}\ \eta + s_C\sqrt{2}\ \eta$$
$$0 = s_A\sqrt{2}\ \eta + s_B(X + \xi) + s_C A \qquad\qquad (9\text{-}35)$$
$$0 = s_A\sqrt{2}\ \eta + s_B A + s_C(X + \xi)$$

where $X = Q - E$.

The character table of group D_{2h} was given on p. 206. The characters of the reducible representation based on structures A, B, and C are

E	$C_2(z)$	$C_2(y)$	$C_2(x)$	i	$\sigma(xy)$	$\sigma(zx)$	$\sigma(yz)$
3	1	1	3	1	3	3	1

and $\Gamma = 2A_g + B_{3u}$. The basis-forming procedure (p. 199) gives, for A_g, that $s_B = s_C$ but s_A/s_B is not determined, and for B_{3u} that $s_B = -s_C$ and $s_A = 0$; and the secular equation reduces to

$$A_g: \quad \begin{aligned} 0 &= s_A(X + A) + s_B 2\sqrt{2}\,\eta \\ 0 &= s_A\sqrt{2}\,\eta + s_B(X + \xi + A) \end{aligned} \tag{9-36}$$

$$B_{3u}: \quad 0 = s_B(X + \xi - A) \tag{9-37}$$

The determinant of the coefficients for the A_g system is

$$\begin{vmatrix} X + A & 2\sqrt{2}\,\eta \\ \sqrt{2}\,\eta & (X + \xi + A) \end{vmatrix} = X^2 + X(\xi + 2A) + (A^2 + \xi A - 4\eta^2) = 0$$

From this

$$X_{1,0} = \frac{-(\xi + 2A) \pm \sqrt{\xi^2 + 16\eta^2}}{2} \tag{9-38}$$

The negative sign before the square root will correspond to the ground state (E_0) and the positive sign to the first excited state (E_1). The experimental excitation energy is about 6 ev. Remembering that $X = Q - E$ we can write that

$$E_1 - E_0 = -\sqrt{\xi^2 + 16\eta^2} = 6\text{ ev} \tag{9-39}$$

For the second excited state (B_{3u}),

$$X + \xi - A = 0$$

hence,

$$X_2 = A - \xi$$

The excitation energy from the ground state is about 7 ev; therefore we have

$$E_2 - E_0 = \frac{\xi}{2} - 2A - \frac{\sqrt{\xi^2 + 16\eta^2}}{2} = 7\text{ ev} \tag{9-40}$$

The assignments on which the values 6 ev and 7 ev are based are now doubtful. They seemed to be definite in 1950 when Craig's work was published. Potts [176] gave reasons to believe that the weak band at about $48,000\text{ cm}^{-1}$ (6 ev) does not represent a separate band system. However, we shall go on with this discussion as if the above assignments were correct.

From Eq. (9-39)

$$\frac{\xi}{2} - 2A + 3\text{ ev} = 7\text{ ev}$$

and
$$\xi = 8\,\text{ev} + 4A \tag{9-41}$$

(9-39) and (9-41) are two equations for the three unknowns A, ξ, and η.

Sklar's value for A was $-1.92\,\text{ev}$ and Craig [173] adopted this for computing the other parameters. We shall not use Sklar's value but, following Craig, we shall use the ionic-covalent resonance energy, estimated by Sklar at $0.19\,\text{ev}$, to secure a third relation.

Since $H_{AA} = X + A$, for the energy of the ground state, if ethylene could be represented by the covalent structure only, we would have simply
$$X_{\text{cov}} = -A$$

Therefore
$$E_{\text{cov}} - E_0 = A - \frac{(\xi + 2A) + \sqrt{\xi^2 + 16\eta^2}}{2}$$

and
$$-\frac{\xi + \sqrt{\xi^2 + 16\eta^2}}{2} = 0.19\,\text{ev} \tag{9-42}$$

From this, using (9-39) we obtain that
$$\xi = 5.62\,\text{ev}$$

and from (9-41) that
$$A = \frac{-8\,\text{ev} + \xi}{4}$$

hence $A = -0.6\,\text{ev}$. Then from
$$\sqrt{\xi^2 + 16\eta^2} = -6\,\text{ev}$$

we obtain, choosing the negative sign, that
$$\eta = -0.53\,\text{ev}$$

which is the same as Craig's value.

There is much to be said about this procedure. We cannot expect too great an accuracy from a method involving so many parameters, which are themselves based on arguable comparisons between theoretical and experimental results. The $\zeta = \theta = A$ equality is not entirely justified. Sklar's $0.19\,\text{ev}$ is also questionable. The obtained value of A is rather low, although there is no real reason to expect it to be the same as that deduced from the homopolar calculation. We may suppose that by choosing A in this way we compensate for some of the other approximations and achieve, at least, a significant improvement with respect to the homopolar approach. This is about the best one can hope for from an empirical calculation under the given circumstances.

In order to simplify the numerical work we shall use
$$\xi = Q' - Q = 5.5\,\text{ev} \quad \text{and} \quad A = \eta = -0.6\,\text{ev}$$

which would correspond to $E_1 - E_0 = 6$ ev, $E_2 - E_0 = 6.95$ ev, and an ionic-covalent resonance energy of 0.25 ev. We are left with only two parameters.

Then, from (9-38)

$$X_0 = +0.85 \text{ ev}, \qquad X_1 = -5.15 \text{ ev}$$

and for the B_{3u} state

$$X_2 = -6.10 \text{ ev}$$

Accordingly,

$$E_0 = Q - 0.85 \text{ ev}, \quad E_1 = Q + 5.15 \text{ ev}, \quad E_2 = Q + 6.10 \text{ ev}$$

Putting X_0 back into the secular equation and normalizing with $d_{AB} = 0$, i.e.,

$$s_A^2 + 2s_B^2 = 1$$

we obtain that for E_0

$$s_A^2 = 0.96, \qquad s_B^2 = s_C^2 = 0.02$$

Thus, in the ground state the covalent structure has 96 per cent of the weight, the two ionic structures only 4 per cent. Similarly for E_1,

$$s_A^2 = 0.04, \qquad s_B^2 = s_C^2 = 0.48$$

which is the reverse situation. For the B_{3u} state clearly

$$s_A^2 = 0, \qquad s_B^2 = s_C^2 = 0.50$$

giving a wholly polar state.

The respective total wave functions are

$$X_0 = 0.98\Psi_A + 0.14\Psi_B + 0.14\Psi_C$$
$$X_1 = 0.20\Psi_A + 0.69\Psi_B + 0.69\Psi_C$$
$$X_2 = \qquad\qquad 0.71\Psi_B - 0.71\Psi_C$$

The $E_1 \leftarrow E_0$ transition is $A_g \leftarrow A_g$ and is forbidden.

The transition moment would be

$$\int X_0 \sum_i e_i r_i X_1 \, d\tau$$

$$= 0.98 \times 0.20 \int \Psi_A \sum_i e_i r_i \Psi_A \, d\tau + 0.14 \times 0.69 \int \Psi_B \sum_i e_i r_i \Psi_B \, d\tau$$

$$+ \; 0.14 \times 0.69 \int \Psi_C \sum_i e_i r_i \Psi_C \, d\tau$$

$$+ \; (0.98 \times 0.69 + 0.14 \times 0.20) \int \Psi_A \sum_i e_i r_i \Psi_B \, d\tau$$

$$+ \; (0.98 \times 0.69 + 0.14 \times 0.20) \int \Psi_A \sum_i e_g r_g \Psi_C \, d\tau$$

$$+ \; (0.14 \times 0.69 + 0.14 \times 0.69) \int \Psi_B \sum_i e_g r_g \Psi_C \, d\tau$$

The first term, referring to the nonionic structure, is zero for reasons given on p. 226. The second and third terms are the dipole moments corresponding to structures B and C, respectively. Since they have the charges opposed, these two terms cancel each other. The next two terms contain one nonpolar and one polar structure eigenfunction each; they contain terms such as

$$\int a(1)b(2) \sum_i e_i x_i \, a(1)a(2) \, d\tau_1 \, d\tau_2$$

$$= e \int a(1)b(2)(x_1 + x_2) a(1)a(2) \, d\tau_1 \, d\tau_2$$

$$= e \int a(1) x_a a(1) \, d\tau_1 \int b(2)a(2) \, d\tau_2$$

$$+ e \int b(2) \frac{x_a + x_b}{2} a(2) \, d\tau_2 \int a(1)a(1) \, d\tau_1$$

$$= eSx_a + \tfrac{1}{2} eS(x_a + x_b)$$

where S is the overlap integral (see p. 192). The second term is zero since $x_a = -x_b$. The first term will cancel out with the similar term of

$$\int a(1)b(2) \sum_i e_i x_i b(1)b(2) \, d\tau_1 \, d\tau_2 = eSx_b + \tfrac{1}{2}eS(x_a + x_b)$$

The last term gives terms such as

$$\int a(1)a(2) \sum_i e_i x_i b(1)b(2) \, d\tau_1 d\tau_2$$

$$= e \int a(1)a(2)(x_1 + x_2)b(1)b(2) \, d\tau_1 d\tau_2$$

$$= 2e \int a(1) \frac{x_a + x_b}{2} b(1) \, d\tau_1 \int a(2)b(2) \, d\tau_2$$

$$= eS^2(x_a + x_b) = 0$$

Thus, the whole transition moment vanishes in accordance with the selection rules ($y_a = y_b = z_a = z_b = 0$ anyway).

As for the $E_2 \leftarrow E_0$ transition, which is ${}^1B_{3u} \leftarrow {}^1A_{1g}$ in character, this is allowed, polarized according to the x axis. The transition moment is

$$\int X_0 \sum_i e_i x_i \, X_2 \, d\tau = 0.14 \times 0.71 \int \Psi_B \sum_i e_i x_i \Psi_B \, d\tau$$

$$- 0.14 \times 0.71 \int \Psi_C \sum_i e_i x_i \Psi_C \, d\tau$$

$$+ 0.98 \times 0.71 \int \Psi_A \sum_i e_i x_i \Psi_B \, d\tau$$

$$- 0.98 \times 0.71 \int \Psi_A \sum_i e_i x_i \Psi_C \, d\tau$$

$$- 0.14 \times 0.71 \int \Psi_B \sum_i e_i x_i \Psi_C \, d\tau$$

$$+ 0.14 \times 0.71 \int \Psi_B \sum_i e_i x_i \Psi_C \, d\tau$$

The two last terms cancel each other. The first and the second do not cancel this time but add together.

$$\int \Psi_B \sum_i e_i x_i \Psi_B \, d\tau = e \int a(1)a(2)[x_1 + x_2]a(1)a(2) \, d\tau_1 \, d\tau_2$$

$$= e \int a(1)x_1 a(1) \, d\tau_1 \int a(2)a(2) \, d\tau_2$$

$$+ e \int a(2) x_2 a(2) \, d\tau_2 \int a(1)a(1) \, d\tau_1$$

$$= 2e x_a$$

If the C=C distance is 1.34 Å, $x_a = 0.67$ Å and we have as the contribution of the first and second terms to the dipole strength:

$$(2 \times 0.14 \times 0.71 \times 2 \times 0.67)^2 = 0.071$$

The third and the fourth terms were shown to cancel each other if they have the same sign. This time they have opposite signs.

$$\int \Psi_A \sum_i e_i x_i \Psi_B \, d\tau$$

$$= \frac{1}{\sqrt{2 + 2S^2}} e \int [a(1)b(2) + a(2)b(1)] (x_1 + x_2) [a(1)a(2)] \, d\tau_1 \, d\tau_2$$

$$= \frac{1}{\sqrt{2 + 2S^2}} eS x_a$$

Then the contribution of the third and fourth terms to the dipole strength, if $S = 0.26$, is

$$\left(0.98 \times 0.71 \frac{4}{2.135} 0.26 \times 0.67\right)^2 = 0.110$$

Finally

$$D \equiv Q^2 = 0.071 + 0.110 = 0.181 \text{ Å}^2$$

and with $E_2 - E_0 = 6.95$ ev $\cong 56{,}337$ cm^{-1}

$$f = 1.085 \cdot 10^{-5} \cdot 56{,}337 Q^2 = 0.111$$

This is lower than the experimental value but approximates it significantly better than the simple LCAO method, which leads to oscillator strengths three to five times the experimental ones.

We shall not try to force the above parameters upon the butadiene molecule. Being based on a questionable interpretation of the spectrum of ethylene they can hardly be expected to lead to good results. Instead we refer to the works of Simonetta and Schomaker [177] and Simonetta [175]. The latter found, with a somewhat different choice of parameters, that the weight of structures A to F is, in the ground state of butadiene:

A	0.809 p.c.
B	0.105
C, D, E, F	0.079
Structures with charges on noncontinuous atoms	0.007

For the ground state of benzene he obtained

The two Kekulé structures	0.631 p.c.
The three Dewar structures	0.175
The 12 ortho-ionic structures	
(with no long bonds)	0.120
The other 42 ionic structures	0.074

Efforts to transform the valence-bond method into a nonempirical method will be mentioned in Chapter 13.

9-5 SOME APPLICATIONS OF THE VALENCE-BOND METHOD TO DYE MOLECULES

In this chapter we shall review certain works on dye molecules, which were done between two and three decades ago but still seem to be of interest.

Dyestuffs possess absorption bands in the visible, i.e., the relatively close-lying energy levels.

After a qualitative treatment by Eistert [178], Bury [179] and Pauling [180] were the first to treat such molecules by quantum-mechanical methods. Later Förster [181, 182] applied the valence-bond method to these problems; Herzfeld and Sklar [183] used both the valence-bond and the simple LCAO molecular orbital method. H. Kuhn studied dye molecules extensively by a "free electron" method, which we shall discuss in a later chapter (p. 333).

Förster's procedure consists in examining the properties of certain classes of dyestuffs in simplified models, which are sufficiently representative of their main structural properties. He studied a straight-chain and a branched-chain model. The straight-chain model is simply the positive ion of a polyenic chain which at both ends is substituted by groups like $-NH_2$ or $-OH$. These substituents possess a lone pair of electrons in a $2p_z$ orbital, which can enter into conjugation with the π electrons of the carbons.

Such an ion may be represented by valence-bond structures among which the following are considered to be the most important.

$$\overset{+}{A}=CH-CH=CH \ \ldots \ CH=CH-A$$
$$A-\overset{+}{C}H-CH=CH \ \ldots \ CH=CH-A$$
$$A-CH=CH-\overset{+}{C}H \ \ldots \ CH=CH-A$$
$$\cdots\cdots\cdots\cdots\cdots\cdots\cdots\cdots\cdots\cdots\cdots$$
$$A-CH=CH-CH=\ldots=CH-CH=\overset{+}{A}$$

where $A = NH_2$, OH, or similar groups.

These are likely to be the most important structures since our model compound is an ion, although the complete disregard of structures containing long bonds is not really justified.

The diagonal elements of the Hamilton operator will be only of two kinds: Q_A for structures with $\overset{+}{A}$ and Q_C for structures containing $\overset{+}{C}$. Among the nondiagonal elements we shall neglect those which represent interactions between structures with a relative shift of the positive charge by more than two carbon atoms. This restricts us to interactions between structures which are neighbors in the above scheme. We shall put all the remaining nondiagonal terms equal to the same exchange integral A. Neglecting the d_{PQ} in the non-diagonal terms, we then have the following secular determinant:

$$\begin{vmatrix} Q_A - E & A & 0 & 0 & \cdots & 0 \\ A & Q_C - E & A & 0 & \cdots & 0 \\ 0 & A & Q_C - E & A & \cdots & 0 \\ \multicolumn{6}{c}{\dotfill} \\ 0 & 0 & 0 & 0 & \cdots & A \quad Q_A - E \end{vmatrix} = 0 \quad (9\text{-}43)$$

The energies depend on the quantity $Q_A - Q_C$, which is the difference of the "energies" of an $\overset{+}{A}$ and a $\overset{+}{C}$ structure.

Instead of assigning values to given substituents Förster computed the energy levels, E_j, for

$$L = \frac{Q_A - Q_C}{A} = 0, \pm 1, \text{ and } \infty$$

(A is a negative quantity.)

Figure 9–10, taken from Förster, shows the results for $L = 0$, where n is the number of the double bonds in the chain and only the five lowest energy levels are given.

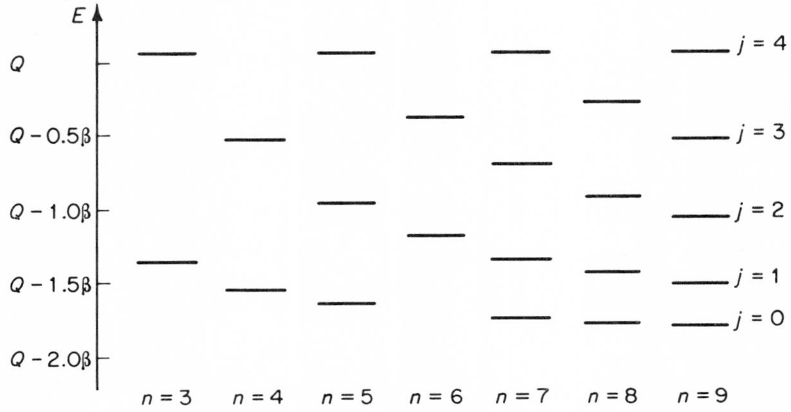

Fig. 9-10

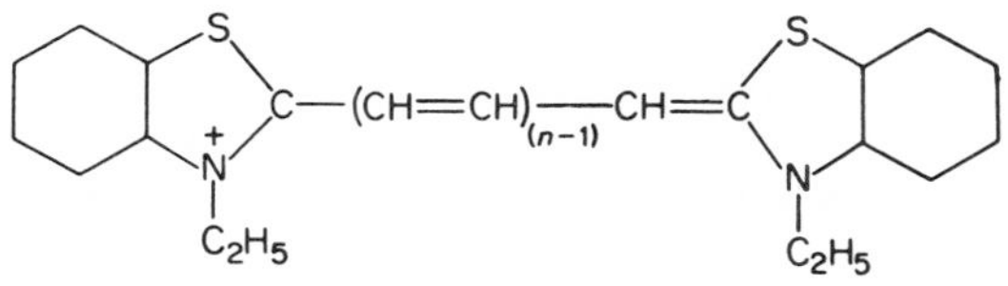

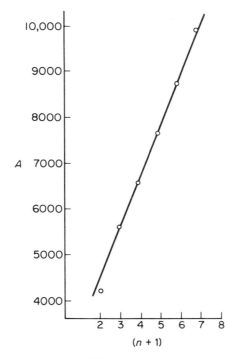

Fig. 9-11

It can be seen immediately that the first band shifts systematically toward longer wavelengths with increasing n. It is also seen that the gap between the first and the second band is appreciable, so that if the first band is in the visible the second band is still in the ultraviolet and, except for very long chains, the first band alone determines the color of the compound.

The shifting of the first band with increasing chain length for polymethine dyes (Fig. 9-11),[1] for example, is given by the straight line in Fig. 9-12 taken from a paper by Herzfeld and Sklar [183].[2]

Fig. 9-12

---

[1] Double bonds were omitted from the figures of this chapter.

[2] It was based on experimental data obtained by L. G. S. Brooker. See footnote 8 in [183].

The distance between the ground level and the first excited level increases with increasing L, that is, when the difference between the electronegativities of carbon and the substituent increases. Thus -NH₂ is a stronger "auxo-chrome" than -OH and gives a deeper color, which means absorption at longer wavelengths. In 1933 Wizinger [184] established an empirical order of the substituents where the auxo-chrome strength increases from left to right:

$$-OCH_3, \ -OH, \ -NH_2, \ -N(CH_3)_2, \ -N(C_2H_5)_2, \ -NHC_6H_5$$

-N(CH₃)₂ is a stronger auxo-chrome than -NH₂. This is because the amino derivatives of benzene are not exactly coplanar. Replacement of the hydrogens by -CH₃ or C₂H₅ groups brings them closer to coplanarity. This is not so for -OH and -OCH₃. -OCH₃ is not quite so good an auxo-chrome as -CH₃ because carbon has a higher electronegativity than hydrogen and this decreases the tendency of the electrons of the $2p_z$ lone pair on the oxygen to move towards the ring [185].

Model I may be considered as representative of dyes of the cyanin, isocyanin, and pseudoisocyanin type.

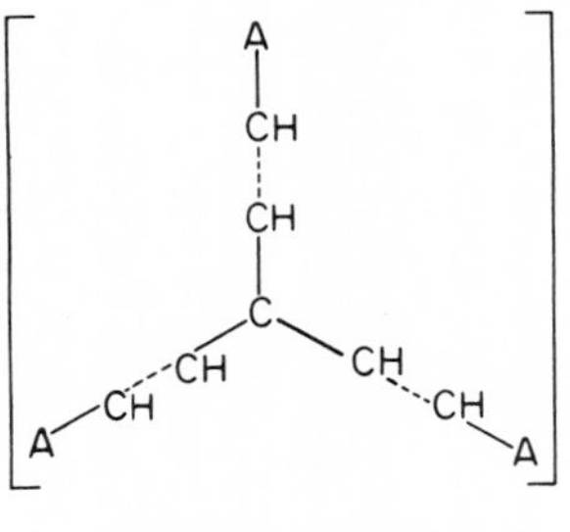

Fig. 9-13

Förster's model II, the branched model (Fig. 9-13), applies to dyes whose main structural element is the triphenylmethyl cation. The setting up of the secular equation follows the same lines as in the case of the linear model and will not be described in detail. The auxochrome effect is also similar and follows Wizinger's series [181, 182]. A few data illustrate this: (The wavelengths corresponding to ϵ_{max} were obtained by taking the arithmetic mean of the two wavelengths at the end of the half-width line right and left of the peak.[3])

___
[3] ϵ is the molar extinction coefficient.

$[C(C_6H_5)_3]^+$	4210 Å
$[C(C_6H_4OCH_3)_3]^+$	4750 Å
$[C(C_6H_4OH)_3]^+$	4790 Å
$[C(C_6H_4NH_2)_3]^+$	5320 Å
$[C(C_6H_4N(CH_3)_2)_3]^+$	5660 Å
$[C(C_6H_4NHC_6H_5)_3]^+$	5920 Å

It is important that for model II the first excited state is doubly degenerate. In solution the band is expected to be slightly split and the two resulting bands will overlap; this is in accord with the great breadth of the observed bands. In case of asymmetrical substitution two separate bands are usually observed. An example is methoxy-malachite green [185].

The known dye molecules do not, in general, correspond exactly to models I or II. In order to obtain results more comparable to experimental findings Förster [182] carried out perturbation calculations. Let us consider a system which differs from I or II by a slight perturbation. We shall assume that the number of valence-bond structures does not change and that there is a one-to-one correspondence between the new and the old structures. Further we shall suppose that both the old and the new structure eigenfunctions are normalized and mutually orthogonal (i.e., the d_{pq} are taken equal to zero). Then the matrix components of the Hamilton operator become (see Section 2-4)

$$H_{kl} = H_{kl}^0 + H_{kl}' \qquad (9\text{-}44)$$

According to first-order perturbation theory we will have for the energy levels:

$$E_j = E_j^0 + E_j'$$

with

$$E_j' = \sum_{k,l} s_{jk} s_{jl} H_{kl}' \qquad (9\text{-}45)$$

where the coefficients are those in the related linear combinations of structure eigenfunctions in the unperturbed problem. This implies that the change in a structure eigenfunction by the perturbation contributes more to the change in the total eigenfunction the greater the coefficient of this structure eigenfunction is in the related total wave function of the unperturbed molecule.

Such a perturbation may be due to the replacement of one auxochrome by another or by a substitution elsewhere in the molecule. For multiple substitution the perturbations are additive in this approximation. This is substantiated by experiment [186, 187]. The λ_{max} value of isocyanin, for example, is close to the arithmetic mean of the related values for pseudo isocyanin and cyanin (Fig. 9-14).

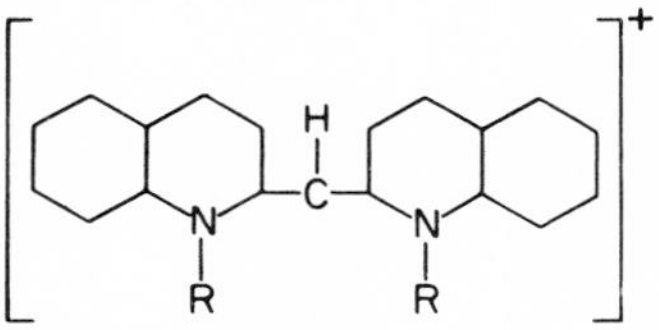

Pseudo–isocyanine
$\lambda_{max} = 5220$ Å

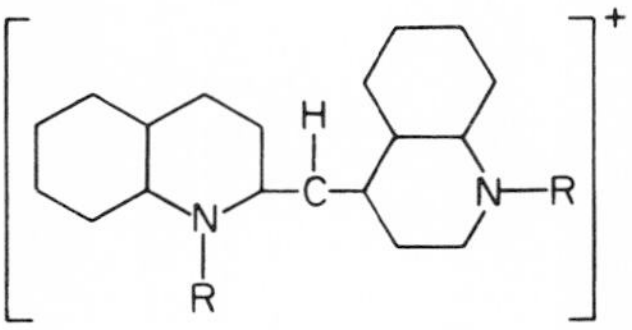

Isocyanine
$\lambda_{max} = 5570$ Å

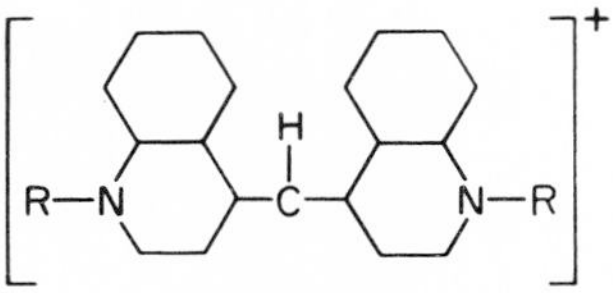

Cyanine
$\lambda_{max} = 5930$ Å

Fig. 9-14

This rule seems to be generally valid—although, of course, only approximate.

An interesting rule can be derived from the additivity of the individual perturbations for multiple substitution in model II. Förster put it this way: "Substitution of an end-hydrogen atom by an auxochrome group or the replacement of a weaker auxochrome by a strong one in one of the three branches of an ion representable by model II brings about a splitting into two of the absorption regions of longest wavelength so that one of them lies at shorter, the other at longer wavelengths. Substitution of a second group at the similar position in another branch makes both these bands shift to longer wavelengths. Substitution of a similar third auxochrome into the third branch again unites the bands into one lone band lying in between."

Applying this rule with some caution to real dye molecules shows that it is confirmed by a number of experimental facts. This is especially the case of triphenylmethyl dyes, substituted in *para-*position with respect to the central carbon atom. The last part of the rule, in particular, gives an explanation of the surprising hypsochromic effect of the third substitution (Wizinger [184]). Thus, by going from malachite green to crystal violet and from Doebner's violet to pararosaniline the first band shifts to shorter wavelengths. The opposite shift of the second band has little influence on the visible color.

Perturbation calculations yield many other qualitative results—for example, the prediction of the hypsochromic effect of a substitution on the central atom for molecules like those which are shown in Fig. 9–15. The hypsochromic effect is linked to the fact that the ground state is considerably lowered while the energy of the first excited state remains practically unchanged. On the contrary, the replacement of the central carbon by nitrogen causes a bathochromic shift (Fig. 9–15).

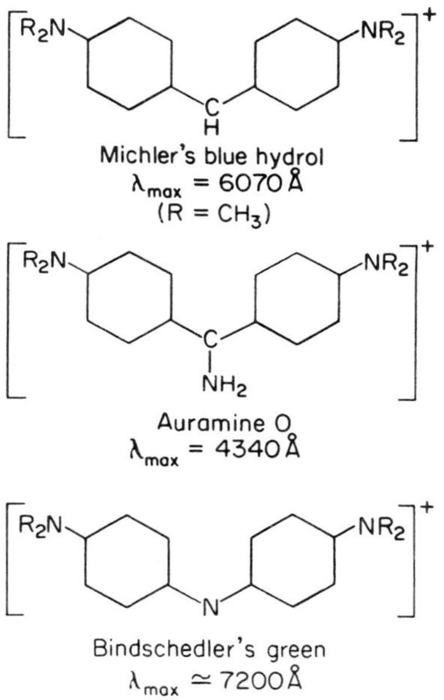

Michler's blue hydrol
$\lambda_{max} = 6070\,\text{Å}$
$(R = CH_3)$

Auramine O
$\lambda_{max} = 4340\,\text{Å}$

Bindschedler's green
$\lambda_{max} \simeq 7200\,\text{Å}$

Fig. 9-15

Herzfeld [189] and Herzfeld and Sklar [183] applied both the valence-bond and the simple molecular orbital method. Herzfeld pointed out, in particular, that using Förster's approximations the form of the secular equations in the two methods is the same. A number of interesting observations were made by Brooker [188].

Antisymmetrized Molecular Orbitals

In the simple linear-combination-of-atomic-orbitals method as we have used it so far the electrons are assigned to molecular orbitals, ϕ_i,

$$\phi_i = c_A \psi_A + c_B \psi_B + c_C \psi_C + \cdots \qquad (10\text{-}1)$$

two electrons at most being allowed to have the same MO, but one with spin projection α, the other with β, and the total wave function is taken as a simple product of the ϕ_i of all the electrons considered.[1]

This way of constructing the total wave function implies two fundamental weaknesses. (1) The Pauli exclusion principle is not adequately taken into account since no spin wave functions were introduced, therefore, spin is not allowed to exert any influence on the energy levels. An obvious consequence is the fact that excited states, where two electrons are in singly occupied orbitals, will have the same energy whether they are singlet or triplet; the method cannot separate them. (2) On the other hand, since every electron has an MO which is computed as if the other electrons were not present, this method actually neglects the mutual repulsion between the electrons.

Some of the shortcomings of the simple LCAO MO method can be compensated for by determining certain quantities such as the coulombic and resonance integrals (α and β or γ) empirically, by com-

[1] Wave functions are supposed to be real throughout chapters 10 to 14.

parison with experimental data, rather than computing them theoretically. In particular we may think of the mutual repulsion energy of the electrons as being averaged out and included in the core potential. Such procedure may be helpful, but clearly it cannot pretend to a high degree of precision.

The next step in improving the method requires us to take spin into account explicitly and make the total spin-orbital wave function of any stationary state antisymmetric with respect to the exchange of the coordinates of any two electrons in order to satisfy the Pauli-principle. We must then have a closer look at the Hamilton-operator and complete it with the necessary terms to represent all interactions between charged particles which constitute a given system. However, magnetic interactions, i.e., interactions between the magnetic moments due to the orbital motion of the electrons and to their spin, will be neglected. This means that levels belonging to the *same* multiplet will have the same energy and that the total wave function of a state will simply be a product of an orbital function and a spin function (cf. Chapter 4, p. 50).

In the old quantum theory the Pauli principle stipulated that in no atom or molecule can there exist two (or more) electrons having all their quantum numbers the same. In wave mechanics this is replaced by the requirement that every complete, spin-orbital wave function must be antisymmetrical, i.e., must change its sign with respect to the exchange of the coordinates of two electrons. The relation between the two forms of the Pauli principle is not obvious. If, however, we consider a wave function written in the form of a determinant, which we have often encountered (Slater determinants), automatically giving an antisymmetrical wave function, it is easy to see that, if we placed two electrons having the same spin projection in the same orbital [see Eqs. (4-10), (4-16) through (4-18), or (10-55)] the determinant would have two identical columns and, therefore, vanish.

As an example, the singlet function on p. 264 is, in determinantal form,

$$\frac{1}{\sqrt{2}}[\phi_1(1)\,\phi_2(2) + \phi_1(2)\,\phi_2(1)]\frac{1}{\sqrt{2}}[\alpha(1)\,\beta(2) - \alpha(2)\,\beta(1)]$$

$$= \frac{1}{2}[\phi_1(1)\,\alpha(1)\,\phi_2(2)\,\beta(2) - \phi_1(1)\,\beta(1)\,\phi_2(2)\,\alpha(2)$$

$$+ \phi_1(2)\,\beta(2)\,\phi_2(1)\,\alpha(1) - \phi_1(2)\,\alpha(2)\,\phi_2(1)\,\beta(1)] \tag{10-2}$$

$$= \frac{1}{\sqrt{2}}\left[\frac{1}{\sqrt{2}}\begin{vmatrix}\phi_1(1)\,\alpha(1) & \phi_2(1)\,\beta(1)\\ \phi_1(2)\,\alpha(2) & \phi_2(2)\,\beta(2)\end{vmatrix} - \frac{1}{\sqrt{2}}\begin{vmatrix}\phi_1(1)\,\beta(1) & \phi_2(1)\,\alpha(1)\\ \phi_1(2)\,\beta(2) & \phi_2(2)\,\alpha(2)\end{vmatrix}\right]$$

This illustrates the fact that there cannot be two (or more) electrons in the same system in exactly the same situation including their spin projections and shows the tendency of electrons with the same spin to avoid each other. Alternatively it can be said that the probability of finding two electrons with the same spin in the same volume element is zero.

Let us take a system with only two electrons, where one electron has MO ϕ_1 and the other ϕ_2. The total, orbital wave function is then

$$\frac{1}{\sqrt{2}}[\phi_1(1)\phi_2(2) \pm \phi_1(2)\phi_2(1)]$$

since both permutations of the electrons are equally acceptable. For the spin function we have four possibilities: $\alpha(1)\alpha(2)$, $\beta(1)\beta(2)$,

$$\frac{1}{\sqrt{2}}[\alpha(1)\beta(2) + \alpha(2)\beta(1)], \qquad \frac{1}{\sqrt{2}}[\alpha(1)\beta(2) - \alpha(2)\beta(1)]$$

Three of these latter are symmetrical (have their sign unchanged) with respect to an exchange of the coordinates of the two electrons (replacing (1) by (2) and vice versa) and the one having the minus sign between the two terms is antisymmetrical.

Thus, if we want a singlet state we must combine the only anti-symmetrical spin function with the symmetrical orbital function (with the plus sign between the two terms), and, if we want a triplet state, the symmetrical spin functions with the antisymmetrical orbital function. In this way the total wave functions will be antisymmetrical in conformity with the Pauli principle. Thus:

Singlet:

$$\frac{1}{\sqrt{2}}[\phi_1(1)\phi_2(2) + \phi_1(2)\phi_2(1)]\frac{1}{\sqrt{2}}[\alpha(1)\beta(2) - \alpha(2)\beta(1)] \quad (10\text{-}3)$$

Triplet:

$$\frac{1}{\sqrt{2}}[\phi_1(1)\phi_2(2) - \phi_1(2)\phi_2(1)][\alpha(1)\alpha(2)]$$

$$\frac{1}{\sqrt{2}}[\phi_1(1)\phi_2(2) - \phi_1(2)\phi_2(1)]\frac{1}{\sqrt{2}}[\alpha(1)\beta(2) + \alpha(2)\beta(1)] \quad (10\text{-}4)$$

$$\frac{1}{\sqrt{2}}[\phi_1(1)\phi_2(2) - \phi_1(2)\phi_2(1)][\beta(1)\beta(2)]$$

10-1 THE EXAMPLE OF ETHYLENE

Goeppert-Mayer and Sklar [190] were the first to use such anti-symmetrized wave functions in their study of the electronic spectrum of benzene. We prefer to begin the description of this method with the simpler example of ethylene. This molecule was first treated by Hartmann [191] and an improved treatment was published later by Parr and Crawford [192].

Only the two π electrons will be included explicitly. The two common LCAO MO orbitals are (see Chapter 3):

$$\phi_1 = \frac{1}{\sqrt{2+2S}}(\psi_a + \psi_b) \tag{10-5}$$

$$\phi_2 = \frac{1}{\sqrt{2-2S}}(\psi_a - \psi_b) \tag{10-6}$$

where the overlap integrals will be taken into account throughout.

In the ground state both electrons are in ϕ_1, one with spin projection α, the other with β. In the first excited state one electron is assigned to ϕ_1 and one to ϕ_2. They may have the same spin or opposite spins, thus giving a singlet and a triplet state. Another excited state is obtained in assigning both electrons to ϕ_2. This configuration can yield only a singlet state.

$$^1E_1 \qquad\qquad {}^1E_2,\, {}^3E_2 \qquad\qquad {}^1E_3$$

The orbital parts of the eigenfunctions for these states will be the following:

$$
\begin{aligned}
{}^1E_1&: \quad \phi_1(1)\phi_1(2) \\
{}^1E_2&: \quad \frac{1}{\sqrt{2}}[\phi_1(1)\phi_2(2) + \phi_1(2)\phi_2(1)] \\
{}^3E_2&: \quad \frac{1}{\sqrt{2}}[\phi_1(1)\phi_2(2) - \phi_1(2)\phi_2(1)] \\
{}^1E_3&: \quad \phi_2(1)\phi_2(2)
\end{aligned} \tag{10-7}
$$

In order to obtain the completely antisymmetrized eigenfunctions we have to multiply these by suitable spin functions, as given above.

Then we have

$$^1\Psi_1 = \phi_1(1)\phi_1(2)\frac{1}{\sqrt{2}}[\alpha(1)\beta(2) - \alpha(2)\beta(1)]$$

$$^1\Psi_2 = \frac{1}{\sqrt{2}}[\phi_1(1)\phi_2(2) + \phi_1(2)\phi_2(1)]\,\frac{1}{\sqrt{2}}[\alpha(1)\beta(2) - \alpha(2)\beta(1)]$$

$$^3\Psi_2 = \begin{cases} \dfrac{1}{\sqrt{2}}[\phi_1(1)\phi_2(2) - \phi_1(2)\phi_2(1)]\alpha(1)\alpha(2), & \text{or} \\[2mm] \dfrac{1}{\sqrt{2}}[\phi_1(1)\phi_2(2) - \phi_1(2)\phi_2(1)]\beta(1)\beta(2), & \text{or} \\[2mm] \dfrac{1}{\sqrt{2}}[\phi_1(1)\phi_2(2) - \phi_1(2)\phi_2(1)]\dfrac{1}{\sqrt{2}}[\alpha(1)\beta(2) + \alpha(2)\beta(1)] \end{cases} \tag{10-8}$$

$$^1\Psi_3 = \phi_2(2)\phi_2(2)\frac{1}{\sqrt{2}}[\alpha(1)\beta(2) - \alpha(2)\beta(1)]$$

Carrying out the multiplications, indicating spin β by a bar above the respective MO, and choosing $\alpha(1)\alpha(2)$ for the triplet state, we write

$$^1\Psi_1 = \frac{1}{\sqrt{2}}[\phi_1(1)\overline{\phi_1(2)} - \overline{\phi_1(1)}\phi_1(2)]$$

$$^1\Psi_2 = \frac{1}{2}[\phi_1(1)\overline{\phi_2(2)} - \overline{\phi_1(1)}\phi_2(2) + \overline{\phi_1(2)}\phi_2(1) - \phi_1(2)\overline{\phi_2(1)}]$$

$$^3\Psi_2 = \frac{1}{\sqrt{2}}[\phi_1(1)\phi_2(2) - \phi_1(2)\phi_2(1)] \tag{10-9}$$

$$^1\Psi_3 = \frac{1}{\sqrt{2}}[\phi_2(1)\overline{\phi_2(2)} - \overline{\phi_2(1)}\phi_2(2)]$$

The Hamiltonian of the system can be written as follows:

$$H = T(1) + T(2) + H_0(1) + H_0(2) + \frac{e^2}{r_{12}} \tag{10-10}$$

where $T(1)$ and $T(2)$ represent the kinetic energies of electrons (1) and (2), $H_0(1)$ and $H_0(2)$ the potential energies arising from the interactions of electrons (1) and (2) with the core that remains from ethylene if we formally remove the two π electrons. e^2/r_{12} is the repulsive potential between the two π electrons (r_{12} is the distance between these latter). This last member is very important. It depends on the coordinates of both electrons and was not explicitly included in the simple LCAO MO treatment.

The energy of the ground "state" is equal to

$$^1E_1 = \int {}^1\Psi_1 H\, {}^1\Psi_1\, d\tau \tag{10-11}$$

since the wave functions are normalized. Writing it out in full detail we have

$$
\begin{aligned}
^1E_1 = \frac{1}{2}\int &[\phi_1(1)\overline{\phi_1(2)} - \overline{\phi_1(1)}\phi_1(2)]\Big[T(1) + T(2) + H_0(1) \\
&+ H_0(2) + \frac{e^2}{r_{12}}\Big][\phi_1(1)\overline{\phi_1(2)} - \overline{\phi_1(1)}\phi_1(2)]\, d\tau_1\, d\tau_2 \\
= \frac{1}{2}\int &\Big\{\phi_1(1)\overline{\phi_1(2)}[T(1) + H_0(1)]\phi_1(1)\overline{\phi_1(2)} \\
&- \phi_1(1)\overline{\phi_1(2)}\,[T(1) + H_0(1)]\overline{\phi_1(1)}\phi_1(2) \\
&- \overline{\phi_1(1)}\phi_1(2)\,[T(1) + H_0(1)]\phi_1(1)\overline{\phi_1(2)} \\
&+ \overline{\phi_1(1)}\phi_1(2)\,[T(1) + H_0(1)]\overline{\phi_1(1)}\phi_1(2) \\
&+ \phi_1(1)\overline{\phi_1(2)}[T(2) + H_0(2)]\phi_1(1)\overline{\phi_1(2)} \\
&- \phi_1(1)\overline{\phi_1(2)}[T(2) + H_0(2)]\overline{\phi_1(1)}\phi_1(2) \\
&- \overline{\phi_1(1)}\phi_1(2)[T(2) + H_0(2)]\phi_1(1)\overline{\phi_1(2)} \\
&+ \overline{\phi_1(1)}\phi_1(2)[T(2) + H_0(2)]\overline{\phi_1(1)}\phi_1(2) \\
&+ \phi_1(1)\overline{\phi_1(2)}\,\frac{e^2}{r_{12}}\,\phi_1(1)\overline{\phi_1(2)} \\
&- \phi_1(1)\overline{\phi_1(2)}\,\frac{e_2}{r_{12}}\,\overline{\phi_1(1)}\phi_1(2)
\end{aligned}
\tag{10-12}
$$

$$- \overline{\phi_1(1)}\,\phi_1(2)\,\frac{e^2}{r_{12}}\,\phi_1(1)\,\overline{\phi_1(2)}$$

$$+ \left. \overline{\phi_1(1)}\,\phi_1(2)\,\frac{e^2}{r_{12}}\,\overline{\phi_1(1)}\,\phi_1(2) \right\} d\tau_1\,d\tau_2$$

Since we have neglected magnetic interactions, the spin functions behave as constants with respect to the Hamiltonian, and since they are mutually orthogonal the same electrons must have the same spin left and right of the operator or else the term vanishes. Furthermore, because of the orthogonality of the ϕ_i if the operator acts upon only one electron, as in the first eight terms, the other electron must be in the same orbital right and left of the operator or else the term again vanishes. Actually, in this simple case, the first rule is sufficient.

Then, we see that the second, third, sixth, seventh, tenth, and eleventh terms are zero and we are left with four terms of the form

$$\begin{aligned}
\epsilon_1 &= \int \phi_1(1)\,\phi_1(2)[T(1) + H_0(1)]\phi_1(1)\,\phi_1(2)\,d\tau_1\,d\tau_2 \\
&= \int \phi_1(1)[T(1) + H_0(1)]\phi_1(1)\,d\tau_1
\end{aligned} \tag{10-13}$$

where we have integrated over the coordinates of electron (2). Since the two electrons play exactly the same role we can also write

$$\epsilon_1 = \int \phi_1(2)[T(2) + H_0(2)]\phi_1(2)\,d\tau_2$$

Besides these there remain two terms having the form

$$\gamma_{11} = \int \phi_1(1)\,\phi_1(2)\,\frac{e^2}{r_{12}}\,\phi_1(1)\,\phi_1(2)\,d\tau_1\,d\tau_2 \tag{10-14}$$

We no longer need the spins; they have done their duty by eliminating half of the terms.

Finally,

$$^1E_1 = 2\epsilon_1 + \gamma_{11} \tag{10-15}$$

ϵ and γ are called *molecular integrals* since they contain the molecular orbitals, ϕ_i. ϵ_1 represents the interaction between a π electron and the core; γ_{11} is a Coulomb integral representing the interaction between the two π electrons.

Similar expressions can be written down for the excited states using the respective eigenfunctions. Only for $^1E_2$ will somewhat more labor be required. We obtain

$$\begin{aligned}
^1E_1 &= 2\epsilon_1 + \gamma_{11} \\
^1E_2 &= \epsilon_1 + \epsilon_2 + \gamma_{12} + \delta_{12} \\
^3E_2 &= \epsilon_1 + \epsilon_2 + \gamma_{12} - \delta_{12} \\
^1E_3 &= 2\epsilon_2 + \gamma_{22}
\end{aligned} \tag{10-16}$$

The meaning of the new symbols is as follows:

$$\epsilon_2 = \int \phi_2(1)[T(1) + H_0(1)]\phi_2(1)\, d\tau_1$$

$$\gamma_{12} = \int \phi_1(1)\phi_2(2)\frac{e^2}{r_{12}}\phi_1(1)\phi_2(2)\, d\tau_1\, d\tau_2$$

$$\gamma_{22} = \int \phi_2(1)\phi_2(2)\frac{e^2}{r_{12}}\phi_2(1)\phi_2(2)\, d\tau_1\, d\tau_2 \tag{10-17}$$

$$\delta_{12} = \int \phi_1(1)\phi_2(2)\frac{e^2}{r_{12}}\phi_1(2)\phi_2(1)\, d\tau_1\, d\tau_2$$

γ_{12} is another Coulomb integral, but δ_{12} is an exchange integral since the electrons are not in the same orbitals left and right of the operator.

Obviously

$$^1E_2 - {}^3E_2 = 2\delta_{12} \tag{10-18}$$

This is the singlet-triplet separation which could not be obtained in the simple LCAO MO approximation; we had to be contented there with their mean.

The energies, so far, are expressed in terms of molecular integrals. These, in turn, can be expressed in terms of atomic integrals, following Goeppert-Mayer and Sklar [190] in replacing the ϕ_i by the corresponding linear combinations of atomic orbitals. Here

$$\phi_1 = \frac{1}{\sqrt{2 + 2S}}(\psi_a + \psi_b) \tag{10-5}$$

$$\phi_2 = \frac{1}{\sqrt{2 - 2S}}(\psi_a - \psi_b) \tag{10-6}$$

Hence by (10-9)

$$^1\Psi_1 = \frac{1}{\sqrt{2}}\frac{1}{2 + 2S}\{[\psi_a(1) + \psi_b(1)][\overline{\psi_a(2)} + \overline{\psi_b(2)}]$$
$$- [\overline{\psi_a(1)} + \overline{\psi_b(1)}][\psi_a(2) + \psi_b(2)]\}$$

$$^1\Psi_2 = \frac{1}{2}\frac{1}{\sqrt{2 + 2S}}\frac{1}{\sqrt{2 - 2S}}\{[\psi_a(1) + \psi_b(1)]$$
$$\times [\overline{\psi_a(2)} - \overline{\psi_b(2)}] - [\overline{\psi_a(1)} + \overline{\psi_b(1)}][\psi_a(2) - \psi_b(2)]$$
$$+ [\overline{\psi_a(2)} + \overline{\psi_b(2)}][\psi_a(1) - \psi_b(1)]$$
$$- [\psi_a(2) + \psi_b(2)][\overline{\psi_a(1)} - \overline{\psi_b(1)}]\} \tag{10-19}$$

$$^3\Psi_2 = \frac{1}{\sqrt{2}}\frac{1}{\sqrt{2 + 2S}}\frac{1}{\sqrt{2 - 2S}}\{[\psi_a(1) + \psi_b(1)][\psi_a(2) - \psi_b(2)]$$
$$- [\psi_a(2) + \psi_b(2)][\psi_a(1) - \psi_b(1)]\}$$

$$^1\Psi_3 = \frac{1}{\sqrt{2}}\frac{1}{2 - 2S}\{[\psi_a(1) - \psi_b(1)][\overline{\psi_a(2)} - \overline{\psi_b(2)}]$$
$$- [\overline{\psi_a(1)} - \overline{\psi_b(1)}][\psi_a(2) - \psi_b(2)]\}$$

Instead of introducing the normalizing factors into these expressions we may use the $\phi_i = c_a\psi_a \pm c_b\psi_b$ with normalized coefficients.

We now introduce the LCAO corresponding to the ϕ_i into the expressions of the molecular integrals ϵ, γ, and δ. Those containing the operator e^2/r_{12} will be considered first. The following short notation is customary:

$$(aa; aa) = \int \psi_a(1)\psi_a(1) \frac{e^2}{r_{12}} \psi_a(2)\psi_a(2) \, d\tau_1 \, d\tau_2$$

$$(aa; bb) = \int \psi_a(1)\psi_a(1) \frac{e^2}{r_{12}} \psi_b(2)\psi_b(2) \, d\tau_1 \, d\tau_2$$

$$(aa; ab) = \int \psi_a(1)\psi_a(1) \frac{e^2}{r_{12}} \psi_a(2)\psi_b(2) \, d\tau_1 \, d\tau_2 \tag{10-20}$$

$$(ab; ab) = \int \psi_a(1)\psi_b(1) \frac{e^2}{r_{12}} \psi_a(2)\psi_b(2) \, d\tau_1 \, d\tau_2$$

With these we obtain

$$\gamma_{11} = \frac{1}{(2 + 2S)^2} [2(aa; aa) + 2(aa; bb) + 8(aa; ab) + 4(ab; ab)]$$

$$\gamma_{22} = \frac{1}{(2 - 2S)^2} [2(aa; aa) + 2(aa; bb) - 8(aa; ab) + 4(ab; ab)]$$

$$\gamma_{12} = \frac{1}{(2 + 2S)(2 - 2S)} [2(aa; aa) + 2(aa; bb) - 4(ab; ab)] \tag{10-21}$$

$$\delta_{12} = \frac{1}{(2 + 2S)(2 - 2S)} [2(aa; aa) - 2(aa; bb)]$$

In notations such as $(aa; bb)$, $(ab; ab)$, etc., the letters stand for the atomic orbitals, not for the electrons; the letters located at one side of the operator—which is represented by a semicolon—correspond to AO containing the same electron. Thus

$$(aa; bb) = \int \psi_a(1)\psi_b(2) \frac{e^2}{r_{12}} \psi_a(1)\psi_b(2) \, d\tau_1 \, d\tau_2$$

$$= \int \psi_a(1)\psi_a(1) \frac{e^2}{r_{12}} \psi_b(2)\psi_b(2) \, d\tau_1 \, d\tau_2$$

is a Coulomb integral and

$$(ab; ab) = \int \psi_a(1)\psi_b(2) \frac{e^2}{r_{12}} \psi_a(2)\psi_b(1) \, d\tau_1 \, d\tau_2$$

$$= \int \psi_a(1)\psi_a(2) \frac{e^2}{r_{12}} \psi_b(1)\psi_b(2) \, d\tau_1 \, d\tau_2$$

$$= \int \psi_a(1)\psi_b(1) \frac{e^2}{r_{12}} \psi_a(2)\psi_b(2) \, d\tau_1 \, d\tau_2$$

is an exchange integral. $(aa; ab) = (bb; ba)$ is a mixed Coulomb-exchange integral.

We still have to express ϵ_1 and ϵ_2 in terms of atomic integrals. This is not quite so easy. The operator has the form $T(1) + H_0(1)$ and contains, besides a kinetic-energy term, all the interactions between electron (1) and the charged particles making up the "core" of the ethylene molecule. Computing all these would lead to great complications. Among the electrons belonging to the core there are $1s$ electrons and σ electrons, which form the single bonds. There will be integrals that contain three or four different atomic orbitals. These are usually difficult to compute. To circumvent the difficulty Goeppert-Mayer and Sklar introduced a method which has been widely used. The hydrogen nuclei are supposed to be completely screened by their $1s$ electrons and are not considered. The carbon nuclei and the electronic charge surrounding them are treated as follows:

For electron (1)

$$H_0(1) = H_a^+(1) + H_b^+(1) \qquad (10\text{-}22)$$

where H_a^+ and H_b^+ represent the potential due to the interaction between π electron (1) and the positive ion which remains from carbon atom a or b after taking a π electron from it. Then they write

$$H_a^+(1) = H_a^*(1) - \int \frac{e^2}{r_{1n}} \psi_a(n)\psi_a(n)\, d\tau_n \qquad (10\text{-}23)$$

meaning that the potential acting upon a π electron due to the positive ion of carbon is equal to the potential due to a neutral carbon atom in the appropriate valence state (trigonally hybridized in this case), minus the repulsion of another hypothetical $2p_z$ electron on that atom (marked by n). (This implies that we neglect exchange terms in computing the related part of the energy [19, pp. 487, 519].)

If we act with the operator $[T(1) + H_a^+(1)]$ upon the atomic wave function $\psi_a(1)$, we may suppose that the following equation holds:

$$[T(1) + H_a^+(1)]\psi_a(1) = W_{2p}\psi_a(1) \qquad (10\text{-}24)$$

where the eigenvalue W_{2p} is the energy of a π electron in the field of carbon a, or the ionization energy for the removal of a π electron in the respective valence state. According to Mulliken [193] its value is close to -11.28 ev.

Then

$$\epsilon_1 = \int \phi_1(1)[T(1) + H_0(1)]\phi_1(1)\, d\tau_1$$

$$= \frac{1}{2+2S}\int [\psi_a(1) + \psi_b(1)][T(1) + H_a^+(1) + H_b^+(1)]$$

$$[\psi_a(1) + \psi_b(1)]\, d\tau_1$$

$$= \frac{1}{2+2S}\left\{\int \psi_a(1)[T(1) + H_a^+(1)]\psi_a\, d\tau_1 \right.$$

$$+ \int \psi_a(1)H_b^+(1)\psi_a(1)\, d\tau_1$$

$$+ \int \psi_a(1)[T(1) + H_a^+(1)]\psi_b(1)\, d\tau_1 \qquad (10\text{-}25)$$

$$+ \int \psi_b(1)[T(1) + H_a^+(1)]\psi_a(1)\, d\tau_1$$

$$+ \int \psi_a(1)H_b^+(1)\psi_b(1)\, d\tau_1$$

$$+ \int \psi_b(1)H_a^+(1)\psi_a(1)\, d\tau_1$$

$$+ \int \psi_b(1)[T(1) + H_b^+(1)]\psi_b(1)\, d\tau_1$$

$$+ \int \psi_b(1)H_a^+(1)\psi_b(1)\, d\tau_1 \Big\}$$

From (10-24)

$$\int \psi_a(1)[T(1) + H_a^+(1)]\psi_a(1)\, d\tau_1 = \int \psi_a(1)\, W_{2p}\psi_a(1)\, d\tau_1 = W_{2p}$$

$$(10\text{-}26)$$

and

$$\int \psi_b(1)[T(1) + H_a^+(1)]\psi_a(1)\, d\tau_1 = \int \psi_b(1)\, W_{2p}\psi_a\, d\tau_1 = W_{2p}S$$

$$(10\text{-}27)$$

Taking these into account we can write

$$\epsilon_1 = \frac{1}{2 + 2S}\Big\{2W_{2p} + 2W_{2p}S + \int \psi_a(1)H_b^+(1)\psi_a(1)\, d\tau_1$$

$$+ \int \psi_b(1)H_a^+(1)\psi_a(1)\, d\tau_1 + \int \psi_a(1)H_b^+(1)\psi_b(1)\, d\tau_1$$

$$+ \int \psi_b(1)H_a^+(1)\psi_b(1)\, d\tau_1 \Big\}$$

$$(10\text{-}28)$$

this way eliminating the kinetic energy.

Now we introduce

$$H_a^+ = H_a^*(1) - \int \frac{e^2}{r_{1n}}\psi_a(n)\psi_a(n)\, d\tau_n$$

We obtain

$$\epsilon_1 = W_{2p} + \frac{1}{2 + 2S}\Big\{\int \psi_a(1)H_b^*(1)\psi_a(1)\, d\tau_1$$

$$- \int \psi_a(1)\psi_a(1)\frac{e^2}{r_{1n}}\psi_b(n)\psi_b(n)\, d\tau_1\, d\tau_n$$

$$+ \int \psi_b(1)H_a^*(1)\psi_a(1)\, d\tau_1 - \int \psi_a(1)\psi_b(1)\frac{e^2}{r_{1n}}\psi_a(n)\psi_a(n)\, d\tau_1\, d\tau_n$$

$$+ \int \psi_a(1)H_b^*(1)\psi_b(1)\, d\tau_1 - \int \psi_a(1)\psi_b(1)\frac{e^2}{r_{1n}}\psi_b(n)\psi_b(n)\, d\tau_1\, d\tau_n$$

$$+ \int \psi_b(1)H_a^*(1)\psi_b(1)\, d\tau_1 - \int \psi_b(1)\psi_b(1)\frac{e^2}{r_{1n}}\psi_a(n)\psi_a(n)\, d\tau_1\, d\tau_n \Big\}$$

$$(10\text{-}29)$$

We shall introduce the following short notation:

$$(A:ab) = - \int \psi_a(1) H_a^*(1) \psi_b(1)\, d\tau_1 = (B:ab)$$

$$(A:bb) = - \int \psi_a(1) H_b^*(1) \psi_a(1)\, d\tau_1 = (B:aa)$$

(10–30)

These are called *penetration integrals*. Then we can write

$$\epsilon_1 = W_{2p} - \frac{1}{1+S}[(A:bb) + (A:ab) + (aa;bb) + (aa;ab)]$$ (10–31)

Similarly, using the linear combination with the minus sign (ϕ_2), we obtain

$$\epsilon_2 = W_{2p} - \frac{1}{1-S}[(A:bb) - (A:ab) + (aa;bb) - (aa;ab)]$$ (10–32)

The one-electron integrals represent interactions between atomic cores and a π electron. Their calculation is rendered easier by the spherical symmetry of H^*. The two-electron integrals are the same as before. However, since n is taken to be a π electron localized on a given atom, the atomic orbitals coming from operators of type

$$\int \frac{e^2}{r_{1n}} \psi_a(n) \psi_a(n)\, d\tau_n$$

do not carry with them normalization factors of the *molecular orbitals* or their coefficients in the latter if $\phi_i = c_a\psi_a + c_b\psi_b$ is used with normalized coefficients. (Compare the normalizing factors of the γ and δ with those of the ϵ.)

We have now expressed all the molecular integrals with atomic integrals. They were of the following types:

1. Two-electron integrals:
   (a) one-center Coulomb integrals such as $(aa;aa)$
   (b) two-center Coulomb integrals such as $(aa;bb)$
   (c) two-center exchange integrals such as $(ab;ab)$
   (d) two-center mixed Coulomb-exchange or hybrid integrals such as $(aa;ab)$
2. One-electron integrals:
   (a) two-center Coulomb-penetration integrals such as $(A:bb)$
   (b) two-center exchange-penetration integrals such as $(A:ab)$
   (c) and, naturally, overlap integrals: S_{ab}

(see also p. 276.)

We need their actual values. The rest of the work is, therefore, mathematical.

10-2 ATOMIC ORBITALS AND INTEGRALS

First we need the form of the atomic orbitals. These are known exactly for the hydrogen atom, and some of them were given on p. 15.

For molecules the exact wave functions are not known, except, in a sense, for the hydrogen molecule (see Chapter 13). Thus, if we build molecular wave functions from atomic wave functions the latter must possess a certain flexibility to be adapted to the various problems. In most molecular calculations Slater atomic orbitals have been used [194].

For the hydrogen atom the Schrödinger equation is separable into three parts, each depending on only one of the spherical coordinates, R, θ, ϕ. The eigenfunctions for $1s$, $2s$, and $2p$ states are

$$\psi_{1s} = \frac{1}{\sqrt{\pi}} \left(\frac{Z}{a_0}\right)^{3/2} e^{-\frac{Z}{a_0}r}$$

$$\psi_{2s} = \frac{1}{\sqrt{32\pi}} \left(\frac{Z}{a_0}\right)^{3/2} \left(2 - \frac{Z}{a_0}r\right) e^{-\frac{Z}{a_0}r}$$

$$\psi_{2p_z} = \frac{1}{\sqrt{32\pi}} \left(\frac{Z}{a_0}\right)^{3/2} \frac{Z}{a_0} re^{-\frac{Z}{2a_0}r} \cos\theta \qquad (10\text{-}33)$$

$$\psi_{2p_x} = \frac{1}{\sqrt{32\pi}} \left(\frac{Z}{a_0}\right)^{3/2} \frac{Z}{a_0} re^{-\frac{Z}{2a_0}r} \sin\theta \cos\phi$$

$$\psi_{2p_y} = \frac{1}{\sqrt{32\pi}} \left(\frac{Z}{a_0}\right)^{3/2} \frac{Z}{a_0} re^{-\frac{Z}{2a_0}r} \sin\theta \sin\phi$$

The radial part for all hydrogen wave functions except those with the lowest energy for a given value of l ($1s, 2p, 3d, \ldots$) has so-called *radial nodes*. Their number is $n - l - 1$. This means that the electron density attains a maximum at a certain distance from the nucleus, then it drops to zero, then it attains another maximum, etc., taking zero value $n - l - 1$ times. This is caused by the presence of the factor $[2 - (Z/a_0)r]$ in the case of $2s$ orbitals, and of similar factors for higher orbitals. $1s, 2p, 3d, \ldots$ orbitals have no radial nodes; for these $n - l - 1 = 0$.

Guillemin and Zener [195] and Zener [196] found on some atomic systems (up to F) that good results can be obtained in using wave functions where the angular parts are the same as in hydrogenlike wave functions and the radial parts are

$$R_{1s} = g_1 e^{-\gamma r}$$
$$R_{2s} = g_2 r^{n^*-1}(1 - \alpha r^{-1})e^{-\delta r} \qquad (10\text{-}34)$$
$$R_{2p} = g_3 r^{n^*-1}e^{-\delta r}$$

where the g are factors of normalization, n^* is an effective principal quantum number, and γ and δ are effective nuclear charges. Their values were fixed by using the variational method, i.e., expressing the energy in the form

$$E = \frac{\int \psi^* H\psi \, d\tau}{\int \psi^* \psi \, d\tau}$$

and minimizing it with respect to the parameters n^*, α, γ, and δ.

The simple hydrogenlike orbitals cannot be used for more complicated systems because they do not take into account the interaction between the electrons.

It turned out that α had little effect on the results. Therefore, Slater [194] suggested putting it equal to zero and introduced nodeless orbitals for all types of orbitals having the form (omitting the normalization factor)

$$r^{n^*-1} e^{-(Z-\sigma)r/n^*} \Theta_{l,m}(\theta) \Phi_m(\phi)$$

Here $(Z - \sigma)/n^*$ corresponds to Zener's δ for $2s$ or $2p$ orbitals. Slater did not carry out variation calculations but adapted the effective principal quantum numbers n^* and effective nuclear charges $(Z - \sigma)$ so as to give a good agreement with experimental energies for all kinds of atoms. He gave empirical rules to determine these constants for any atom.[2]

As for n^*, this is the same as n, for the first three rows of the periodic table. It has to be modified for the others:

n	1	2	3	4	5	6
n^*	1	2	3	3.7	4	4.2

$Z_{eff} = Z - \sigma$, where Z is the nuclear charge and σ is a screening constant, which takes into account the screening effect of all other electrons on an electron in a given orbital. In other words, the attraction by the nucleus at the given electron will not be such as it would be according to Z but, owing to the presence of the other electrons, $Z - \sigma$.

To find the appropriate value for σ the orbitals have to be divided into the following groups:
$(1s); (2s, 2p); (3s, 3p); (3d); (4s, 4p); (4d); (4f); (5s, 5p); \ldots$
Then the following rules can be applied:

1. Electrons in orbitals belonging to groups succeeding the one of the electron under consideration have no effect on σ.

2. Each occupied orbital belonging to the same group contributes 0.35 to σ except for $1s$ orbitals, from which the contribution is 0.30.

3. Each occupied orbital belonging to the group preceding the one of the orbital considered contributes 0.85 to σ if the considered orbital is s or p, 1.00 if it is d or f.

4. All other orbitals, closer to the nucleus, contribute 1.00.

Thus, for an electron in the $2p$ orbital of carbon, $C\ 1s^2\ 2s^2\ 2p^2$,

$$\sigma = 2 \times 0.85 + 3 \times 0.35 = 2.75$$
$$Z_{eff} = 6 - 2.75 = 3.25$$

[2] l is the azimuthal quantum number, and m is the magnetic quantum number.

Zener obtained 3.18 by the variational method, and this is the value which has been most often used in actual calculations. (For nitrogen his value is 3.84; for oxygen, 4.48.)

The Slater atomic orbitals are not all orthogonal, which is sometimes a cause of difficulties. Thus $1s$ and $2s$ are not mutually orthogonal, and this is the case of any two functions with the same l value. Orthogonalized Slater functions can be constructed using linear combinations of the nonorthogonalized ones. More complicated functions, such as self-consistent wave functions, can also be built from the latter. The reader is advised to consult a paper by Moffitt and Coulson on this subject [197].

The nodeless, unorthogonalized Slater orbitals have been used in most molecular calculations. The atomic integrals based on them may be found in tables of integrals computed by several authors. The most extensive collections are the following:

Kotani, Amemiya, Ishiguro, and Kimura, *Table of Molecular Integrals* (Tokyo: Maruzen, 1955).

Preuss, *Integraltafeln zur Quantenchemie*, 4 vols. (Berlin: Springer-Verlag, 1956, 1957, 1961, 1960).

Roothaan, *Two-center Coulomb Integrals between 1s, 2s, and 2p Orbitals*, Special Technical Report (The University of Chicago, Laboratory of Molecular Structure and Spectra, 1955).

Miller, Gerhauser, and Matsen, *Quantum Chemistry Integrals and Tables* (Austin: University of Texas Press, 1958).

Sahni and Cooley, *Derivation and Tabulation of Molecular Integrals*, Technical Note D-146-I (Washington, D.C.: National Aeronautics and Space Administration, 1959).

More data can be found in the following publications:

Kotani, Amemiya, and Simose, *Proc. Phys. Math. Soc. Japan,* **20,** extra number 1 (1938); **22,** extra number 1 (1940).

Kopineck, *Z. Naturforschung,* **5a,** 420 (1950); **6a,** 177 (1951); **7a,** 785 (1952).

Barnett and Coulson, *Phil. Trans. Roy. Soc. London,* **A243,** 221 (1951).

Roothaan, *J. Chem. Phys.,* **19,** 1445 (1951).

Ruedenberg, *J. Chem. Phys.,* **19,** 1459 (1951).

Ruedenberg, Roothaan, and Jaunzemis, *J. Chem. Phys.,* **24,** 210 (1956).

Roothaan, *J. Chem. Phys.,* **24,** 947 (1956).

Preuss, *Z. Naturforschung,* **8a,** 270 (1953); **9a,** 375 (1954).

Boys, Cook, Reeves, and Shavitt, *Nature,* **178,** 1207 (1956).

Mulliken, Rieke, Orloff, and Orloff, *J. Chem. Phys.,* **17,** 1248 (1949) (overlap integrals).

Coulson, *Proc. Cambridge Phil. Soc.*, **38**, 210 (1941).

Parr and Crawford, *J. Chem. Phys.*, **16**, 1049 (1948).

Brennan and Mulligan, *J. Chem. Phys.*, **20**, 1635 (1952).

Scrocco and Salvetti, *La Ricerca Scientifica*, **21**, 1629 (1951); **22**, 1766 (1952); **23**, 98 (1953).

Murai and Araki, *Progr. Theoret. Phys.*, **8**, 615 (1952) (heteronuclear).

However, this list is far from complete.

These publications contain either numerical tables or general formulas from which the numerical values may be computed.

The normalized Slater atomic orbitals have the general form

$$(2\zeta)^{n-1}(2n!)^{-1/2}r^{n-1}e^{-\zeta r}\Theta_{l,m}(\theta)\Phi_m(\phi)$$

where $\zeta = Z_{eff}/n$, and r is to be taken in atomic units ($r_0 = 1$ a. u. $= 0.5292$ Å). The types of atomic integrals were listed above. We may add the kinetic-energy integrals, which have the following form:

One-center: $\int \psi_a(1)\left(-\frac{1}{2}\nabla^2\right)\psi_a(1)\,d\tau$

Two-center: $\int \psi_a(1)\left(-\frac{1}{2}\nabla^2\right)\psi_b(1)\,d\tau$

where ∇^2 is the Laplace operator.

If we wish to consider explicitly more than one electron from a given center we shall have integrals such as $(A: aa')$, a one-center, monoelectronic integral with two different AO; $(aa'; a''a''')$, a one center, bielectronic integral with four different AO; $(aa'; b''b''')$, a two-center, bielectronic integral with two different AO on each center, and so on. The operators have to be taken in atomic units too. (The atomic unit for the electronic charge is the charge of an electron. Thus we shall have simply $1/r_a$, $1/r_{ab}$, and so on.)

In the tables the integrals are found, in the homoatomic case, as functions of a parameter

$$\rho = \zeta R$$

where R is the internuclear distance in atomic units and $\zeta = Z_{eff}/n$. For one-center integrals we have, naturally, $R = 0$.

In the heteropolar case the situation is more complicated. Overlap integrals, for example, may be given as functions of two parameters, τ and ρ (or t and p):

$$\tau = \frac{\zeta_a - \zeta_b}{\zeta_a + \zeta_b} \quad \text{and} \quad \rho = \frac{1}{2}(\zeta_a + \zeta_b)R$$

In molecules with more than two atoms, three- and four-center integrals also occur since the MO then are linear combinations of more than two AO. More-than-four-center integrals cannot occur, since the operators are at most bielectronic and an electron can be only in one AO left and in one right of the operator. A three-center integral, for example, is

$$(B:ac) = \int \psi_a(1) \frac{1}{r_b} \psi_c(1) \, d\tau$$

or

$$(aa;bc) = \int \psi_a(1)\psi_a(1)\frac{1}{r_{12}}\psi_b(2)\psi_c(2) \, d\tau$$

A four-center integral, for example, is

$$(ab;cd) = \int \psi_a(1)\psi_b(1)\frac{1}{r_{12}}\psi_c(2)\psi_d(2) \, d\tau$$

These three- and four-center integrals constitute a formidable problem. In spite of efforts by Barnett and Coulson [198], Taylor [199], Barker and Eyring [200], Shavitt and Karplus [201], and others, few of them are accurately known. There are, however, methods which make it possible to obtain them in a fair approximation. One such method is due to Mulliken. [202]. He replaced the charge distribution $\psi_a\psi_b$ by $\frac{1}{2}S_{ab}[\psi_a^2 + \psi_b^2]$, where S_{ab} is the overlap integral. Thus, for example, we would have

$$
\begin{aligned}
(ab;cc) &= \int \psi_a(1)\psi_b(1)\frac{1}{r_{12}}\psi_c(2)\psi_c(2) \, d\tau \\
&= \tfrac{1}{2}S_{ab}\Big[\int \psi_a(1)\psi_a(1)\frac{1}{r_{12}}\psi_c(2)\psi_c(2) \, d\tau \\
&\quad + \int \psi_b(1)\psi_b(1)\frac{1}{r_{12}}\psi_c(2)\psi_c(2) \, d\tau \\
&= \tfrac{1}{2}S_{ab}[(aa;cc) + (bb;cc)]
\end{aligned}
\tag{10-35}
$$

Similarly

$$(ab;cd) = \tfrac{1}{4}S_{ab}S_{cd}[(aa;cc) + (aa;dd) + (bb;cc) + (bb;dd)] \tag{10-36}$$

Another approximation was used by Sklar [203]. According to it

$$(ab;cd) = S_{ab}S_{cd} \int K_{ab}(1)K_{ab}(1)\frac{1}{r_{12}}K_{cd}(2)K_{cd}(2) \, d\tau \tag{10-37}$$

where K_{ab} is an atomic orbital with its center located halfway between nucleus a and nucleus b. If a and b are different atoms, K_{ab} may be placed closer to the more electronegative atom, proportionally to the electronegativities, for example [206].

We return now to the discussion of the ethylene molecule and we shall follow the treatment by Parr and Crawford [192]. The nuclei A and B will be considered as the origin of coordinates (x_a, y_a, z_a) and (x_b, y_b, z_b), respectively. Then we introduce spherical coordinates instead of the Cartesian ones, (r_a, θ_a, ϕ) and (r_b, θ_b, ϕ), and obtain as the normalized 2p Slater eigenfunctions:

$$a = \psi_a = \left(\frac{Z^5}{32\pi}\right)^{1/2} r_a e^{-Zr_a/2} \sin\theta_a \cos\phi$$

$$a_s = \psi_{as} = \left(\frac{Z^5}{32\pi}\right)^{1/2} r_a e^{-Zr_a/2} \sin\theta_a \sin\phi$$

$$a_r = \psi_{ar} = \left(\frac{Z^5}{32\pi}\right)^{1/2} r_a e^{-Zr_a/2} \cos\theta_a$$

$$b = \psi_b = \left(\frac{Z^5}{32\pi}\right)^{1/2} r_b e^{-Zr_b/2} \sin\theta_b \cos\phi$$

$$b_s = \psi_{bs} = \left(\frac{Z^5}{32\pi}\right)^{1/2} r_b e^{-Zr_b/2} \sin\theta_b \sin\phi$$

$$b_r = \psi_{br} = \left(\frac{Z^5}{32\pi}\right)^{1/2} r_b e^{-Zr_b/2} \cos\theta_b$$

(10-38)

Here the normalization factors due to both the radial and angular part were taken into account and the coordinates refer to either electron (1) or electron (2). Because of the choice of the coordinates our π orbitals will be ψ_a and ψ_b. (ψ_{ar} and ψ_{br} are those p orbitals whose axes lie in the internuclear axis, ψ_{as} and ψ_{bs} those whose axes are perpendicular to both ψ_a and ψ_{ar} or ψ_b and ψ_{br}).

We are reproducing here (Table 10-1) the table of integrals used by Parr and Crawford in 1948 [204]. Some of them might have been changed since then, but we prefer not to depart from the authors' original work. Also their table is of moderate size, so that it can be included here fairly conveniently.

TABLE 10-1

Intégral	$\rho = 0$	3	4	5
$Z^{-1}(aa; bb)$.	0.3914	0.3151	0.3476	0.2890
$Z^{-1}(aa; b_s b_s)$.	0.3492	0.3164	0.2909	0.2710
$Z^{-1}(aa_s; bb_s)$.	0.0211	0.0156	0.0121	0.0090
$Z^{-1}(aa; b_r b_r)$.	0.3492	0.338	0.324	0.305
$Z^{-1}(aa_r; bb_r)$.	0.0211	0.0056	−0.0009	−0.0044
$Z^{-1}(a_r a_r; b_r b_r)$.	0.3914	0.359	0.346	0.332
$Z^{-1}(ab; bb)$.	0.3914			
$Z^{-1}(ab; b_s b_s)$.	0.3492			
$Z^{-1}(ab_s; bb_s)$.	0.0211			
$Z^{-1}(ab; ab)$.	0.3914			
$Z^{-1}(ab; a_s b_s)$.	0.3492			
$Z^{-1}(ab_s; ab_s)$.	0.0211		0.005	0.005
$Z^{-1}(ab_r; ab_r)$.	0.0211	0.043	0.030	0.039
$Z^{-1}(ab_r; a_r b)$.	−0.0211	−0.043	−0.030	−0.039
$Z^{-1}(A; bb)$.	0.5859			
$Z^{-1}(A; ab)$.	0.5859			
S_{ab}	1.000			
$S_{a_r b_r}$	1.000			

INTÉGRAL	$\rho = 6$	7	8	8,37	9
$Z^{-1}(aa; bb)$.	0.2616	0.2367	0.2163	0.2086	0.1972
$Z^{-1}(aa; b_s b_s)$.	0.2484	0.2273	0.2097	0.2036	0.1928
$Z^{-1}(aa_s; bb_s)$.	0.0066	0.0047	0.0033	0.0025	0.0022
$Z^{-1}(aa; b_r b_r)$.	0.285	0.262	0.241		0.220
$Z^{-1}(aa_r; bb_r)$.	-0.0064	-0.0067	-0.0062		-0.0053
$Z^{-1}(a_r a_r; b_r b_r)$.	0.315	0.296	0.278		0.252
$Z^{-1}(ab; bb)$.	0.1538			0.0766	
$Z^{-1}(ab; b_s b_s)$.	0.1399			0.0704	
$Z^{-1}(ab_s; bb_s)$.	0.0069			0.0031	
$Z^{-1}(ab; ab)$.	0.073			0.022	
$Z^{-1}(ab; a_s b_s)$.	0.066			0.020	
$Z^{-1}(ab_s; ab_s)$.	0.0035	0.0025		0.0012	
$Z^{-1}(ab_r; ab_r)$.	0.028	0.021	0.015		0.010
$Z^{-1}(ab_r; a_r b)$.	-0.028	-0.021	-0.015		-0.010
$Z^{-1}(A; bb)$.	0.0773			0.01976	
$Z^{-1}(A; ab)$.	0.1200			0.04364	
S_{ab}	0.46800			0.25995	
$S_{a_r b_r}$					

INTÉGRAL	$\rho = 10$	12	14,5	16,7	20
$Z^{-1}(aa; bb)$.	0.1806	0.155	0.131	0.115	0.097
$Z^{-1}(aa; b_s b_s)$.	0.1774				
$Z^{-1}(aa_s; bb_s)$.	0.0016				
$Z^{-1}(aa; b_r b_r)$.	0.200				
$Z^{-1}(aa_r; bb_r)$.	-0.0042				
$Z^{-1}(a_r a_r; b_r b_r)$.	0.231				
$Z^{-1}(ab; bb)$.	0.0448		0.0087		
$Z^{-1}(ab; b_s b_s)$.	0.0415		0.0082		
$Z^{-1}(ab_s; bb_s)$.	0.0016		0.0003		
$Z^{-1}(ab; ab)$.	0.0082	0.0031	0.0006	0.0001	0.0000
$Z^{-1}(ab; a_s b_s)$	0.0074				
$Z^{-1}(ab_s; ab_s)$.	0.0004				
$Z^{-1}(ab_r; ab_r)$.	0.006				
$Z^{-1}(ab_r; a_r b)$.	-0.006				
$Z^{-1}(A; bb)$.	0.00703	0.00182	0.00031	$0.0_4 6$	$0.0_5 46$
$Z^{-1}(A; ab)$.	0.02090				
S_{ab}	0.16396	0.08874	0.03883	0.01798	
$S_{a_r b_r}$			-0.15356	0.08946	

Adopting the values $Z_{eff} = 3.18$ and $R = 1.353$ Å, we have $\rho = 8.13$. (For benzene we should have $\rho = 8.37$.)

Let us determine the one-center integral $(aa; aa)$ from the table. Then, since $a = b$, $R = 0$ and $\rho = 0$, and we find in the table

$$Z^{-1}(aa; bb) = 0.3914$$

We take as the atomic unit of energy

$$\frac{e^2}{2a_0} = 2.1792 \times 10^{-11} \text{ erg/atom} = 13.602 \text{ ev}$$

where a_0 is the Bohr radius. Thus, to have $(aa; aa)$ in atomic units we have to multiply the number found in the table by 3.18, and if we want it in electron-volts, by $3.18 \times 13.602 = 43.254$. It is important to remark that most other tables are constructed in such a way that we have to multiply by twice this the number found in the table (i.e., then e^2/a_0 is taken as the atomic energy unit).

For the other integrals we have to interpolate for $\rho = 8.13$. We obtain the following values:

$$S_{ab} = 0.2772$$
$$Z^{-1}(A:bb) = 0.0229$$
$$Z^{-1}(A:ab) = 0.0477$$
$$Z^{-1}(aa;aa) = 0.3914$$
$$Z^{-1}(aa;bb) = 0.2140$$
$$Z^{-1}(ab;ab) = 0.0250$$
$$Z^{-1}(aa;ab) = 0.0827$$

All we have to do now is use the expressions (10–21), (10–31), and (10–32) for the molecular integrals ϵ, γ, and δ.

We obtain

$$Z^{-1}(\epsilon_1 - W_{2p}) = -0.2876, \qquad \epsilon_1 - W_{2p} = -12{,}440 \text{ ev}$$
$$Z^{-1}(\epsilon_2 - W_{2p}) = -0.1474, \qquad \epsilon_2 - W_{2p} = -6.376 \text{ ev}$$
$$Z^{-1}\gamma_{11} = 0.3023, \qquad \gamma_{11} = 13.076 \text{ ev}$$
$$Z^{-1}\gamma_{22} = 0.3107, \qquad \gamma_{22} = 13.439 \text{ ev}$$
$$Z^{-1}\gamma_{12} = 0.3008, \qquad \gamma_{12} = 13.011 \text{ ev}$$
$$Z^{-1}\delta_{12} = 0.0961, \qquad \delta_{12} = 4.157 \text{ ev}$$

From these, using (10–16), we obtain the following energy levels:

$$^1E_3 = 2W_{2p} + 0.688 \text{ ev}$$
$$E_V = {}^1E_2 = 2W_{2p} - 1.648 \text{ ev}$$
$$E_T = {}^3E_2 = 2W_{2p} - 9.961 \text{ ev}$$
$$^1E_1 = 2W_{2p} - 11{,}804 \text{ ev}$$

Actually, these values should be diminished by the mutual repulsion of the two C^+ cores. This is equal to $e^2/r = 10.59$ ev. Thus, the true value of $^1E_1$ is $2W_{2p} - 1.21$ ev, and so on.

After having invested all this labor we may hope for results in good agreement with experiment. Unfortunately, this is not the case. The first singlet-singlet excitation energy would be 10.156 ev, which is much too high, and the singlet-triplet separation, 8.313 ev, is also much too great. We have to remember, however, that all we did was to antisymmetrize the orbitals and to make the Hamiltonian explicit, but nothing new has been done to improve the energy values, i.e., to improve the minimization process employed in the simple LCAO MO method.

The next step is to introduce configuration interaction.

10-3 CONFIGURATION INTERACTION

The Schrödinger equation is linear and homogeneous. Therefore, if $^1\Psi_1$, $^1\Psi_2$, $^3\Psi_2$, and $^1\Psi_3$ are solutions, then the general solution is

$$\Psi = s_1 \, ^1\Psi_1 + s_2 \, ^1\Psi_2 + s_3 \, ^3\Psi_2 + s_4 \, ^1\Psi_3 \qquad (10\text{-}39)$$

Normalization requires that

$$\sum_i |s_i|^2 = 1$$

the Ψ_i being mutually orthogonal. If the system is in a given stationary state then the corresponding coefficient is equal to 1, and all others are equal to zero. However, our eigenfunctions were obtained by an approximate, variational treatment and they are not the true, exact eigenfunctions. Consequently it may happen that more than one coefficient is different from zero. As to the energy, it would be exactly

$$\int \Psi_i H \Psi_i \, d\tau \qquad (10\text{-}40)$$

in any given stationary state, and terms involving two different eigenfunctions would be zero. Since we do not have the true eigenfunctions, some of the

$$\int \Psi_i H \Psi_j \, d\tau, \qquad i \neq j \qquad (10\text{-}41)$$

may not be zero.

In other words, the matrix of the Hamilton operator will not contain only diagonal terms. Therefore, we may consider the ψ_i as eigenfunctions belonging to the unperturbed Hamiltonian and then set up the secular determinant of the perturbation calculation (see Sec. 2-4).

Two important simplifying factors facilitate this work. First, states of different multiplicity will not interact because of the orthogonality of the spin functions. (No physical phenomenon is meant by "interacting." By not interacting we mean simply that $\int {}^1\Psi H \, {}^3\Psi \, d\tau$ is equal to zero.) Second, states belonging to different irreducible representations will not interact either, since the integral must be totally symmetrical with respect to all symmetry operations of the related group.

Ethylene belongs to group D_{2h}. $^1\Psi_1$ and $^1\Psi_3$ belong to A_{1g} since they have all electrons in closed orbitals, but $^1\Psi_2$ belongs to B_{3u} (pp. 206, 296). Hence only $^1E_1$ and $^1E_3$ "interact."

Coulson and Fischer [205], who introduced configuration interaction into molecular orbital theory, suggested that what we have been calling *states* should be called *configurations* and the word "state" should be reserved for the energy levels obtained as a result of a configuration interaction calculation. Thus

are configurations.

The secular determinant can be written as follows:

$$\begin{vmatrix} {}^1E_1 - E & \int {}^1\Psi_1 H\, {}^1\Psi_3\, d\tau \\ \int {}^1\Psi_1 H\, {}^1\Psi_3\, d\tau & {}^1E_3 - E \end{vmatrix} = 0 \qquad (10\text{-}42)$$

The off-diagonal term becomes

$$\begin{aligned}
\int {}^1\Psi_1 H\, {}^1\Psi_3\, d\tau &= \tfrac{1}{2} \int [\phi_1(1)\,\overline{\phi_1(2)} - \overline{\phi_1(1)}\,\phi_1(2)] \\
&\quad \times \left[T(1) + T(2) + H_0(1) + H_0(2) + \frac{e^2}{r_{12}} \right] \\
&\quad [\phi_2(1)\,\overline{\phi_2(2)} - \overline{\phi_2(1)}\,\phi_2(2)]\, d\tau_1\, d\tau_2 \\
&= \int \phi_1(1)\,\phi_1(2)\,\frac{e^2}{r_{12}}\,\phi_2(1)\,\phi_2(2)\, d\tau_1\, d\tau_2 \\
&= \int \phi_1(1)\,\phi_2(1)\,\frac{e^2}{r_{12}}\,\phi_1(2)\,\phi_2(2)\, d\tau_1\, d\tau_2 \\
&= \delta_{12}
\end{aligned} \qquad (10\text{-}43)$$

The other members vanish because of the orthogonality of the ϕ_i. Now we can solve the secular determinant using the previously obtained values of ${}^1E_1$, ${}^1E_3$, and δ_{12}. Then two values are obtained for E; the one of lower energy will be called E_N, the other E_Z. The new energy scheme is given in Fig. 10-1, taken from Parr and Crawford [192]. N, T, V, and Z are states, 1 and 2 are only configurations as obtained previously for ${}^1E_1$ and ${}^1E_3$. T and V were alone and were not affected by configuration interaction ($E_N = -13.061$ ev; $E_z = 1.945$ ev).

The main result is the stabilization of the ground state by about 1.3 ev. Naturally, there is no physical phenomenon involved here; only our calculation has been improved.

The eigenfunctions corresponding to states N and V are now of the form

$$X_N = s_1\, {}^1\Psi_1 + s_2\, {}^1\Psi_3 \qquad (10\text{-}44)$$

where s_1 and s_2 are obtained from the secular equation by substituting the respective value for E. With E_N we have

$$\begin{aligned}
0 &= s_1(-11.804 + 13.061) + s_2(4.157) \\
0 &= s_1(4.157) + s_2(0.688 + 13.061)
\end{aligned} \qquad (10\text{-}45)$$

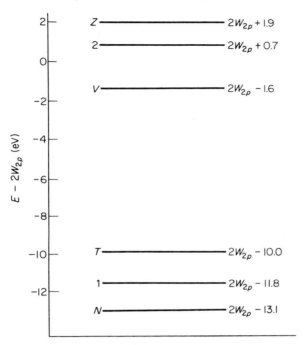

Fig. 10-1

Taking into account that

$$s_1^2 + s_2^2 = 1$$

we have for the coefficients:

$$s_1 = 0.958, \qquad s_2 = -0.288$$

Then we may compute the transition moment for transition $V \leftarrow N$.

$$Q_{V \leftarrow N} = \int (0.958 \,^1\Psi_1 - 0.288 \,^1\Psi_3)\, x\,^1\Psi_2\, d\tau$$

$$= 0.958 \int\,^1\Psi_1 x\,^1\Psi_2\, d\tau - 0.288 \int\,^1\Psi_3 x\,^1\Psi_2\, d\tau$$

with x taken in the direction of the internuclear axis. The first integral becomes

$$\int\,^1\Psi_1 x\,^1\Psi_2\, d\tau = \frac{1}{2\sqrt{2}} \int [\phi_1(1)\overline{\phi_1(2)} - \overline{\phi_1(1)}\phi_1(2)][x(1) + x(2)]$$

$$[\phi_1(1)\overline{\phi_2(2)} - \overline{\phi_1(1)}\phi_2(2) + \overline{\phi_1(2)}\phi_2(1)$$

$$- \phi_1(2)\overline{\phi_2(1)}]\, d\tau$$

$$= \sqrt{2} \int \phi_1\, x\phi_2\, d\tau$$

$$= \frac{\sqrt{2}}{\sqrt{2 + 2S}\,\sqrt{2 - 2S}} \int (\psi_a + \psi_b)\, x\, (\psi_a - \psi_b)\, d\tau$$

$$= \sqrt{\frac{1}{2 - 2S^2}} \left[\int \psi_a x \psi_a \, d\tau - \int \psi_b x \psi_b \, d\tau \right]$$

$$= \frac{1}{\sqrt{2 - 2S^2}} (x_a - x_b) = 0.736 \times 1.353 \,\text{Å} = 0.996 \,\text{Å}$$

where $x_a = 1.353/2$ Å and $x_b = -1.353/2$ Å. The second integral obviously has the same value, since ϕ_1 and ϕ_2 play the same role. Hence

$$Q_{V \leftarrow N} = 0.958 \times 0.996 - 0.288 \times 0.996$$
$$= 0.667 \,\text{Å} \tag{10-46}$$

and $\qquad Q_{V \leftarrow N}^2 = 0.445 \,\text{Å}^2$

Without configuration interaction, i.e., taking only the first term in Q_{V-N}, we should obtain 0.910 for Q^2. Thus, we see that configuration interaction lowered the intensity, which is proportional to Q^2 by a factor of 2.04. This is a definite improvement over the simple LCAO MO method, where Q^2 was always too high by a factor of from three to five (see Chapter 3).

It is important to point out that—as is implicit in the above deduction—antisymmetrization does not in itself change the transition moment (or the dipole moment of a given configuration); only configuration interaction does [206, 207].

In conclusion we can say that in the case of ethylene, configuration interaction improved the energy of the ground state and the transition moment, but the excitation energies are still rather far from reality, the experimental value for the first transition being certainly not higher than 7 ev.

Craig [208] introduced some refinements into this method. In particular, for different states he used different values for Z_{eff} and for the internuclear distances.

10-4 RULES FOR THE COMPUTATION OF MATRIX COMPONENTS IN CONFIGURATION INTERACTION

In the simple case of ethylene, with only two electrons considered explicitly, it was easy to determine the matrix components necessary to set up the secular equation. This becomes increasingly more difficult if the number of the electrons increases, since there will be generally many more interacting configurations. Furthermore, at low molecular symmetry, configurations containing only doubly occupied orbitals will interact with configurations containing singly occupied orbitals, and this introduces new types of integrals. Therefore, it is useful to set up rules for the practical evaluation of these matrix components. Such rules were given by Chalvet, Daudel, Roux, Sandorfy, and Vroelant [209]. We shall describe them slightly differently.

As stated above, configurations of different multiplicity do not interact and, if the molecule has symmetry, only configurations belonging to the same irreducible representation interact with one other. Hence there will be as many determinants for each multiplicity as there are irreducible representations to which configurations belong.

The rules will refer to configurations with fixed spins. This greatly simplifies the evaluation of the matrix components. In order to characterize a configuration we shall use two sets of parentheses; we write in the first one, in the natural order, the indices of the occupied spin orbitals with α spin, and in the second one those with β spin.

For example, the following configuration will be designated as $(1, 3, 5)\,(1, 3, 4)$:

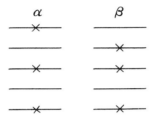

As we have seen, the Hamilton operator can be written as the sum of kinetic-energy operators $T(1), T(2), \ldots, T(n)$, if n electrons are considered; operators representing the interaction between a given electron and the core consisting of the nuclei and a certain number of electrons around them which are not considered explicitly, $H_0(1), H_0(2), H_0(3), \ldots$; and operators representing the mutual repulsion between the electrons, $e^2/r_{12}, e^2/r_{13}, \ldots$,

$$H = T(1) + T(2) + \cdots + H_0(1) + H_0(2) + \cdots + \sum_{\substack{u, v \\ u<v}} \frac{e^2}{r_{uv}} \qquad (10\text{-}47)$$

if u and v are general indices for the electrons. We have to compute matrix components of the type

$$H_{pq} = \int \Psi_p H \Psi_q \, d\tau \qquad (10\text{-}48)$$

where Ψ_p and Ψ_q are wave functions for configurations with fixed spins. H_{pq} will contain molecular integrals of the following types.

There will be monoelectronic integrals such as

$$\epsilon_i \equiv (ii) \equiv \int \phi_i(u)[T(u) + H_0(u)]\phi_i(u) \, d\tau \qquad (10\text{-}49)$$

which are like those we encountered in the case of ethylene, but there may also be integrals such as

$$\epsilon_{ij} \equiv (ij) \equiv \int \phi_i(u)[T(u) + H_0(u)]\phi_j(u) \, d\tau \qquad (10\text{-}50)$$

which occur when doubly and singly filled orbitals interact.

Then, there are bielectronic integrals such as

$$\gamma_{ii} \equiv (ii; ii) = \int \phi_i(u)\,\phi_i(v)\,\frac{e^2}{r_{uv}}\,\phi_i(u)\,\phi_i(v)\,d\tau_u\,d\tau_v \qquad (10\text{-}51)$$

$$\gamma_{ij} \equiv (ii; jj) = \int \phi_i(u)\,\phi_j(v)\,\frac{e^2}{r_{uv}}\,\phi_i(u)\,\phi_j(v)\,d\tau_u\,d\tau_v \qquad (10\text{-}52)$$

$$\delta_{ij} \equiv (ij; ij) = \int \phi_i(u)\,\phi_j(v)\,\frac{e^2}{r_{uv}}\,\phi_i(v)\,\phi_j(u)\,d\tau_u\,d\tau_v \qquad (10\text{-}53)$$

$$\zeta_{ij}^{kl} \equiv (ij; kl) = \int \phi_i(u)\,\phi_k(v)\,\frac{e^2}{r_{uv}}\,\phi_j(u)\,\phi_l(v)\,d\tau_u\,d\tau_v \qquad (10\text{-}54)$$

The last integral did not occur in the simple case of ethylene. It contains three or four different molecular orbitals. Two notations are used. The one using $\epsilon, \gamma, \delta,$ and ζ comes from Craig [213]; the other is obvious with the remark that the ϕ_i with the same electron are collected at one side of the operator sign (;).

First we deduce the rules for the diagonal matrix components, H_{pp}.

(a) *Rules for evaluating the diagonal matrix components, H_{pp}.*

The argument is very similar to that used in the valence-bond method (Chapter 4) except that now we have molecular orbitals instead of atomic orbitals and the MO are really orthogonal.

The eigenfunction of a configuration with doubly filled orbitals only can be given in the form of *one* Slater determinant. For example, for the ground configuration of butadiene treated as a four π-electronic problem,

$$
\begin{array}{l}
\phi_4 \ \underline{\hspace{4cm}} \\
\phi_3 \ \underline{\hspace{4cm}} \\
\phi_2 \ \underline{\quad\times\quad\quad\times\quad} \\
\phi_1 \ \underline{\quad\times\quad\quad\times\quad}
\end{array}
$$

we have

$$
^1\Psi_1 = \frac{1}{\sqrt{4!}}
\begin{vmatrix}
\phi_1(1)\alpha(1) & \phi_1(1)\beta(1) & \phi_2(1)\alpha(1) & \phi_2(1)\beta(1) \\
\phi_1(2)\alpha(2) & \phi_1(2)\beta(2) & \phi_2(2)\alpha(2) & \phi_2(2)\beta(2) \\
\phi_1(3)\alpha(3) & \phi_1(3)\beta(3) & \phi_2(3)\alpha(3) & \phi_2(3)\beta(3) \\
\phi_1(4)\alpha(4) & \phi_1(4)\beta(4) & \phi_2(4)\alpha(4) & \phi_2(4)\beta(4)
\end{vmatrix}
$$

$$
= \frac{1}{\sqrt{4!}}(\phi_1\overline{\phi_1}\phi_2\overline{\phi_2}) \qquad (10\text{-}55)
$$

where in the short expression the bar means spin projection β.

Since in the matrix component $\int {}^1\Psi_1 H\, {}^1\Psi_1\, d\tau$ each of the permutations encounters all of the other 4! permutations, the integrals can be written as the sum of $(4!)^2$ terms. However, since all permutations are equivalent, one of the 4! cancels out with the normalization factor, and it is sufficient to consider the terms between one permutation at the left with all 4! permutations at the right (Slater [15]).

Then, it is seen immediately that a monoelectronic operator like

$$T(u) + H_0(u)$$

gives only one nonzero term with any occupied spin orbital, an ϵ_i or (ii). Indeed, since the operator acting on (u) is monoelectronic, all other electrons must be in the same orbitals at both sides of the operator or else the orthogonality of the ϕ_i will make the term zero. Thus, the two permutations must be the same, which happens only once since all permutations are different.

If not all orbitals are doubly occupied, as in the following configuration of butadiene,

$$\phi_4 \quad \text{————————————}$$
$$\phi_3 \quad \text{————————✗————}$$
$$\phi_2 \quad \text{————✗————————}$$
$$\phi_1 \quad \text{————✗————✗————}$$

the situation is more complicated, inasmuch as more than one Slater determinant will be needed to describe the configuration. In this example

$$^1\Psi_2 = \frac{1}{\sqrt{2}} \frac{1}{\sqrt{4!}} [(\phi_1 \overline{\phi_1} \phi_2 \overline{\phi_3}) - (\phi_1 \overline{\phi_1} \overline{\phi_2} \phi_3)]$$

In general the additional factor of normalization is $1/\sqrt{2^m}$, where m is the number of pairs of electrons in simply occupied orbitals. However, each one of the Slater determinants is just one fixed-spin configuration, which we have defined in using spin orbitals.

Hence our previous rule is still valid, and every occupied spin orbital contributes one $\epsilon_i \equiv (ii)$ to H_{pp}. For example, the diagonal matrix component corresponding to fixed-spin configuration $(1, 2, 4)$ $(3, 4)$ (which may be a configuration of a free radical) will contain

$$\epsilon_1 + \epsilon_2 + \epsilon_3 + 2\epsilon_4 \quad \text{or} \quad (11) + (22) + (33) + 2(44)$$

For configuration $(1, 3, 5)$ $(1, 3, 4)$ we obtain similarly:

$$2\epsilon_1 + 2\epsilon_3 + \epsilon_4 + \epsilon_5$$

There will be no terms of type $\epsilon_{ij} \equiv (ij)$. Since there is the same function on both sides of the operator, if electron (u) is once in ϕ_i and once in ϕ_j there must be another electron, which is not in the same ϕ left and right of the operator. Then the term is zero because the operator is monoelectronic.

There will be, however, bielectronic terms. Every doubly occupied orbital introduces one $\gamma_{ii} \equiv (ii; ii)$, any other pair of electrons one $\gamma_{ij} \equiv (ii; jj)$. There will be only one of each, since the operator is only bielectronic and no permutation can be tolerated except between the orbitals of the two electrons on which the operator operates. The latter possibility introduces one $-\delta_{ij} \equiv -(ij; ij)$ for every pair of spin orbitals with the same spin. Of course, $\delta_{ii} = \gamma_{ii}$ and should not be counted twice.

For $(1, 2, 4)$ $(3, 4)$ we finally have

$$H_{pp} = \epsilon_1 + \epsilon_2 + \epsilon_3 + 2\epsilon_4 + \gamma_{12} + \gamma_{13} + 2\gamma_{14} + \gamma_{23}$$
$$+ 2\gamma_{24} + 2\gamma_{34} + \gamma_{44} - \delta_{12} - \delta_{14} - \delta_{24} - \delta_{34}$$

Similarly for $(1, 3, 5)$ $(1, 3, 4)$ we have:

$$H_{pp} = 2\epsilon_1 + 2\epsilon_3 + \epsilon_4 + \epsilon_5 + \gamma_{11} + \gamma_{33} + 4\gamma_{13} + 2\gamma_{15} + 2\gamma_{14} + 2\gamma_{35}$$
$$+ 2\gamma_{34} - 2\delta_{13} - \delta_{15} - \delta_{35} - \delta_{14} - \delta_{34}$$

(b) *Rules for evaluating the nondiagonal matrix components, H_{pq}.*

The matrix component between two configurations differing in the assignments of more than two electrons is zero since the operators are, at most, bielectronic.

Next we take the case of two fixed-spin configurations which differ in the assignments of two electrons. We suppose that electrons (u) and (v) are in orbitals $\phi_i(u)$ and $\phi_j(v)$ in one configuration and in $\phi_k(u)$ and $\phi_l(v)$ in the other. Then we shall have an integral

$$\zeta_{ik}^{jl} \equiv (ik; jl)$$

where the lower indices refer to electron (u) and the upper indices to electron (v), corresponding to the two sides in $(ik; jl)$.

The sign of this integral depends on the sign of the wave functions of the two configurations it involves. Since only $|\Psi|^2$ has physical meaning, a convention has to be adopted for obtaining these signs relative to each other. We give the positive sign in Ψ to the permutation which in the two brackets places the variables (1), (2), ... in the natural order of the occupied ϕ, with the first bracket (the one of the α) containing the first variables. We convene too that if $i \neq j$, i comes before j in the notation of p and if $k \neq l$, k comes before l in the notation of q.

Then, if n is the number of permutations necessary to transform the notation of q into a notation where the spin orbitals are in the same order as in the notation of p inasmuch as they are the same, the sign of ζ_{ij}^{kl} will be $(-1)^n$. If $k \neq l$, k comes before l.

Outside of ζ_{ij}^{kl} we may have an integral where the electrons having the same spin are exchanged. This is

$$\zeta_{il}^{jk} \equiv (il; jk)$$

and its sign is the opposite of the sign of ζ_{ij}^{kl} if ϕ_i and ϕ_j have the same spin. (If not, the term is zero.)

Finally we have

$$H_{pq} = (-1)^n[(ik;jl) + \tau(il;jk)]$$

where τ is equal to -1 or 0.

If we are interested in the H_{pq} of two fixed-spin configurations derived from the same configuration we have $i = l$ and $j = k$. For this ϕ_i and ϕ_j must have different spins; otherwise there would be only one Slater function. Then

$$H_{pq} = (-1)^n \zeta_{ij}^{ij} = (-1)^n(ij;ij) = \delta_{ij}$$

$$
\begin{array}{cccc}
\alpha & \beta & \alpha & \beta \\
\phi_j \quad\; \underrightarrow{\;\times\;} & & \phi_k \; \underrightarrow{\;\times\;} & \\
\phi_i \; \underrightarrow{\;\times\;} & & \phi_l & \underrightarrow{\;\times\;} \\
\underbrace{\qquad\qquad}_{p} & & \underbrace{\qquad\qquad}_{q} &
\end{array}
$$

If $i = j$ and $k = l$ which corresponds to a case like

$$
\begin{array}{cccc}
\alpha & \beta & \alpha & \beta \\
\phi_i \; \underrightarrow{\;\times\;} & \phi_j \; \underrightarrow{\;\times\;} & & \\
& & \phi_k \; \underrightarrow{\;\times\;} & \phi_l \; \underrightarrow{\;\times\;} \\
\underbrace{\qquad\qquad}_{p} & & \underbrace{\qquad\qquad}_{q} &
\end{array}
$$

we have

$$H_{pq} = (-1)^n \zeta_{ik}^{ik} = (-1)^n(ik;ik) = \delta_{ik}$$

This was the case of the interaction between the two configurations

$$
\begin{array}{cc}
\underline{\qquad} & \underrightarrow{\;\times\;\;\times} \\
\underrightarrow{\;\times\;\;\times} & \underline{\qquad}
\end{array}
$$

of ethylene.

If $i = j$ but $k \neq l$ we have

$$H_{pq} = (-1)^n \zeta_{ik}^{il} \equiv (-1)^n(ik;il)$$

An example would be

$$
\begin{array}{cccc}
\alpha & \beta & \alpha & \beta \\
\underline{\qquad} & & \underrightarrow{\;\times} & \\
\underline{\qquad} & & \underrightarrow{\;\times} & \\
\underrightarrow{\;\times\;\;\times} & & \underline{\qquad} & \\
\underrightarrow{\;\times\;\;\times} & & \underrightarrow{\;\times\;\;\times} &
\end{array}
$$

An interesting case is the one where the two fixed-spin configurations differ in the assignment of one electron only. Then the monoelectronic operators will give a nonzero term of the $\epsilon_{ik} \equiv (ik)$ type where $i \neq k$ and ϕ_i belongs to p and ϕ_k belongs to q.

The bielectronic operator in this case will produce interaction terms involving the electron which is in ϕ_i and ϕ_k respectively in the two configurations and any other electron. These will be of the $\phi_{ik}^{rr} \equiv (ik; rr)$ type where ϕ_r is any occupied spin orbital except ϕ_i and ϕ_k and, in addition, there will be terms like $-\phi_{is}^{ks}$ if ϕ_s is an occupied spin orbital having the same spin as ϕ_i, different from ϕ_i and ϕ_k.

The result for this case is

$$H_{pq} = (-1)^n [(ik) + \sum (ik; rr) - \sum (is; ks)]$$

We take as an example the case

$$p = (1, 2, 5)\,(3, 4), \qquad q = (1, 3, 5)\,(3, 4)$$

Then $n = 0$, since no permutation is necessary to transform the notation of q into that of p. Hence $(-1)^n = 1$ and

$$H_{pq} = \epsilon_{23} + \zeta_{23}^{11} + \zeta_{23}^{55} + \zeta_{23}^{33} + \zeta_{23}^{44} - \zeta_{21}^{31} - \zeta_{25}^{35}$$

(If, say, 5, were to occur in both parentheses, we should have $2\zeta_{23}^{55}$).

The matrix based on fixed-spin configurations is of higher degree than the matrix based on configurations in the usual sense. We can, however, reduce the degree of the matrix again if we remember that fixed-spin configurations are equivalent to one Slater function. In order to obtain H_{PQ}, where P and Q are now the complete, free-spin configurations, we have merely to add all the H_{pq}, p and q being the fixed-spin configurations derived from P and Q. In doing this we do not have to forget the normalization factors, which are $1/\sqrt{m_1}$ and $1/\sqrt{m_2}$, where m_1 and m_2 are the number of Slater functions in the eigenfunctions of P and Q, respectively (or $1/\sqrt{2^m}$, if m is the number of pairs of electrons in singly occupied orbitals in the case of an even number of electrons). They depend only on the number of electrons in singly occupied orbitals. If the number of electrons is odd, say 7, it is sufficient to consider the fixed-spin configurations with 4 and 3 electrons having α and β spin respectively while those with 3 and 4 may be omitted, or vice versa.

Good examples for the application of the rules described in this chapter may be found in a paper by Chalvet and Daudel [210].

10-5 CONFIGURATION INTERACTION: OTHER MOLECULES

Hydrocarbons. Benzene was treated by the method of antisymmetrized molecular orbitals as early as 1938 by Goeppert-Mayer and Sklar [190]. This classical work was refined and completed by a series of authors, in particular by A. London [211], Parr and Crawford [212], and Craig [213], and a very extensive treatment was given by Parr, Craig, and Ross [214].

We shall not go into a detailed discussion of these works, which differ from the case of ethylene mainly by their greater complexity. The method is always the same: first the simple LCAO orbitals are computed—taking overlap integrals into account—using symmetry as much as possible; then they are multiplied by appropriate spin functions and written in the form of Slater functions. The energy is expressed first in terms of molecular integrals and then in terms of atomic integrals, which in many cases can be found in tables. Then configuration interaction is applied, which requires a number of other molecular integrals equally transformable into sums of atomic integrals. Symmetry helps in determining the number of interacting configurations, and the rules given in the preceding chapter help in expressing the matrix components in terms of molecular integrals.

The number of configurations is usually very great. Since two configurations whose energies are very different usually do not interact much, a selection may often be made without much loss in accuracy. Craig [213] and Craig, Parr, and Ross [214] took into account all the configurations, which are obtained from the ground configuration by "exciting" one or two electrons.

When the molecular integrals are transformed into atomic integrals, three- and four-center integrals come in. These are generally difficult to compute and are approximated by Sklar's or Mulliken's method (see p. 277).

Table 10-2, taken from Parr, Craig, and Ross [214], summarizes the results obtained for benzene. The number in parentheses beside the group-theoretical symbols giving the symmetry of the various states is the number of configurations taken into account in computing its energy. The other columns give the energies obtained by using antisymmetrized molecular orbitals without configuration interaction (ASMO), with configuration interaction taking into account two-center integrals only (CI 2), with configuration interaction taking into account all the integrals (CI 2, 3, 4), and finally by the valence-bond method including polar structures (VB). In the last column are the energy values based on the observed spectrum. The energies are in electron-volts, with the ground-state energy taken as zero everywhere.

TABLE 10–2

	SINGLET	STATES		
	ASMO	CI 2	CI 2, 3, 4	VB	OBS
A_{1g} (9)	0.0	0.0	0.0	0.0	0.0
A_{2g} (3)	11.1	—	12.5	—	—
B_{1u} (6)	7.3	4.5	9.0	—	—
B_{2u} (5)	5.9	2.0	4.4	4.7	4.9
E_{1u} (11)	9.8	6.2	9.9	7.9	7.0
E_{2g} (11)	10.9	—	7.7	6.6	6.2

	TRIPLET	STATES	
	ASMO	CI 2, 3, 4	OBS
A_{1g} (4)	13.6	14.9	
A_{2g} (7)	11.1	11.8	
B_{1u} (5)	3.1	4.1	3.8
B_{2u} (4)	5.8	8.2	
E_{1u} (12)	4.4	4.7	
E_{2g} (9)	8.3	6.4	

The results yield strong evidence in favor of the $^1B_{2u} \leftarrow {}^1A_{1g}$ assignment of the first band system of benzene. This can be considered to be definite in view of a great amount of accumulated experimental and theoretical evidence. For the second band the data seem to indicate $^1E_{2g} \leftarrow {}^1A_{1g}$ rather than $^1B_{1u} \leftarrow {}^1A_{1g}$, although the former is forbidden by the Laporte rule. The third band would be $^1E_{1u} \leftarrow {}^1A_{1g}$. The first singlet-triplet transition would be $^3B_{1u} \leftarrow {}^1A_{1g}$. This latter would correspond to an extremely weak band found at about 3400 Å.

We shall discuss the spectrum of benzene in Chapter 15.

The results emphasize the importance of three- and four-center integrals, which in certain cases modify the order of the states. Chalvet and Daudel [210] confirmed this on other examples.

Configuration interaction was applied to naphthalene by Jacobs [215]; it was one of the first applications of this method. Julg and Pullman treated fulvene [216].

Longuet-Higgins [217] has shown that the method of molecular orbitals completed with configuration interaction and the valence-bond method including polar structures yield the same wave function, provided all configurations and all structures are taken into account. This can hardly ever be done in practice, however.

Substituted and Heteroatomic Molecules. In 1939 Sklar [218] made an attempt to apply the method of antisymmetrized molecular orbitals to benzene derivatives. They were of the "aniline type" where the substituent brings two $2p_z$ electrons, which can join with the π electron system of the benzene ring. Aniline, phenol, and fluorobenzene are of this type. Sklar considered toluene as being of the same type (see p. 339).

Toluene and fluorobenzene absorb about twice as strongly as benzene; phenol and aniline about ten to twenty times. We refer here to the $^1B_{2u} \leftarrow {}^1A_{1g}$ band system, which is forbidden for benzene itself and appears weakly at about 2550 Å thanks to a nontotally symmetrical vibration of the benzene ring.

Sklar's idea was to consider the substituted benzene molecule as a diatomic molecule. Then the wave function of the substituted molecule is written as a linear combination of a wave function representing the substituent (generally an sp^2 hybrid) and of a wave function representing the unperturbed benzene molecule. Sklar had to make many approximations but he was able to obtain the intensities of the first band in the right order of magnitude for phenol, aniline, fluorobenzene, and toluene. He was able to interpret the great difference of intensity between the two former and the two latter. (For details, see [218]).

Sklar [219] gave a treatment of the di- and polysubstituted benzene derivatives as well. In particular, he could interpret the curious fact that among benzene derivatives with *ortho-para* orienting substituents the *ortho*-disubstituted and the *meta*-disubstituted derivatives have a band with approximately the same intensity as that of the monosubstituted derivative but the intensity of the band of the *para*-disubstituted derivative is much greater. Sklar's calculations lead to the result that the intensities for the derivatives under discussion are in the relation

$$mono : ortho : meta : para = 1 : 1 : 1 : 4$$

which is in good agreement with experiment [219, 220].

This result was obtained for identical substituents but it may be generalized to the case of different substituents.

For *meta*-orienting substituents Sklar found that the transition moment is exactly antiparallel to the one for *ortho-para* orienting substituents. Two *meta*-directing substituents give the same result as two *ortho-para* directing substituents.

The combination of one *ortho-para* directing and one *meta*-directing substituent, provided the monosubstituted derivatives absorb with approximately equal intensity, yields the following relationship:

$$mono : ortho : meta : para = 1 : 3 : 3 : 0$$

a rather astonishing result.

Among tri (hydroxy) substituted benzene derivatives, $C_6H_3P_3$, where P is an *ortho-para* directing substituent, the symmetrical derivative, phloroglucine, has high enough symmetry to have its first band forbidden, like benzene itself. It appears weakly due to nontotally symmetrical vibrations. The intensity of the 1,2,3 derivative (pyrogallol) is zero too, not because of its symmetry but simply because the contributions of the three substituents cancel each other. The band will appear weak for the same reason as for phloroglucine. (For the extinction curves see Kiss [225]). The 1,2,4 isomer, hydroxyhydroquinone, should absorb three times as strongly as the monosubstituted derivative.

Sklar examined only the intensities. It is found that the frequencies exhibit similar phenomena. *Ortho-* and *meta*-$C_6H_4P_2$ absorb at about the same frequency, but *para*-$C_6H_4P_2$ undergoes a pronounced bathochromic shift with respect to the two other isomers. This fact was interpreted by Förster [223]. He particularly examined the case of the chlorobenzenes for which Conrad-Billroth had previously found [224] that isomers containing the same number of pairs of *para*-substituents (p) have similar spectra but that with the increase of this number p a proportionate shift to longer wavelengths is found. On the basis of valence-bond considerations, Förster established the following formula for the frequencies of substituted benzene derivatives:

$$\nu = \nu_0 - nB - \left(\frac{n(3-n)}{2} + 3p\right)C \qquad (10\text{-}56)$$

Here ν_0 is the frequency for benzene, B and C are positive constants whose value depends on the substituent, and n is the number of substituents.

Naturally, all these rules have to be treated with caution. They are based on certain approximations and it is not particularly surprising to find departures from them, especially for substituents exerting a strong perturbation on the benzene ring. Recently Forbes [226] gave examples to this effect.

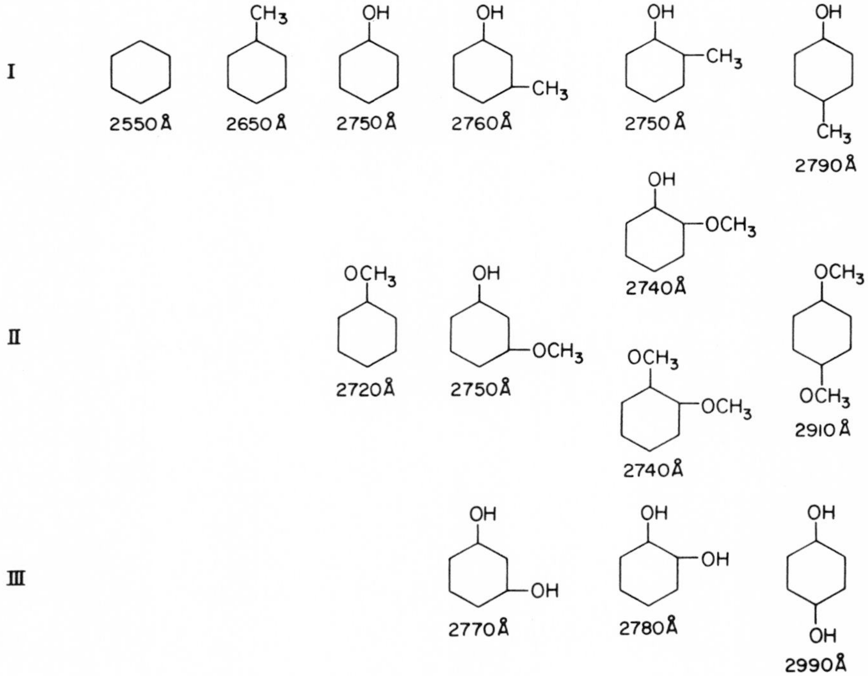

Fig. 10-2

Figure 10–2, taken from a paper by Kiss, Molnar, and Sandorfy [225], compares the λ_{max} values of a number of phenol derivatives, including some phenol ethers. Similar diagrams were given previously by Pauling [32].

Goeppert-Mayer and McCallum [227] in 1942 applied the antisymmetrized molecular orbital method to the positive ion of *para*-phenylendiamine. In this interesting work the idea of configuration interaction was already implicit.

The Semiempirical Method of
Pariser and Parr

The transition from empirical to nonempirical methods was, to some extent, disappointing. Considering only spectral quantities we may conclude from the examples of the preceding chapter that while lower and, therefore, better energy values are obtained for the ground states when configuration interaction is introduced, and there was a significant improvement in the transition moment, the excitation energies obtained were rather far from reality. One may say in a perhaps unscientific manner that in removing about half of the approximations involved with the empirical methods we diminished the chance for the various errors to cancel each other.

Therefore, Moffitt [229, 230] and Pariser and Parr [231, 232] proposed to compromise by reintroducing a reasonable amount of empiricism into the nonempirical methods.

We are going to describe Pariser and Parr's method on the example of ethylene [232], considered again as a two-π-electronic problem.

The two LCAO molecular orbitals, which were the starting point of the nonempirical calculation, were

$$\phi_1 = \frac{1}{\sqrt{2}} (\psi_a + \psi_b) \qquad B_{1u}$$

$$\phi_2 = \frac{1}{\sqrt{2}} (\psi_a - \psi_b) \qquad B_{2g}$$

(11-1)

The atomic orbitals are not mutually orthogonal, and by writing the normalization factor simply as $1/\sqrt{2}$ we ignore this fact. The energies computed in Chapter 10 in terms of molecular integrals were as follows:

$$^1E_1 = 2\epsilon_1 + \gamma_{11}$$
$$^1E_2 = \epsilon_1 + \epsilon_2 + \gamma_{12} + \delta_{12}$$
$$^3E_2 = \epsilon_1 + \epsilon_2 + \gamma_{12} - \delta_{12}$$
$$^1E_3 = 2\epsilon_2 + \gamma_{22}$$

Setting $S = 0$, we have for the molecular integrals representing electronic repulsion

$$\gamma_{11} = 1/4\,[2(aa;aa) + 2(aa;bb) + 8(aa;ab) + 4(ab;ab)]$$
$$\gamma_{22} = 1/4\,[2(aa;aa) + 2(aa;bb) - 8(aa;ab) + 4(ab;ab)]$$
$$\gamma_{12} = 1/4\,[2(aa;aa) + 2(aa;bb) - 4(ab;ab)]$$
$$\delta_{12} = 1/4\,[2(aa;aa) - 2(aa;bb)]$$

$$(11\text{-}2)$$

Now Pariser and Parr request not only that the atomic orbitals are to be treated as if they were orthogonal but that differential overlap

$$\psi_a(v)\,\psi_b(v)\,d\tau_v$$

is zero. Then obviously any integral containing the product ab at one side or at both sides of the operator vanishes and only the purely coulombic integrals remain. (Equating the overlap *integral* to zero would not do this.) Thus under these conditions we obtain that

$$\gamma_{11} = \gamma_{22} = \gamma_{12} = \tfrac{1}{2}\,[(aa;aa) + (aa;bb)]$$
$$\delta_{12} = \tfrac{1}{2}\,[(aa;aa) - (aa;bb)]$$

$$(11\text{-}3)$$

We still need the core integrals ϵ_1 and ϵ_2. Before introducing the Goeppert-Mayer and Sklar potential, we had, with H_0 being the Hamiltonian not including the electron repulsion term, e^2/r_{12},[1]

$$\epsilon_1 = \frac{1}{2} \int (\psi_a + \psi_b)\,H_0(\psi_a + \psi_b)\,d\tau$$
$$= \int \psi_a H_0 \psi_a\,d\tau + \int \psi_a H_0 \psi_b\,d\tau$$

and

$$\epsilon_2 = \frac{1}{2} \int (\psi_a - \psi_b)\,H_0(\psi_a - \psi_b)\,d\tau$$
$$= \int \psi_a H_0 \psi_a\,d\tau - \int \psi_a H_0 \psi_b\,d\tau$$

$$(11\text{-}4)$$

taking into account that ψ_a and ψ_b are equivalent. It is seen immediately that the two integrals occuring in ϵ_1 and ϵ_2 are quantities

[1] But including, this time, the kinetic energy term.

analogous to the coulombic and resonance integrals used in the simple empirical LCAO method. So we write

$$\alpha = \int \psi_a H_0 \psi_a \, d\tau = \int \psi_b H_0 \psi_b \, d\tau$$

and   (11-5)

$$\beta = \int \psi_a H_0 \psi_b \, d\tau$$

With these the core energies become

$$\epsilon_1 = \alpha + \beta, \qquad \epsilon_2 = \alpha - \beta \qquad (11\text{-}6)$$

α could be calculated from Eq. (10-25) on p. 270, which was an expression for ϵ_1. All we have to do is to replace ϕ_1 not by $(\psi_a + \psi_b)$ but simply by ψ_a, leaving the operator unchanged, and introduce the Goeppert-Mayer and Sklar potential. It is obtained that

$$\alpha = W_{2p} - [(aa;bb) + (A:bb)] \qquad (11\text{-}7)$$

A term may be added to represent the attraction due to the hydrogen atoms. This is nonzero if there is overlap between the carbon and hydrogen atomic orbitals.

However, α is not needed for spectral excitation energies, as it cancels out between two states.

β is treated as an empirical parameter and is chosen to give agreement with experiment.

The bielectronic integrals $(aa;aa)$ and $(aa;bb)$ can be calculated using Slater orbitals. Pariser [233] and Moffitt [230] have shown, however, that there are good reasons to modify these.

To integral $(aa;aa)$ a certain physical meaning can be given. Pariser reasoned the following way: consider two neutral, infinitely separated C atoms in their sp^2 valence states. The energy necessary to remove one π-electron from each is $2W_{2p}$, W_{2p} being the ionization energy for a π-electron. We now transfer one π-electron from one carbon to the other, obtaining thereby the ion pair C^+ and C^-. The energy necessary to remove the two π-electrons from C^- is now $2W_{2p} + (aa;aa)$, since we have to take into account the mutual repulsion of the two. Thus $(aa;aa)$ was just the energy necessary to form the ion pair. On the other hand, this energy is equal to the ionization energy, I, of a neutral carbon atom minus its electron affinity, A. So we can write that

$$(aa;aa) = I - A \qquad (11\text{-}8)$$

Pariser first used experimental values given by Mulliken [234]: $I = -11.22$ ev, $A = 0.69$ ev. Then $(aa;aa) = -10.53$ ev. Later he modified this value to -10.96 ev. [235].

The theoretical value of the integral, using Slater orbitals, is

-16.93 ev. This is a great discrepancy. Moffitt has shown that it is due in great part to not considering the change in the energy of the σ electrons when the ion pair is formed. On the other hand, Stewart [236] has shown that $(aa; aa)$ becomes considerably smaller if Z_{eff} is varied.

By similar arguments it is found that the value of $(aa; bb)$ also must be lowered. In the case of ethylene, according to Pariser and Parr, it goes from -9.25 ev. to -7.38 ev. This semiempirical method is probably the best for computing excitation energies in the case of larger molecules. (see Chapter 15.)

The parameter β is chosen so that we have agreement with the first observed excitation energy. Then, broadly speaking, the Pariser and Parr method with the nonempirical integrals is capable of duplicating the results of the nonempirical calculations (antisymmetrized molecular orbitals plus configuration interaction), and with the integrals adjusted as above it gives a very reasonable agreement with the other experimental excitation energies.

The generalization of the method to larger molecules does not introduce any special difficulty. All we have to do is to express the energies in terms of molecular integrals, express the latter in terms of atomic integrals, and retain only the Coulomb integrals. The core integrals are easily obtained, too, by using the simple linear combinations of atomic orbitals, and neglecting the overlap integrals.

The following, very pertinent question remains to be answered. How is it that we were able to obtain good results by using such a drastic approximation as neglecting differential overlap? This is contrary to all the usual ideas associating strong bonds with great overlap between atomic orbitals. The flexibility provided by the introduction of an empirical parameter can only be a partial explanation.

The answer is that in this method we need not consider the atomic orbitals as ordinary atomic orbitals. It is entirely possible, instead of these, to use orbitals which are truly orthogonal and then form molecular orbitals from these orthogonal orbitals.

Such orbitals were introduced into the theory of metals by Wannier [237] and into molecular theory by Löwdin [238].

One way of building such orthogonal orbitals is to "mix" into ψ_a and ψ_b, localized on a and b, respectively, a certain amount of the orbital localized on the other center:

$$\psi_a' = c_a\psi_a + c_b\psi_b$$
$$\psi_b' = c_b\psi_a + c_a\psi_b \tag{11-9}$$

To have these two semilocalized orbitals normalized and orthogonal we must satisfy the conditions

$$c_a^2 + c_b^2 + 2c_a c_b S_{ab} = 1$$

and

$$2c_a c_b + (c_a^2 + c_b^2) S_{ab} = 0$$

(11-10)

to obtain

$$\psi_a' = \frac{1}{2}\left[\frac{1}{\sqrt{1+S_{ab}}} + \frac{1}{\sqrt{1-S_{ab}}}\right]\psi_a + \frac{1}{2}\left[\frac{1}{\sqrt{1+S_{ab}}} - \frac{1}{\sqrt{1-S_{ab}}}\right]\psi_b$$

$$\psi_b' = \frac{1}{2}\left[\frac{1}{\sqrt{1+S_{ab}}} - \frac{1}{\sqrt{1-S_{ab}}}\right]\psi_a + \frac{1}{2}\left[\frac{1}{\sqrt{1+S_{ab}}} + \frac{1}{\sqrt{1-S_{ab}}}\right]\psi_b$$

(11-11)

Supposing that in our previous deduction ψ_a and ψ_b were actually ψ_a' and ψ_b' justifies the omission of overlap *integrals*. It justifies, however, putting differential overlap equal to zero as well. This can be seen if we compute integrals like $(a'a'; a'b') \equiv (\psi_a'\psi_a'; \psi_a'\psi_b')$. The intervention of the overlap integral, S_{ab}, makes certain terms cancel, so that such integrals are very small (see [19, p. 503] and [239] to [243]).

In this way the Pariser and Parr procedure is justified if it is thought to be based on orthogonal semilocalized orbitals instead of the usual atomic orbitals localized on one center.

Pariser applied this method with great success to aromatic molecules [244]. Heteroatomic molecules have also been treated [245].

12

The Self-Consistent Field Method

12-1 GENERAL PRINCIPLES

In most molecular problems in wave mechanics the approximation is made that each electron can be regarded as being in a stationary state in the field of the nuclei and the other electrons. As a consequence the molecular wave function is expressed as a product of one-electron wave functions or spin orbitals,

$$\Psi = \phi_1(1)\phi_2(2)\cdots\phi_n(n) \tag{12-1}$$

We quote from D. R. Hartree, *Calculation of Atomic Structures* [246, p. 18]: "For such an approximate wave function Ψ, $|\phi_1(j)|^2$ gives the average charge density resulting from the presence of electron j in wave function ϕ_1, and this suggests that each one of these functions $\phi_1, \phi_2, \ldots, \phi_n$ should be determined as a solution of Schrödinger's equation for one electron in the field of the nucleus and of the total average charge distribution of the electrons in the *other* wave functions. In such a treatment, the field of the average electron distribution derived from the wave functions $\phi_1, \phi_2, \ldots, \phi_n$ must be the same as the field used in evaluating these wave functions. This aspect has led to the term 'self-consistent field' for the atomic field so determined."

This idea implies the iterative nature of the method. For if we want to determine the field acting on a given electron we have to know the wave functions of all the others. However, we do not know more about them than about the chosen one. Now we quote from Coulson [11, p. 32]:

"Suppose that there are n electrons in our atom. Then let us first guess plausible wave functions for each of these electrons. . . . Now choose one of the electrons and find the average field provided by all the others. . . . This process allows us to write down, and then to solve, the wave equation for our chosen electron. We obtain what may be called a first-improved wave function for this electron. This new function may next be used to calculate the average field for a second electron, and enables us to get a first-improved wave function for this electron also. The process is continued until we have a complete bunch of first-improved orbitals. In the same way starting with these we may improve them, one by one, and calculate second-order a.o's. This technique is continued until successive iteration makes no appreciable difference to the orbitals. We may then say that the set of a.o's are self-consistent."

This idea of self-consistency is then coupled with a variational treatment whose well-known energy expression is

$$E = \frac{\int \Psi^* H \Psi \, d\tau}{\int \Psi^* \Psi \, d\tau} \qquad (12\text{-}2)$$

It has to be minimized with respect to the adjustable parameters contained in the wave functions. It is important to show that this can be achieved by varying the wave functions of the individual electrons. (The exact wave function would, of course, be self-consistent.)

The basic equations for the self-consistent field method have been laid down by Hartree [247] for atomic systems. Self-consistent atomic orbitals can also be used for building molecular wave functions.

Fock [248] adapted the method to the very important case where the wave functions are given in the form of Slater determinants. As we know, these are of fundamental importance in treating molecular problems.

We are going to outline, up to a certain point, the Hartree-Fock method, following a description by Roothaan [249]. We shall consider the closed-shell ground state of a molecule, represented by one Slater determinant.

The "best" orbitals making up this Slater determinant are those which make the energy reach its minimum. This means that we have to minimize the energy, at the same time satisfying the requirement that the orbitals form an orthonormal set.

The energy for a closed-shell state has the form

$$E = 2 \sum_i I_i + \sum_{ij} (2J_{ij} - K_{ij}) \qquad (12\text{-}3)$$

This is entirely the same expression as in the antisymmetrized molecular orbital method, but we changed the notation to conform to general practice in self-consistent field theory. I_i is the core energy for electron i,

$$I_i = \int \phi_i(u)[T(u) + H_0(u)]\phi_i(u)\, d\tau = \epsilon_i \qquad (12\text{-}4)$$

J_{ij} is the Coulomb integral,

$$J_{ij} = \int \phi_i(u)\phi_j(v) \frac{e^2}{r_{uv}} \phi_i(u)\phi_j(v)\, d\tau = \gamma_{ij} \qquad (12\text{-}5)$$

and K_{ij} is the exchange integral,

$$K_{ij} = \int \phi_i(u)\phi_j(v) \frac{e^2}{r_{uv}} \phi_i(v)\phi_j(u)\, d\tau = \delta_{ij} \qquad (12\text{-}6)$$

where ϵ_i, γ_{ij}, and δ_{ij} follow Craig's notation which we have used in the preceding chapters.

We suppose that the ϕ_i are real functions. It can be seen that (12-3) is in agreement with the rules for counting the molecular integrals given in Chapter 10, if we remember that $K_{ii} = J_{ii}$.

We can define a Coulomb and an exchange operator,

$$J_i(v)\phi_j(u) \equiv e^2 \left(\int \frac{\phi_i(v)\phi_i(v)}{r_{uv}}\, d\tau_v \right) \phi_j(u)$$

and

$$K_i(v)\phi_j(u) \equiv e^2 \left(\int \frac{\phi_i(v)\phi_j(v)}{r_{uv}}\, d\tau_v \right) \phi_i(u) \qquad (12\text{-}7)$$

the latter exchanging the electrons between ϕ_i and ϕ_j.

The Coulomb and exchange integrals may be expressed as one-electronic integrals by using these operators.

$$J_{ij} = \int \phi_i J_j \phi_i\, d\tau = \int \phi_j J_i \phi_j\, d\tau \qquad (12\text{-}8)$$

$$K_{ij} = \int \phi_i K_j \phi_i\, d\tau = \int \phi_j K_i \phi_j\, d\tau \qquad (12\text{-}9)$$

Now each molecular orbital ϕ_i will be varied by an infinitesimal amount, $\delta\phi_i$. Then the variation of the energy will be

$$\begin{aligned}
\delta E &= 2\sum_i \delta I_i + \sum_{ij} (2\delta J_{ij} - \delta K_{ij}) \\
&= 2\sum_i (\delta\phi_i) I_i \phi_i\, d\tau + \sum_{ij} \left\{ \int (\delta\phi_i)(2J_j - K_j)\phi_i\, d\tau \right. \\
&\quad \left. + \int (\delta\phi_j)(2J_i - K_i)\phi_j \right\} d\tau + 2\sum_i \int \phi_i I_i(\delta\phi_i)\, d\tau \\
&\quad + \sum_{ij} \left\{ \phi_i(2J_j - K_j)(\delta\phi_i)\, d\tau + \int \phi_j(2J_i - K_i)(\delta\phi_j) \right\} d\tau
\end{aligned} \qquad (12\text{-}10)$$

In the braces, if the summation is carried out over i and j, the second term gives the same result as the first term.

Thus we can write

$$\delta E = 4 \sum_i \int (\delta\phi_i)\{I_i + \sum_j (2J_j - K_j\}\phi_i \, d\tau \qquad (12\text{-}11)$$

since the functions were supposed to be real.

The condition that E has a minimum (or a maximum) is that δE vanishes. At the same time, however, we have to satisfy the condition of orthogonality,

$$\int \phi_i\phi_j \, d\tau = 0, \qquad i \neq j$$

Varying this expression gives

$$\int (\delta\phi_i)\phi_j \, d\tau + \int (\delta\phi_j)\phi_i \, d\tau = 0 \qquad (12\text{-}12)$$

The standard mathematical technique to deal with an extreme value problem under accessory conditions is the method of Lagrange multipliers, or undetermined multipliers.

Equations (12-11) and (12-12) contain the same variables and integrations between the same limits. Furthermore the (12-12) are equal to constants (zero in this case). If we multiply each condition (12-12) by a constant, but undetermined, multiplier $-2\epsilon_{ji}$ and add them to δE we obtain $\delta E'$, which has to vanish as well as δE to allow E to reach its minimum.

The requirement that $\delta E' = 0$ will also fix the values of the Lagrangian multipliers. To make $\delta E'$ vanish, the coefficients of each $\delta\phi_i$ in the sum have to vanish, and we obtain the conditions

$$\{I_i + \sum_j (2J_j - K_j)\}\phi_i = \sum_j \phi_j\epsilon_{ji} \qquad (12\text{-}13)$$

There is one such equation for each ϕ_i. This minimization process is essentially the same as the one that led us to the secular determinants of the molecular orbital and valence-bond methods.

Roothaan has shown [249] that the Hartree-Fock method may be applied with the molecular orbitals ϕ_i taken as linear combinations of atomic orbitals.

We are going to continue our discussion in terms of an example. It will be that of *trans*-butadiene, following an article by Parr and Mulliken [250].

12-2 THE EXAMPLE OF *TRANS*-BUTADIENE

The molecular orbitals are of the usual form

$$\phi_i = c_{ia}\psi_a + c_{ib}\psi_b + c_{ic}\psi_c + c_{id}\psi_d \qquad (12\text{-}14)$$

where i stands for the MO and a, b, c, d for the four carbon atoms.

The energy of the ground configuration with two electrons in ϕ_1 and ϕ_2 is

$$E_N = 2I_1 + 2I_2 + J_{11} + J_{22} + 4J_{12} - 2K_{12} \qquad (12\text{-}15)$$

The integrals I_i, I_{ij}, and K_{ij} may be expressed in terms of atomic integrals by substituting the respective linear combinations of atomic orbitals for the ϕ_i.

If H is the operator for the total energy, then Eq. (12-13) gives that for every ϕ_i

$$H\phi_i = \sum_j \phi_i \epsilon_{ji} \qquad (12\text{-}16)$$

or, multiplying by ϕ_i and integrating over the whole space,

$$\int \phi_i H \phi_i \, d\tau = \epsilon_i \int \phi_i \phi_i \, d\tau \qquad (12\text{-}17)$$

since the ϕ_i are mutually orthogonal. Then the same minimization procedure as used in the case of the simple LCAO method Section 3-1 leads to the following conditions:

$$c_{ip}(H_{pp} - \epsilon_i) + \sum_{q \neq p} c_{iq}(H_{pq} - S_{pq}\epsilon_i) = 0 \qquad (12\text{-}18)$$

For butadiene this gives a system of four equations:

$$\begin{aligned}
&c_{ia}(H_{aa} - S_{aa}\epsilon_i) + c_{ib}(H_{ab} - S_{ab}\epsilon_i) + c_{ic}(H_{ac} - S_{ac}\epsilon_i) \\
&\quad + c_{id}(H_{ad} - S_{ad}\epsilon_i) = 0 \\
&c_{ia}(H_{ba} - S_{ba}\epsilon_i) + c_{ib}(H_{bb} - S_{bb}\epsilon_i) + c_{ic}(H_{bc} - S_{bc}\epsilon_i) \\
&\quad + c_{id}(H_{bd} - S_{bd}\epsilon_i) = 0 \\
&c_{ia}(H_{ca} - S_{ca}\epsilon_i) + c_{ib}(H_{cb} - S_{cb}\epsilon_i) + c_{ic}(H_{cc} - S_{cc}\epsilon_i) \\
&\quad + c_{id}(H_{cd} - S_{cd}\epsilon_i) = 0 \\
&c_{ia}(H_{da} - S_{da}\epsilon_i) + c_{ib}(H_{db} - S_{db}\epsilon_i) + c_{ic}(H_{dc} - S_{dc}\epsilon_i) \\
&\quad + c_{id}(H_{dd} - S_{dd}\epsilon_i) = 0
\end{aligned} \qquad (12\text{-}19)$$

In order to obtain the ϵ_i the determinant of the coefficients c_{ip} has to be set equal to zero. But first we need the matrix elements H_{pq}. We may write

$$\begin{aligned}
H_{pq} &= \int \psi_p H \psi_q \, d\tau = \int \psi_p [I_i + \sum_j (2J_j - K_j)] \psi_q \, d\tau \\
&= \int \psi_p I_i \psi_q \, d\tau + \sum_j 2 \int \psi_p J_j \psi_q \, d\tau - \sum_j \int \psi_p K_j \psi_q \, d\tau \\
&= I_{pq} + G_{pq} \qquad (12\text{-}20)
\end{aligned}$$

Furthermore, using (12-7),

$$\begin{aligned}
G_{pq} &= \sum_j 2 \int \phi_i(v) \psi_p(u) \frac{e^2}{r_{uv}} \phi_i(v) \psi_q(u) \, d\tau_v \, d\tau_u \\
&\quad - \sum_j \int \phi_i(v) \psi_p(u) \frac{e^2}{r_{uv}} \phi_i(u) \psi_q(v) \, d\tau_v \, d\tau_u \qquad (12\text{-}21) \\
&= \sum_j (2J_{i,\, pq} - K_{i,\, pq})
\end{aligned}$$

and

$$J_{i,\,pq} = \sum_{r,\,s} c_{ir} c_{is} \int \psi_r(v)\psi_p(u) \frac{e^2}{r_{uv}} \psi_s(v)\psi_q(u)\, d\tau_v\, d\tau_u \quad (12\text{-}22)$$

$$K_{i,\,pq} = \sum_{r,\,s} c_{ir} c_{is} \int \psi_r(v)\psi_p(u) \frac{e^2}{r_{uv}} \psi_s(u)\psi_q(v)\, d\tau_v\, d\tau_u \quad (12\text{-}23)$$

It is seen that no LCAO coefficient appears in I_{pq} and only two appear in $J_{i,\,pq}$ and $K_{i,\,pq}$. Now we start computing the H_{pq}. For this we need the coefficients. We may use those obtained in the simple Hückel approximation (see p. 184), but any set of coefficients can be taken provided they are normalized and molecular symmetry is respected. With these we compute the H_{pq} and substitute them into the secular equation (12-19). We solve the secular equation, obtaining the ϵ_i. For the two ϵ_i of lowest energy we compute the c_{ip} from the secular equation. Then with these first-improved coefficients we again compute the H_{pq}, feed them back into the secular equation, and repeat this iteration process until the coefficients remain unchanged to the desired precision between two successive steps.

As an example we shall compute H_{ab} for *trans*-butadiene. First we evaluate I_{ab}.

$$I_{ab} = \int \psi_a(v)\, I(v)\, \psi_b(v)\, d\tau_v$$
$$= \int \psi_a(v)[T(v) + H_a^+(v) + H_b^+(v) + H_c^+(v) + H_d^+(v)]\psi_b(v)\, d\tau_v$$

Since

$$[T(v) + H_a^+(v)]\psi_a(v) = W_{2p}\psi_a(v)$$

we can write that (p. 270)

$$\int \psi_b(v)[T(v) + H_a^+(v)]\psi_a(v)\, d\tau_v = W_{2p}S_{ab}$$

For the three other members in the operator we introduce the Goeppert-Mayer and Sklar potential (p. 270):

$$H_b^+(v) = H_b^*(v) - \int \frac{e^2}{r_{vu}} \psi_b(n)\psi_b(n)\, d\tau_v$$

Then we are led to the following expression:

$$I_{ab} = S_{ab} W_{2p} - [(B\!:\!ab) + (C\!:\!ab) + (D\!:\!ab)$$
$$+ (ab;aa) + (ab;cc) + (ab;dd)]$$

where

$$(B\!:\!ab) = -\int \psi_a H_b^* \psi_b\, d\tau$$

The integral $(A\!:\!ab)$ does not occur, it is in $W_{2p}S_{ab}$. For the latter, Parr and Mulliken [250] used the value $W_{2p} = -11.28$ ev. The other integrals are found in Parr and Crawford's tables (Table 10-1). They are given with $Z_{\text{eff}} = 3.18$ and the internuclear distances taken as $a - b = 1.35$ Å, $b - c = 1.46$ Å, and the angle $abc \not\lessgtr$ as $124°$ in Parr and Mulliken's Table I, which we reproduce (Table 12-1).

TABLE 12–1

Integral	Value cis-	trans-	Integral	Value cis-	trans-
Overlap integrals			Coulomb-exchange Integrals		
S_{ab}	0.27854	0.27854	$aa;aa$	$0.3914 \times Z$	$0.3914 \times Z$
S_{bc}	0.23281	0.23281	$aa;bb$	0.2136	0.2136
S_{ac}	0.03371	0.03371	$bb;cc$	0.2010	0.2010
S_{ad}	0.01188	0.00218	$aa;cc$	0.1277	0.1277
Penetration			$aa;dd$	0.1083	0.0885
integrals			$aa;ab$	0.0834	0.0834
$A:ab$	$0.0527 \times Z$	$0.0527 \times Z$	$bb;bc$	0.0678	0.0678
$B:bc$	0.0377	0.0377	$bb;cd$	0.0447	0.0447
$A:bb$	0.0228	0.0228	$aa;bc$	0.0384	0.0384
$B:cc$	0.0156	0.0156	$aa;cd$	0.0334	0.0291
$B:ac$	0.0070	0.0070	$aa;ac$	0.0069	0.0069
$A:ac$	0.0012	0.0012	$aa;bd$	0.0053	0.0043
$A:bc$	0.0008	0.0008	$bb;ac$	0.0107	0.0107
$B:cd$	0.0007	0.0007	$aa;ad$	0.0024	0.0004
$B:ad$	0.0003	0.0004	$bb;ad$	0.0026	0.0007
$A:cc$	0.0002	0.0002	$ab;ab$	0.0252	0.0252
$A:ad$	0.0002	0.0000	$bc;bc$	0.0169	0.0169
$A:bd$	0.0001	0.0000	$ab;bc$	0.0147	0.0147
$A:cd$	0.0000	0.0000	$ab;cd$	0.0110	0.0107
$A:dd$	0.0000	0.0000	$ab;ac$	0.0029	0.0029
Core			$ab:bd$	0.0019	0.0016
integrals			$bc;ac$	0.0025	0.0025
$-I_{aa}$	$0.4726 \times Z$	$0.4528 \times Z$	$ab;ad$	0.0008	0.0001
$-I_{bb}$	0.5809	0.5809	$bc;ad$	0.0007	0.0002
$-I_{ab}$	0.2149	0.2106	$ac;ac$	0.0004	0.0004
$-I_{bc}$	0.1839	0.1839	$ac;bd$	0.0003	0.0002
$-I_{ac}$	0.0312	0.0301	$ac;ad$	0.0001	0.0000
$-I_{ad}$	0.0084	0.0026	$ad;ad$	0.0001	0.0000

With these values,

$$I_{ab} = -11.28 \cdot 0.27854 - 13.602 \cdot 3.18$$
$$\cdot [0.0527 + 0.0007 + 0.0000 + 0.0834 + 0.0447 + 0.0291]$$
$$= -11.28 \cdot 0.27854 - 13.602 \cdot 3.18 \cdot 0.2106 = -12.2513 \text{ ev}$$

where one atomic unit of energy is taken as $\dfrac{e}{2a_0} = -13.602$ ev.

Next we compute the term G_{ab}. From (12–21):

$$G_{ab} = 2J_{1,ab} + 2J_{2,ab} - K_{1,ab} - K_{2,ab}$$

All four terms depend on the coefficients and vary from step to step. We shall use the coefficients obtained by Parr and Mulliken at the end of the iteration procedure, when self-consistence was achieved.

For $\phi_1, c_{1a} = 0.3540 = c_{1d}; c_{1b} = 0.4687 = c_{1c}$.

For $\phi_2, c_{2a} = 0.5081 = -c_{2d}; c_{2b} = 0.4229 = -c_{2c}$.

Substituting these, we may write

$$J_{1,ab} = \int \psi_a(v)[0.3540\psi_a + 0.4687\psi_b$$
$$+ 0.4687\psi_c + 0.3540\psi_d](u)\frac{e^2}{r_{uv}}[0.3540\psi_a$$
$$+ 0.4687\psi_b + 0.4687\psi_c + 0.3540\psi_d](u)\psi_b(v)\,d\tau_u\,d\tau_v$$

$$
\begin{aligned}
= \; & 0.3540\cdot0.3540 \quad (aa; ab) \\
& + 0.4687\cdot0.3540 \quad (ba; ab) \\
& + 0.4687\cdot0.3540 \quad (ca; ab) \\
& + 0.3540\cdot0.3540 \quad (da; ab) \\
& + 0.3540\cdot0.4687 \quad (ab; ab) \\
& + 0.4687\cdot0.4687 \quad (bb; ab) \\
& + 0.4687\cdot0.4687 \quad (cb; ab) \\
& + 0.3540\cdot0.4687 \quad (db; ab) \\
& + 0.3540\cdot0.4687 \quad (ac; ab) \\
& + 0.4687\cdot0.4687 \quad (bc; ab) \\
& + 0.4687\cdot0.4687 \quad (cc; ab) \\
& + 0.3540\cdot0.4687 \quad (dc; ab) \\
& + 0.3540\cdot0.3540 \quad (ad; ab) \\
& + 0.4687\cdot0.3540 \quad (bd; ab) \\
& + 0.4687\cdot0.3540 \quad (cd; ab) \\
& + 0.3540\cdot0.3540 \quad (dd; ab)
\end{aligned}
$$

With the integrals of Table 12–1 this gives

$$J_{1,ab} = 0.06213 \quad \text{atomic units}$$

For $J_{2,ab}$ the integrals remain the same but the coefficients are those of ϕ_2. The result is

$$J_{2,ab} = 0.06013 \quad \text{a.u.}$$

For $K_{1,ab}$ and $K_{2,ab}$ the coefficients are the same as for $J_{1,ab}$ and $J_{2,ab}$, respectively, and the integrals are the same for $K_{1,ab}$ and $K_{2,ab}$. We compute $K_{2,ab}$.

$$K_{2,ab} = \int \psi_a(v)[0.5081\psi_a + 0.4229\psi_b - 0.4229\psi_c$$
$$- 0.5081\psi_d](u)\frac{e^2}{r_{uv}}\psi_b(u)[0.5081\psi_a + 0.4229\psi_b$$
$$- 0.4229\psi_c - 0.5081\psi_d](v)\,d\tau_v\,d\tau_u$$

$$
\begin{aligned}
= \; & 0.5081\cdot0.5081 \quad (aa; ab) \\
& + 0.4229\cdot0.5081 \quad (ba; ab) \\
& - 0.4229\cdot0.5081 \quad (ca; ab) \\
& - 0.5081\cdot0.5081 \quad (da; ab) \\
& + 0.5081\cdot0.4229 \quad (aa; bb)
\end{aligned}
$$

$$+ \ 0.4229 \cdot 0.4229 \quad (ba; bb)$$
$$- \ 0.4229 \cdot 0.4229 \quad (ca; bb)$$
$$- \ 0.5081 \cdot 0.4229 \quad (da; bb)$$
$$- \ 0.5081 \cdot 0.4229 \quad (aa; cb)$$
$$- \ 0.4229 \cdot 0.4229 \quad (ba; cb)$$
$$+ \ 0.4229 \cdot 0.4229 \quad (ca; cb)$$
$$+ \ 0.5081 \cdot 0.4229 \quad (da; cb)$$
$$- \ 0.5081 \cdot 0.5081 \quad (aa; db)$$
$$- \ 0.4229 \cdot 0.5081 \quad (ba; db)$$
$$+ \ 0.4229 \cdot 0.5081 \quad (ca; db)$$
$$+ \ 0.5081 \cdot 0.5081 \quad (da; db)$$

$$K_{2, ab} = +0.07324 \quad \text{a.u.}$$
$$K_{1, ab} = +0.08237 \quad \text{a.u.}$$

Hence, $G_{ab} = 13.602 \cdot 3.18 \cdot 0.08892 = 3.8462 \quad \text{ev}$

and $H_{ab} = H_{ab}^{SCF} = -12.2513 + 3.8462 = -8.4051 \quad \text{ev}$

Naturally, certain terms will be equal because of symmetry, and symmetry might also be used in solving the secular equations in the usual way.

Roothaan has worked out his LCAO SCF theory for closed-shell ground states. Mulligan [251] applied it to the CO_2 molecule, Parr and Taylor [252] to allene, Berthier to fulvene [253], and Julg to azulene [254]. Streitwieser lists a number of other works using this method [132, pp. 454–454]. Encouraging results were obtained.

The calculation of the energies of excited states is not so simple. In most cases excited configurations contain simply filled orbitals, and their wave function consists of more than one Slater function. The conditions of self-consistency for such wave functions were established in four different ways by Lefebvre [255], McWeeny [256], Roothaan [257], and Masse [258]. The energies are expressed in terms of molecular integrals according to the rules of Chapter 10. In the minimization procedure account must be taken of the requirement that the wave function of any excited state be orthogonal to those of the other states. In the case of degenerate states a set of Slater functions must be used, causing similar problems. However, the difficulty arising from the orthogonality conditions does not concern the states of lowest energy belonging to a given irreducible representation, since wave functions belonging to different representations are automatically orthogonal to one other.

Although the handling of excited states by Roothaan's SCF method turned out to be somewhat less prohibitive than it was originally thought, it is nevertheless true that this method always requires a great amount of labor. As a simpler but less accurate method of treating excited states within the framework of LCAO SCF theory

Roothaan suggested using molecular orbitals obtained from the secular equation of the ground state to build the excited configurations. The procedure of the antisymmetrized molecular orbital method is then applied, the LCAO coefficients now resulting from the SCF treatment of the ground configuration. (In the case of butadiene, for example, the secular determinant yields four ϵ_i and four corresponding ϕ_i of which two are used for the ground configuration). These orbitals *are* mutually orthogonal. Complications arise in the case of degenerate orbitals (see Roothaan [249, p. 79]).

Such wave functions may be improved by configuration interaction as has been suggested by Lefebvre and Moser [259].

For the first singlet-singlet excitation energy for butadiene, Parr and Mulliken found 7.8 ev for the *cis-* and 8.2 ev for the *trans*-isomer using the orbitals obtained from the SCF treatment of the ground configuration. The observed value is about 6 ev. For benzene Roothaan and Parr [260] obtained 5.8 ev instead of 4.9 ev. Fulvene was treated by the LCAO SCF method by Berthier [253] and by the method of configuration interaction by Julg and A. Pullman [216]. Table 12-2 summarizes some of their results. The oscillator strengths were computed with the observed frequencies. The numerical agreement for the excitation energies is not very good. Yet the results substantiate the shift toward lower frequencies of the bands of fulvene with respect to those of benzene and butadiene.

TABLE 12–2

	Excitation energies		
	LCAO SCF	CI	*Observed*
$V_1 \leftarrow N$	4.95 ev	4.87	3.4
$V_2 \leftarrow N$	7.51 ev	9.06	4.6
	Oscillator strengths		
$V_1 \leftarrow N$	0.013	0.033	0.012
$V_2 \leftarrow N$	0.55	0.43	0.32

The theoretical values of the oscillator strengths are much more encouraging; in some cases the agreement between theory and experiment is excellent.

12-3 A SEMIEMPIRICAL APPROXIMATION TO THE LCAO SCF METHOD

The configuration interaction method and the LCAO SCF method may be considered as being of the same degree of elaborateness. It may be said of both methods that in view of the great amount of labor required to treat a larger molecule, the agreement obtained with experimental data is disappointing. From this Pariser and Parr have drawn the conclusion that a certain amount of semiempirical data should be reintroduced; and their method, which was described in Chapter 11, has shown itself to be very successful. It was then a logical step to introduce Pariser and Parr's assumptions into Roothaan's LCAO SCF theory. This has been done by Pople [261].

As has been shown, Roothaan's equations for a closed-shell configuration have the form:

$$c_{ip}(H_{pp} - \epsilon_i) + \sum_{q \neq p} c_{iq}(H_{pq} - S_{pq}\epsilon_i) = 0 \qquad (12\text{-}18)$$

Since $H_{pq} = I_{pq} + G_{pq}$, we may write, by analogy with the simple Hückel theory, that

$$H_{pp} = \alpha_p + G_{pq}, \qquad \text{where } \alpha_p = I_{pp}$$
$$H_{pq} = \beta_{pq} + G_{pq}, \qquad \text{where } \beta_{pq} = I_{pq} \qquad (12\text{-}24)$$

Then we break down these expressions in terms of atomic integrals, and we put equal to zero all those expressions which contain differential overlap. Then only the Coulomb integrals remain, making the calculations much easier.

$$\alpha_p = W_{2p} - [\sum_{q \neq p} (qq;pp) + \sum_{q \neq p} (P:qq)] \qquad (12\text{-}25)$$

where the Goeppert-Mayer and Sklar potential can be used. β_{pq} is treated as an empirical quantity. Thus the iteration procedure becomes much less tedious.

This method has been widely used, and Pople has reviewed its applications up till 1957 [262]. In a series of works by Pople, Dewar, Longuet-Higgins, Murrell, and McEwen [263–268] re-examined the spectra of aromatic hydrocarbons and their derivatives, combining the LCAO SCF method with perturbation calculations. They also studied some of the ions and free radicals of these molecules. Lefebvre, Moser, and Brion proposed other ways of obtaining SCF wave functions [270].

An interesting point is that the similarity of this method to the simple Hückel method makes it possible to justify the basic approximations of the latter in the case of conjugated hydrocarbons. This is surprising and encouraging at the same time. Actually the coefficients obtained by the Pariser-Parr-Pople method and the Hückel method resemble each other fairly closely. The simple LCAO and valence-bond methods are sometimes called "naive" methods. As Daudel puts it, "The naive methods are less naive than they seem to be" [271].

A formal justification of the assumptions of the Hückel method has been given by Simpson.[1]

[1] W. T. Simpson, J. Chem. Phys. **28** : 972 (1958).

13

Summing Up. What Next?

Quantum chemistry is like a progression with an upper limit: the Schrödinger equation is good for atomic and molecular systems—if only we could solve it accurately! So all we do is search for better and better approximations to the Schrödinger equation for a given system, and we should say for a given system in a given environment. We are trying to fill a given frame; there cannot be any sensational discoveries ahead of us; all we may expect is hard work.

We have examined three types of methods: empirical ones, such as the simple molecular orbital or valence-bond methods; nonempirical ones, such as the method of antisymmetrized molecular orbitals completed with configuration interaction or the LCAO self-consistent-field method; and finally, semiempirical methods, such as the Pariser and Parr method, which can be fitted to any of the two former elaborate methods.

In reality these three types of methods differ only in the amount of empirical element introduced into them. Only for a handful of small molecular species is it possible to say: we have so many nuclei and so many electrons, let us determine from the Schrödinger equation what kind of system their interaction will yield. Internuclear distances are taken from experiment even in the so-called nonempirical methods, at least at the start, and the general frame of the molecule is borrowed from experimental chemistry. In empirical methods, in addition, some theoretical quantities, usually with the dimensions of energy, are also chosen to give agreement with experiment. Semiempirical methods constitute a compromise between the two extremes—which are not really extremes.

There is no doubt that so far as agreement with observed data is concerned, for all but the smallest molecules the semiempirical Pariser-Parr-Pople method was the most successful. There is something rewarding and something frustrating in every compromise. We obtain agreement, but theory becomes a connecting link between two sets of experimental quantities. What to do? The answer of the more mathematically minded quantum chemists was radical: let us stop working on large molecules and return to small, two- or three-atomic systems and treat them as rigorously as possible. This is one of the main streams of quantum chemistry today. Its future depends largely on the evolution of digital computers permitting extension to larger systems.

The more chemically minded quantum chemists did not give up their large molecules so easily. They have something in their favor. So far almost all of the real successes of quantum chemistry have been achieved by very approximate methods. Most of them are connected with spectral phenomena: the classification of the spectra of aromatic and other conjugated compounds by the free-electron method of Platt [272], or by the simple LCAO method in the Hückel approximation; the prediction of the existence of $n \to \pi^*$ transitions by McMurray and Mulliken [273, 274] by molecular orbital considerations; the explanation of the spectra of certain types of dye molecules by Kuhn using another free-electron model (Sec. 14-2); the explanation of the visible absorption of the transition metal ions having incomplete d or f shells by Ilse and Hartmann [275]; the explanation of the spectra of charge-transfer complexes by Mulliken [276]; the near quantitative matching of the ultraviolet spectra of aromatic hydrocarbons by Pariser [277]. So let us continue to use theory as a link between sets of experimental values. What we want is to understand nature by whatever means are available to us. This line of thought constitutes the other main stream of present-day quantum chemistry.

We shall attempt to summarize briefly some of the works characteristic of these two lines.

13-1 WORK ON LARGE MOLECULES

Our examples treated in the preceding chapters were all π-electronic problems. It has been tacitly assumed that sufficient account was taken of the σ electrons by considering them as part of the cores and that it was a good approximation to study the behavior of the π electrons in the field formed by the cores and the other π electrons.

Thus the interaction between σ and π electrons has not been treated explicitly. This procedure originated in considerations of Hückel pointing out that the π orbitals have a nodal plane where the σ orbitals have their greatest amplitude and, therefore, overlap between σ and π orbitals may be neglected [278]. The validity of this assumption has been subjected to tests in a few cases.

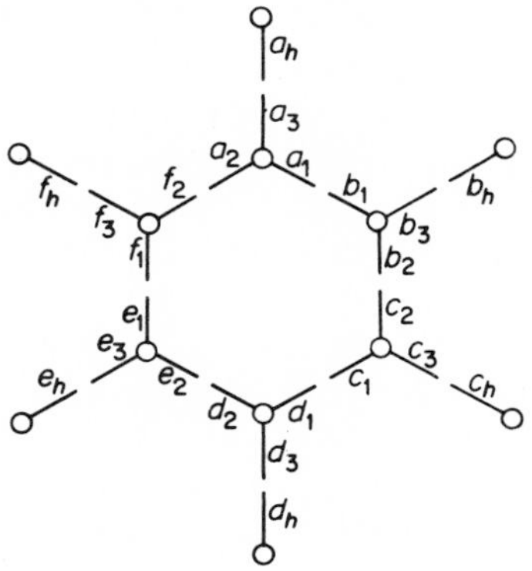

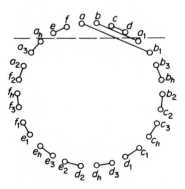

Fig. 13-1

Altmann [279] made a treatment of benzene by the valence-bond method including both σ and π electrons. Let a, b, c, d, e, and f (unindexed) be symbols for the six π orbitals and let the σ orbitals and hydrogen $1s$ orbitals be represented as in Fig. 13-1. Then the canonical circle may be written as in Fig. 13-2, taken from Altmann. The structure represented there is canonical since no lines connecting pairs of orbitals cross. This is correct, since according to Rumer's theorem (p. 78) the canonical circle is not required to resemble the

Fig. 13-2

actual molecule in any way. The problem does not involve new principles but it is very complicated. If the valence-bond method is to be used as an empirical method new parameters are needed. If it is used as a nonempirical method a number of integrals are required.

Altmann chose the latter way in the case of ethylene, which he treated as a twelve-electron problem, putting into the core the carbon $1s$ electrons only. He found that σ-π interactions have a considerable influence on the sequence and value of the energy levels.

Ross [280] carried out calculations on the acetylene molecule by the method of the antisymmetrized molecular orbitals including configuration interaction. He found that some of the levels are purely π, but, some others are mixed π-σ in character. Ross found, however, that the lowest such level is higher than the ground level by 22.6 ev and practically does not interact with the purely π levels. The situation becomes worse when the C—C distance increases, but Ross estimated that if it does not exceed 1.50 Å the effect of the σ electrons on the π levels remains unimportant.

These results depend on the validity of certain approximations made in the process of the calculations, but it seems to be confirmed at present that the separation of the σ and π orbitals is a fair approximation.

Empirical molecular orbital calculations on saturated hydrocarbons by Sandorfy and Daudel [138, 139] were mentioned in Chapter 8. Other treatments were offered by R. D. Brown [281] (bond orbital method), Dewar and Pettit [282] (a perturbation treatment), Lennard-Jones and Hall [283] (equivalent orbital method), Franklin [284] (a united atom treatment), by Fukui, Kato, and Yonezawa [285], and by others. Most of these, however, dealt with bond energies, heats of formation, ionization potentials, and other molecular properties but not with spectral quantities. The LCAO SCF method has been tried on methane by Besnainou and Roux [286]. An interesting perturbation method was offered by Julg [287], who also presented an improved LCAO method [288]. Daudel gave a recent review of these and other methods related to saturated hydrocarbons [271, pp. 115–140].

There is, however, no basic difference in the treatment of σ-electronic problems, or π-electronic problems, or problems with two or more types of orbitals; everything is a matter of integrals. Problems involving π orbitals are simpler only because only one orbital has to be taken on each core.

A sample group-theoretical treatment of benzene as a 42-electron problem has been given by Roothaan [289]. Tinkham's description [114, p. 259] is also a good one to consult in this respect.

One possible improvement of the wave functions lies in the variation of the effective nuclear charge, Z_{eff}, which occurs in the exponent of every atomic orbital. Zener's 3.18 may not, and usually does not, give the lowest possible energy in the case of molecules. Varying the total energy with respect to Z_{eff} may lead to considerable improvement [290, 291].

Another feature that might be improved is Goeppert-Mayer and Sklar's core potential. One way of doing this is to include exchange terms; this has been attempted in the case of CO_2 by Mulligan [292]. It would be even better to dispense with the whole idea of a core and instead to treat explicitly all the interactions between electrons and nuclei present in the molecule. Efforts in this direction have been made by Scherr [293] and by Sahni [294] on N_2 and BH, respectively. Such calculations require a very great number of integrals and become extremely complicated for all but diatomic molecules.

One may think of mixing into the atomic orbitals other atomic orbitals of the same symmetry but of higher energy, such as $3p$ into $2p$. This would be equivalent, in configuration interaction language, to including configurations in which $2p$ electrons are formally excited to $3p$ orbitals. Recently Hartmann [295] stressed the importance of this procedure. (See also Jacobs [296].)

A very important point to make is that although Slater atomic orbitals have been used in the great majority of quantum-chemical calculations up to the present time, they are, of course, approximate functions. Using screening constants is not necessarily the best way of taking into account the mutual repulsion between the electrons.

A decisive departure from Slater functions was made by Boys [297], who uses as basis functions sets of functions of the type $r^m e^{-kr}$ or $r^m e^{-kr^2}$ for building more complicated functions. Integrals involving these functions are easier to evaluate. In the future this method might well turn out to be one of the most powerful ones [298, 299, 300].

Recently Zauli [301] and Mangini and Zauli [302] published an interesting work in which the valence-bond method is used as a non-empirical method including overlap and exchange integrals of all orders. Mulliken's approximation (see p. 277) was used in computing three- and four-center integrals. Subsequently Magnusson and Zauli [303] computed many integrals by numerical methods.

13-2 WORK ON SMALL MOLECULAR SPECIES

We have already mentioned the work of Scherr and Sahni on N_2 and BH, respectively. These were calculations using Roothaan's LCAO SCF method including all the electrons. Similar calculations have been made by Kotani [304] (ground and low excited states of O_2 and Li_2), Duncan [305], and Kaplan [306] (NH_3).

In recent years great advances have been made in programming, for large, electronic, digital computers, the computation of integrals needed in molecular calculations. Because of these advances the time needed for solving problems like the ones mentioned above has been decreased by several orders of magnitude. Much of this work on programming was initiated in Cambridge by Boys and his collaborators, and by Mulliken, Roothaan, Ransil, McLean, and others at the University of Chicago.

Many of the papers resulting from this fundamental work appeared in the Technical Reports of the Laboratory of Molecular Structure and Spectra of the University of Chicago (1957–59, 1959–60, 1961). Another good source of information is the April, 1960, number of the *Reviews of Modern Physics.*

SCF wave functions with an exact, all-electron treatment approximate the total energy rather closely, about 99 per cent [307]. The agreement is not so good, however, for some other physical properties [308]. The shortcomings of the method are due mainly to the incomplete account taken of the mutual repulsion between electrons. True, the e^2/r_{uv} term is included in the Hamiltonian, but the *wave function* does not take it into account explicitly, being constructed as a product of one-electron orbitals. The result is that the electrons—in particular, electrons of opposite spin—in the same orbital get "too close to each other too often." The corresponding correction to the total energy value is often called *correlation energy.*

The improvement can be expected from the introduction of the interelectronic distance into the wave function itself. This problem first came up in the case of the helium atom, where there are two $1s$ electrons. The near-perfect solution of the problem by Hylleraas [309] in 1929 constituted one of the greatest triumphs of the first period of wave mechanics.

Hylleraas [310, 311] tried several functions, of which the one most often called *Hylleraas function* has the following form:

$$[Ke^{-Zr_1}e^{-Zr_2}(1 + cr_{12})] \tag{13-1}$$

where K is a normalizing factor and the function is to be multiplied by the appropriate spin function. Z and c are considered as variational parameters. The minimization of the energy gives $Z = 1.816$ and $c = 0.364$. An even better function given by Hylleraas is

$$[Ke^{-Zr_1-Zr_2}(1 + c_1r_{12} + c_2(r_1 - r_2)^2)] \tag{13-2}$$

which approximates the experimental value of the total energy of helium to 0.03 ev. With a six-term polynomial this is improved to 0.01 ev. (This is still about 80 cm^{-1}.)

In recent times these Hylleraas-type, "correlated" wave functions were again taken up with the hope of application to larger systems. Roothaan and Weiss [308] investigated two functions on heliumlike systems:

$$\Phi_c = \phi(r_1)\phi(r_2)\chi(r_{12}) \qquad (13\text{-}3)$$

and

$$\Phi_0 = [\phi(r_1)\psi(r_2) + \psi(r_1)\phi(r_2)]\chi(r_{12}) \qquad (13\text{-}4)$$

where the first function applies to closed shells and the second one to open shells. ϕ and ψ are two different orbitals, and χ is called the *correlation function*. ϕ, ψ, and χ are expressed as linear expansions in terms of suitable basis functions. The coefficients in the expansion are determined by the variational method. For details and other references we refer to Roothaan and Weiss' paper. This approach constitutes probably one of the best hopes for the future. Another is linked to the other great success of early quantum mechanics: the treatment of the hydrogen molecule by James and Coolidge in 1933 [312–314]. They, too, introduced the interelectronic separation r_{12} into the variation function.

They used the elliptic coordinates

$$\xi_1 = \frac{r_{A_1} + r_{B_1}}{r_{AB}}, \qquad \xi_2 = \frac{r_{A_2} + r_{B_2}}{r_{AB}}$$

$$\eta_1 = \frac{r_{A_1} - r_{B_1}}{r_{AB}}, \qquad \eta_2 = \frac{r_{A_2} - r_{B_2}}{r_{AB}}$$

and

$$v = \frac{2r_{12}}{r_{AB}}$$

where r_{AB} is the internuclear distance, r_{A_1} is the distance between proton A and electron 1, and so on. Then the James and Coolidge variation function is as follows [9, p. 349]:

$$\Phi = \frac{1}{2\pi} e^{-\delta(\xi_1 + \xi_2)} \sum_{mnjkp} c_{mnjkp} (\xi_1^m \xi_2^n \eta_1^j \eta_2^k v^p + \xi_1^n \xi_2^m \eta_1^k \eta_2^j v^p) \qquad (13\text{-}5)$$

The exponents m, n, j, k, and p are integers which can take 0 or positive values; $j + k$ must be even so that the function is symmetric in the coordinates of the nuclei. δ and c are variational parameters. The accuracy of the results depends on the number of terms taken in the summation. In carrying out the calculations for a series of internuclear distances a potential curve can be constructed and the dissociation energy may be determined. The experimental dissociation energy of the hydrogen molecule is 4.7466 ± .0007 ev.

Their results were as follows:

Number of terms	D_e (ev)
1	2.56
5	4.504
11	4.685
13	4.698

James, Coolidge, and Present carried out similarly successful calculations on some of the excited states of the H_2 molecule [314].

Kolos and Roothaan in 1959 [315, 316] made a two-fold attack on the ground state and lower excited states of the hydrogen molecule. First they used the correlated wave functions described above. The best wave functions of form (13-3) and (13-4) yielded, respectively, 4.6955 and 4.7061 ev.

Then they took the James and Coolidge type function with up to 50 terms. They obtained $D_e = 4.7467$ ev against the experimental 4.7466 ± .0007 ev [76]. For the internuclear distance they obtained 0.74127 Å, the latest experimental value being 0.74116 Å [317].

There is hope for quantum chemistry.

14

Free-Electron Methods

In free-electron methods the wave functions of the electrons in a conjugated system are those of particles moving freely along the bonds. This idea was introduced by Pauling [318], Lonsdale [319], and Schmidt [320]; more recently, it was developed into a comprehensive system for the treatment of conjugated molecules by Platt [272] (rotator model) and by Bayliss [321], Simpson [322], and Kuhn [323] (metallic or electron gas model). First we shall describe Platt's rotator model.

14-1 THE ROTATOR MODEL

We shall describe this method following a work by Platt dealing with cata-condensed hydrocarbons [272]. These are condensed ring aromatic compounds in which no carbon atom is a part of more than two rings. (So, for example, anthracene is cata-condensed, but pyrene and coronene are peri-condensed.) The basic idea of the method is the following:

"The π electrons of a planar conjugated system are free to move along the bonds throughout the system under a potential field which is, in first approximation, constant." Then, "the classification of π orbitals in cata-condensed systems is like that of the orbitals of a free electron traveling in a one-dimensional loop of constant potential around the perimeter."

In first approximation the perimeter may be regarded as a circle of the same length. Then we have a plane rotator, which constitutes one of the simplest examples for the application of the Schrödinger equation (see, for example, [8, p. 198]).

The quantized energy levels of the plane rotator are

$$E = \frac{q^2 h^2}{2ml^2} = 1.21 \times 10^6 \frac{q^2}{l^2} \qquad (14\text{-}1)$$

where h is Planck's constant, m is the mass of the electron, $q = 0, 1, 2, \ldots$ is a quantum number, and l is the length of the perimeter in angstroms. E is measured in cm^{-1} with the constant potential taken as the zero level.

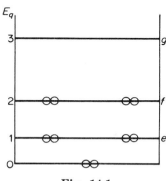

Fig. 14-1

Figure 14-1 shows the spacing of the levels, which depends on q^2. All the levels except the one with $q = 0$ are doubly degenerate, since the electrons may rotate around the perimeter in clockwise or counterclockwise direction.

Platt (after Hückel) calls q the *orbital ring quantum number*. For the circle it measures the angular momentum; for real cata-condensed molecules it no longer represents the angular momentum but it still determines the number of nodes on the perimeter and remains therefore a good quantum number. The nodes are in the molecular plane, as they should be for π electrons.

The lowest level may be occupied by two electrons of opposite spin and the degenerate levels by two such pairs each. Since the system is only one-dimensional we may add algebraically the q values belonging to the individual electrons, putting q or $-q$ according to the direction. Their sum Q is defined as the *total ring quantum number* of the system.

In a cata-condensed system containing n *rings* the number of carbon atoms is $2(2n + 1)$ and every carbon atom contributes one π electron. For benzene, $n = 1$, and there are two electrons in the shell with $q = 0$ and four in the shell with $q = 1$. Naphthalene, with $n = 2$, has two electrons with $q = 0$, four electrons with $q = 1$, and four electrons with $q = 2$. Quite generally the highest occupied level is the one with $q = n$. Platt calls this shell the f shell and designates the others the following way:

$$q = n - 1: \quad e \text{ shell}$$
$$q = n: \qquad f \text{ shell}$$
$$q = n + 1: \quad g \text{ shell}$$
$$q = n + 2: \quad h \text{ shell}$$

Thus the electrons of the outer shells, which are responsible for most chemical and optical phenomena, are designated by the same letters, independently of the number of rings.

The total ring quantum number Q is, because of the two possible directions of rotation, equal to zero for closed shells. If a transition takes place from the f shell to the next empty shell (g), then the new total quantum number will be

$$Q = (n + 1) + n = 2n + 1$$

or

$$Q = (n + 1) - n = 1$$

since in the g level the electron may have the one or the other direction of rotation. States with $Q = 0, 1, 2, \ldots$ are called $A, B, C, \ldots$ states, and those with $2n, 2n + 1, 2n + 2, \ldots$ are called $K, L, M, \ldots$ states, independently of n. $2n + 2$ may correspond to an $f \to h$ transition with $(n + 2) + n = 2n + 2$; $2n$ to an $e \to g$ transition: $(n - 1) + (n + 1) = 2n$.

All states except the A state will be doubly degenerate since the total momentum may be in either direction.

So far we have not taken any account of the crosslinks. If we introduce them and at the same time take, instead of the constant potential, a potential that has periodic variations along the perimeter because of the atoms located on it, the degeneracy of the levels will be removed except for molecules of very high symmetry, like benzene or triphenylene.

Platt gives to the two new states resulting from the splitting of a degenerate one the indices a and b. Thus, from the $f \to g$ transition we obtain four states:

$$Q = (n + 1) + n = 2n + 1, \quad L_a, \quad L_b$$
$$Q = (n + 1) - n = 1, \qquad B_a, \quad B_b$$

We can have a singlet and a triplet for all of these, since in nonclosed shells the spins are free. Finally the configuration of f^3g which results from the $f \to g$ transition give eight states:

$$^1B_a, \, ^1B_b, \, ^1L_a, \, ^1L_b, \, ^3B_a, \, ^3B_b, \, ^3L_a, \, ^3L_b$$

Table 14-1, taken from Platt, gives similar results for the lower configurations. The configurations are characterized by the arithmetic sum of the q of the individual electrons, $\sum q$, and $\Delta \sum q$ is counted from the ground state. [J corresponds to $(n + 1) + (n - 2) = 2n - 1$.]

TABLE 14-1

$\Delta\sum q$	Configuration	States		
3	$f^3 i$	$^{1,3}D_{a,b}$	$^{1,3}N_{a,b}$	
	$e^3 f^4 h$	$^{1,3}D_{a,b}$	$^{1,3}L_{a,b}$	
	$d^3 e^4 f^4 g$	$^{1,3}D_{a,b}$	$^{1,3}J_{a,b}$	
2	$f^3 h$	$^{1,3}C_{a,b}$	$^{1,3}M_{a,b}$	
	$e^3 f^4 g$	$^{1,3}C_{a,b}$	$^{1,3}K_{a,b}$	
1	$f^3 g$	$^{1,3}B_{a,b}$	$^{1,3}L_{a,b}$	
0	f^4		^1A	

For smaller molecules, where the spacing goes increasingly near the f shell, the lowest levels will be of the $f \to g$ type, followed, toward higher frequencies, by those of $e \to g$ type and then those of $f \to h$ type. This is the case of the molecules of interest to us. In large systems the spacing becomes almost equal (l is great) and configurations belonging to the same $\sum q$ will give states of similar energies. According to Hund's rule (p. 124) triplet states will lie below the corresponding singlet states, and among states of the same multiplicity those with high Q values will lie below those of low Q values. For example, ^3L will lie below ^1L and ^1L will lie below ^1B.

Concerning selection rules, singlet-triplet transitions are, naturally, forbidden; furthermore, for molecules possessing a center of symmetry we have the rule that ΔQ and $\Delta \sum q$ must be odd for a transition to be allowed. This latter rule is the equivalent to the Laporte rule, $g \longleftrightarrow u, g \not\leftrightarrow g, u \not\leftrightarrow u$. This is because the wave function of the rotator, which has the form $\psi = N \sin q\phi$ or $\psi = N \cos q\phi$ (degeneracy), changes its sign on inversion ($\phi \to \phi + \pi$) if q is odd, and conserves its sign if q is even. The total eigenfunction is taken as a product of the wave functions of the individual electrons, hence it is even if $\sum q$ is even, and it is odd if $\sum q$ is odd. If the perimeter were a circle, only transitions with $\Delta Q = \pm 1$ would be allowed as dipole transitions (cf. the selection rule for molecular rotation). Even though the perimeter is not actually a circle, these transitions are expected to cause the strongest bands in the spectrum. Among those of the $f \to g$ type these are the B bands.

Platt gave a simple diagrammatic method to determine the polarization of the various transitions. In the rotator wave functions, q determines the number of nodes on the perimeter. In general it is $2q$. Using Q instead of q for the total wave function we see that for the

$Q = 0$ ground state (A) the wave function has no node on the perimeter, for a B state $(Q = 1)$ it has two nodes, and so on. The transition moment is naturally

$$\int \Psi_{\text{ground}} \sum e_i r_i \Psi_{\text{exc}} \, d\tau$$

Now we may use Platt's prescription: "Draw the perimeter line. Indicate the atom positions, and mark where the line is cut by planes of symmetry. Expand the line to a circle. For the transition between the ground state and a state of momentum number Q, draw the nodes of a free-electron standing-wave orbital of momentum number $q = Q$. Since the orbitals are doubly degenerate, there will be two independent sets of these nodes. Each set will have $2Q$ nodal cuts across the perimeter. The nodes of one set will lie at antinodes of the other set.

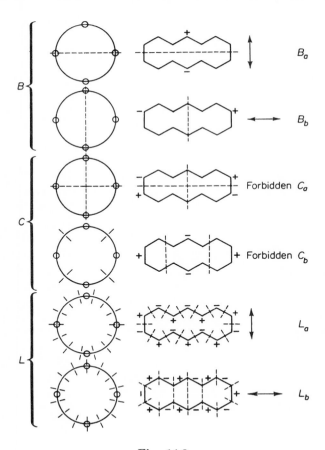

Fig. 14-2

Where there is a symmetry axis, they are easy to construct. In one set the nodes will lie on the axis, in the other set the antinodes. We will call that set, a, which proves to have a nodal line cutting crosslinks (Fig. 14-2) when the perimeter is returned to its normal shape; b, that set in which the crosslinks are uncut. The polarizations of transitions from the ground state will be the same as if we located $+$ and $-$ point charges at alternate antinodes, shrank the perimeter back to its normal shape, and determined the direction of the resulting electric moment."

We may normalize the sum of all $+$ charges to $+\frac{1}{4}$ and the sum of all $-$ charges to $-\frac{1}{4}$, and then the dipole moment will give an idea of the transition moment. This is, of course, only a rough estimate, but Platt has shown that it is a reasonable assumption considering the distribution of the effective charges over the molecule [272].

Let us look at the example of benzene. The length of the perimeter is

$$l = 8.4 \text{ Å}$$

and with this value the rotator energies become

$$E = 17,000q^2 \text{ cm}^{-1}$$

This simple formula does not contain any parameter and supposes only the knowledge of the C—C distance in benzene.

The first bands result from the excitation of an electron from the f level to the g level.

$$f^3 g: \begin{cases} {}^1B & {}^3B & Q = (n+1) - n = 1 \\ {}^1L_a & {}^3L_a & Q = (n+1) + n = 3 \\ {}^1L_b & {}^3L_b \end{cases}$$

$$f^4 \qquad {}^1A \qquad\qquad\qquad\qquad (n = 1)$$

Many other higher excited states may be obtained by using further configurations; however, we shall not consider these.

Because of the high symmetry of benzene the state B does not split into B_a and B_b but remains degenerate (cf. the group-theoretical treatment in Secs. 8-3 and 9-2). The state L, however, splits into L_a and L_b, the six nodes being at the six nuclei for L_a and at the middle of the C—C bonds for L_b.

According to the above approximate formula the transition moment for ${}^1B \leftarrow {}^1A$ is one-fourth of the benzene diameter, that is, $\frac{1}{4} \cdot 2.8 = 0.7$ Å. This gives an oscillator strength $f = 0.59$, which compares well with the experimental 0.79. (The simple LCAO method leads to 2.35.) Zero would be obtained for ${}^1L_a$ and ${}^1L_b$.

Platt's second example is anthracene. The length of the perimeter is $l = 19.6$ Å and

$$E = 3150q^2 \text{ cm}^{-1}$$

The states are, of course, denoted the same way. Since there are three rings in the anthracene molecule, $n = 3$, and thus for B states

$$Q = (3 + 1) - 3 = 1$$

and for L states

$$Q = (3 + 1) + 3 = 7$$

The polarizations are obtained from the diagrams of Fig. 14-2. They need little comment. It is seen, for example, that in the case of the forbidden transitions of type C the dipoles cancel each other. Some of the C-type transitions may be made allowed by nontotally symmetrical vibrations. For the other diagrams the direction of the resultant transition dipole is indicated by an arrow. There are two nodes for B, four for C ($Q = 2$), and fourteen for L. The points on the circles are the points of intersection with the symmetry planes; the dotted lines indicate the location of the nodes.

Table 14-2 summarizes the main results.

TABLE 14-2

Transition	Polarization	Q Estimated	νcm^{-1}	f	f observed
$^1A \to {}^1B_a$	trans	0.7 Å	54,000	0.30	0.65
$^1A \to {}^1B_b$	long	1.8 Å	39,000	1.4	2.28
$^1A \to {}^1L_a$	trans	0.1 Å	26,000	0.003	0.10
$^1A \to {}^1L_b$	long	0.00 Å	(28,000)	0.000	(0.002)

For ^1B_b the transition moment is one-fourth of the length of the anthracene molecule, which is 7.2 Å. For ^1B_a it is $\frac{1}{4} \cdot 2.8$ Å, the quarter of the short axis. For ^1L_a the two end rings have balanced charges and there remains the contribution of the central atoms. Giving every $-$ and every $+$ the same weight, this yields $\frac{1}{7} \cdot \frac{1}{4} \cdot 2.8$ Å $= 0.1$ Å. For ^1L_b we obtain zero from the diagram, provided all effective charges are equal and the rings are perfectly hexagonal. Otherwise a small longitudinal moment would result [324]. The corresponding band in the spectrum is hidden by the stronger ^1L_a band and its f value is estimated from the phenanthrene spectrum.

Klevens and Platt [325] examined the spectra of a number of aromatic hydrocarbons experimentally and made a very successful attempt to correlate them by the free-electron method. Their findings will be discussed in Chapter 15 and will only be referred to briefly here. They pointed out: "Levels of a given type have unambiguous identifying characteristics, which do not change from compound to compound." (Intensity, polarization and vibrational fine structure.) "Levels of a given type move in a systematic way from compound to compound."

These rules greatly facilitate the assignment of observed band systems. Figure 14-3, taken, like the others, from Platt's work, represents the observed spectra of the acenes and the related assignments made by the free-electron method. The scale in log ε is indicated at the head of each diagram.

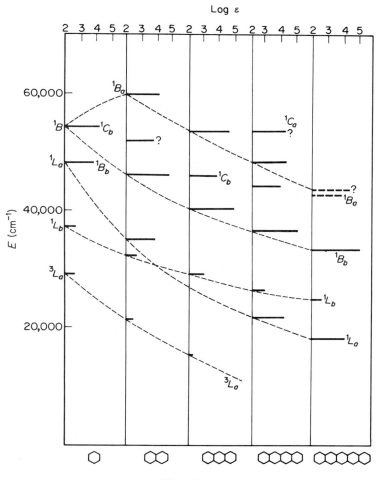

Fig. 14-3

Perhaps the most interesting feature is the change of place of the ^1L_a and ^1L_b levels from naphthalene to anthracene. The longest-wavelength singlet-singlet transition is long-axis polarized in naphthalene but it is short-axis polarized in anthracene.

The shift toward lower frequencies with increasing number of rings is well pronounced.

Comparisons with the LCAO MO (Hückel) method were made in Platt's paper [324].

The weakness of this method, as of all the free-electron methods, is essentially that it is based on a model. An electron in a molecule is, of course, not a free rotator. However, the method has many attractive features. One is that it is not based on atomic orbitals and, therefore, avoids excessive individualization of the atoms in the molecule: another, that comparisons between molecules are not obscured by their differing symmetries. Anyway, we may use any suitable function as a variation function, and the rotator functions are easily susceptible to improvements. Moffitt [327] gave a very interesting interpretation of the spectra of benzene derivatives using such improved free-electron wave functions.

Ham and Ruedenberg [328] presented a configuration interaction treatment, based on antisymmetrized products of free-electron molecular orbitals. They used the complete Hamiltonian including electronic repulsion terms, and computed all the necessary integrals.

In the case of cata-condensed aromatic compounds their calculations led to an agreement with experiment comparable with that obtained by the Pariser and Parr method.

14-2 THE PARTICLE-IN-A-BOX MODEL[1]

Just as the rotator model suggests itself for application to the aromatic hydrocarbons, the particle-in-a-box model may be fitted to linear conjugated systems such as polyenes and many dye molecules containing a polyenic system.

Both models are among the simplest examples of the application of wave-mechanical principles (see, for example, Linnett, *Wave Mechanics and Valency*, p. 6). The particle in a one-dimensional box is essentially a particle of mass m moving freely on a line of length L taken along the x axis, where the potential, V_0, is constant but at the two ends of the line the potential jumps to infinite, restricting the particle to the. one-dimensional "box."

The Schrödinger equation for within the box is

$$\frac{d^2\psi}{dx^2} + \frac{8\pi^2 mE}{h^2} = 0 \qquad (14\text{-}2)$$

which, taking into account the conditions at the limits, yields the normalized eigenfunctions:

[1] Also called the electron-gas or metallic model.

$$\psi_n = \sqrt{\frac{2}{L}} \sin n\pi \, \frac{x}{L}, \qquad n = 1, 2, 3, \ldots \qquad (14\text{-}3)$$

and the eigenvalues:

$$E_n = \frac{n^2 h^2}{8mL^2} \qquad (14\text{-}4)$$

Thus, the energies are given by the same formula as for the free rotator except that here L is the length of the (one-dimensional) box while there it is the length of the perimeter. Another difference is that for the rotator the quantum number can be zero but for the box it cannot. (To-and-fro motions have zero-point energy, circular motions have none.)

For $V = $ const., the Schrödinger equation is equivalent to the de Broglie equation. Therefore, instead of solving the Schrödinger equation we could simply apply the

$$\lambda = \frac{h}{mv}$$

formula, taking into account the condition that at the two extremities of the box ψ must reach the value zero. Then

$$\frac{\lambda}{2} = \frac{L}{n}, \qquad n = 1, 2, 3, \ldots$$

$(n - 1)$ gives the number of internal nodes and n the number of half-waves fitted into the box (Fig. 14-4). From the above two formulas

$$mv = \frac{h}{\lambda} = \frac{nh}{2L}$$

and

$$E_n = \frac{1}{2} mv^2 = \frac{(mv)^2}{2m} = \frac{n^2 h^2}{8mL^2}$$

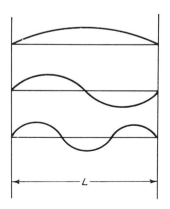

Fig. 14-4

The constant potential energy should be added. This result is general. Quantum numbers can always be interpreted as quantities defining the number of nodes in the available space. The orbital of lowest energy has no nodes, the next lowest has one, and so on. Walsh [330] has pointed out that even in the most complicated wave-mechanical methods we are actually fitting half-waves into the available space.

The energy increases with n^2 and decreases with L^2, i.e., when the box becomes larger. This latter fact is at the root of the homopolar bond; for example, if two hydrogen atoms are brought together the available space for both electrons is almost doubled; hence the energy diminishes and stability is increased.

In the case of molecules the limits of the "box" are determined by the attraction between the π electrons and the partly shielded nuclei. In the case of *trans*-butadiene, for example, the particle-in-a-box orbitals of the π electrons, which have their nodal plane in the plane of the molecule determined by the σ bonds, are as in Fig. 14-5. [330] Clearly, the wavelength diminishes and the energy increases from (a) to (d). It is very interesting to remember that the LCAO MO orbitals (p. 184) have exactly the same nodal properties.

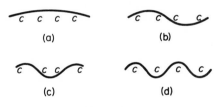

$$
\begin{array}{cc}
\text{(a)} & \text{(b)} \\
\text{(c)} & \text{(d)}
\end{array}
$$

Fig. 14-5

We are interested in spectroscopic quantities. In the ground state there are two electrons in each of the orbitals (a) and (b). The first transition consists in the jumping of an electron from (b) to (c) while n changes from 2 to 3. Therefore, the excitation energy for this $V_1 \leftarrow N$ transition is equal to

$$\frac{(9-4)h^2}{8mL^2} = \frac{5h^2}{8mL^2}$$

Here L designates the length of the butadiene molecule, which has to be extended somewhat beyond the two extreme carbon nuclei. For the ethylene molecule (Fig. 14-6) the related excitation energy is

Fig. 14-6

$$\frac{(4-1)h^2}{8mL^2} = \frac{3h^2}{8mL^2}$$

but L is only half of its value for butadiene. Thus, the excitation energy for the $V_1 \leftarrow N$ transition of ethylene is greater than for butadiene, and it is easy to see that for hexatriene it is lower than for butadiene. This is the familiar shift of this band toward lower frequencies with an increasing number of conjugated double bonds.

The theory of metals of Sommerfeld is based on similar considerations [330]. In this theory the electrons of a metallic crystal are treated as a one-dimensional gas subject to a constant potential field. In a series of papers, O. Schmidt [331] applied a similar treatment to the π electrons of conjugated systems and interpreted many of their physicochemical properties on this basis.

More recently, in 1948, Bayliss [332, 333], Kuhn [334, 335], and Simpson [322] used the one-dimensional electron gas model to account for the spectra of linear conjugated molecules. First we examine some of Bayliss' work.

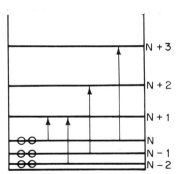

Fig. 14-7

Figure 14-7 (of Bayliss [321]) represents the case of hexatriene. In general, if N indicates the number of double bonds in the system and $2N$ the number of π electrons for polyenes, the wave number (in cm^{-1}) of the first transition is equal to

$$\omega = \frac{E_{N+1} - E_N}{hc} = \frac{h}{8mcL^2}(2N+1) \qquad (14\text{-}5)$$

since N is equal to n for the highest filled orbital of the ground state and $(N+1)^2 - N^2 = 2N + 1$.

Introducing the numerical values of the constants and measuring L in angstrom units one has, for the wave number and the wavelength,

$$\omega = 3.033 \times 10^5(2N+1)/L^2 = B\frac{2N+1}{L^2}$$

and $$\lambda = 329.7\,L^2/2N + 1 \qquad (14\text{-}6)$$

respectively. L is to be taken along the bonds, i.e., the molecule has to be drawn out into a straight line with the true C—C distances.

The transition moment from an orbital with quantum number n to an orbital with quantum number m is equal to

$$Q = \int_0^L \psi_n x \psi_m \, d\tau \qquad (14\text{-}7)$$

Substituting the expressions of the wave functions and with $\theta = \pi x/L$ we have

$$Q = \frac{2\sqrt{2}\,L}{\pi^2} \int_0^\pi \theta \sin n\theta \sin m\theta \, d\theta \qquad (14\text{-}8)$$

The reasons for the factor $\sqrt{2}$ are given on p. 192. It is seen, if the integration is carried through, that the integral is zero if $(m - n)$ is even and is equal to

$$Q = \frac{2\sqrt{2}\,L}{\pi^2}\left[\frac{1}{(m+n)^2} - \frac{1}{(m-n)^2}\right] \qquad (14\text{-}9)$$

if $(m - n)$ is odd.

The strongest band is obtained when $\Delta n = (N + 1) - N = 1$.

$$Q(N, N+1) = \frac{2\sqrt{2}\,L}{\pi^2}\left[\frac{1}{(2N+1)^2} - 1\right] \cong \frac{2L}{\pi^2} \qquad (14\text{-}10)$$

The oscillator strength may be calculated from the formula

$$f = 1.085 \times 10^{11}\,\omega Q^2$$

Computing ω and Q from (14-6) and (14-9) we obtain that

$$f(N, N+1) \cong 0.268(2N + 1)$$

It is seen that f is independent of the length of the system and depends only on the number of double bonds.

There are three transitions[2] with $n = 3$:

$$\omega(N - 2, N + 1) = \frac{B}{L^2}(6N - 3)$$

$$\omega(N - 1, N + 2) = \frac{B}{L^2}(6N + 3)$$

$$\omega(N, N + 3) = \frac{B}{L^2}(6N + 9)$$

The oscillator strength for the first one is

$$f(N - 1, N + 2) \cong 0.010(2N + 1)$$

Comparing these results with experiment we can say that the method predicts correctly the bathochromic shift and gradual increase

[2] Here, at the left hand side, the expressions in parentheses are used as indices.

in intensity of the $V_1 \leftarrow N$ transition with an increasing number of double bonds. The predicted intensities are in reasonable agreement with experimental data, but the frequencies are usually not and they are too sensitive to slight changes in L.

Kuhn examined by the same method the spectra of polymethine dyes.

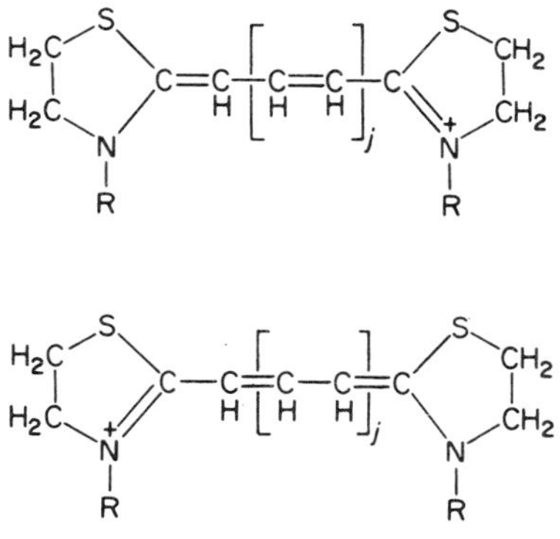

Fig. 14-8

First he studied the symmetrical cyanines, where the chromophoric group is a polyenic chain with a nitrogen at both ends. These substances are colored in the form of cations. Kuhn [323] supposed that they may be represented by the two structures in Fig. 14-8, which have the same weight. Then the bonds in these chains do not alternate as almost double and almost single bonds, but they all have the same double-bond character, as in benzene, for example. This suggestion had been made earlier by Arndt and Eistert [336]. For this reason a constant potential may be a good approximate representation of the actual field for the symmetrical cyanines, while for simple polyenic chains it is not and a periodic potential has to be assumed.

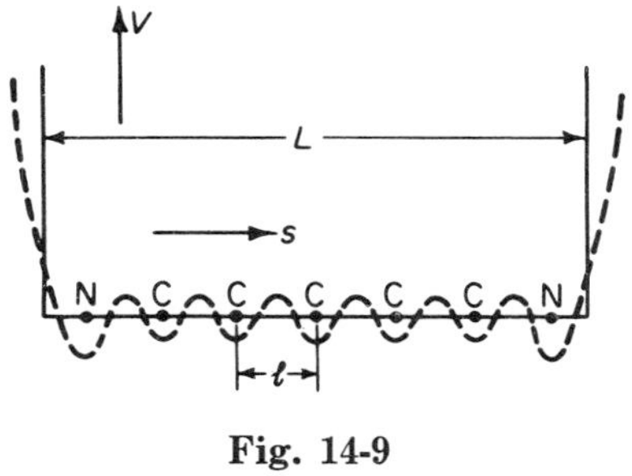

Fig. 14-9

A π electron having freedom of motion in one dimension has its potential energy increased or decreased when it approaches or moves away from a core (carbon or nitrogen), and the potential energy increases suddenly at the ends of the chain. Figure 14-9 [334] represents such a potential. Replacing the inner part of it by a straight line would be a fair approximation for symmetrical cyanine dyes but not for simple polyenes. In applying the formula (14-5) to cyanines we have to remember that one of the nitrogens contributes two π electrons, the other only one, and there is an odd number of carbon atoms in this case. Carbon and nitrogen atoms are treated alike in this approximation. Table 14-3, taken from Kuhn [334], compares the results with experiment for a number of carbocyanines of the type given in Fig. 14-10. The agreement is very satisfactory.

TABLE 14-3

Number of π electrons	λ_1 Theor.	λ_1 Exp.
10	5790	5900
12	7060	7100
14	8340	8200
16	9590	9300

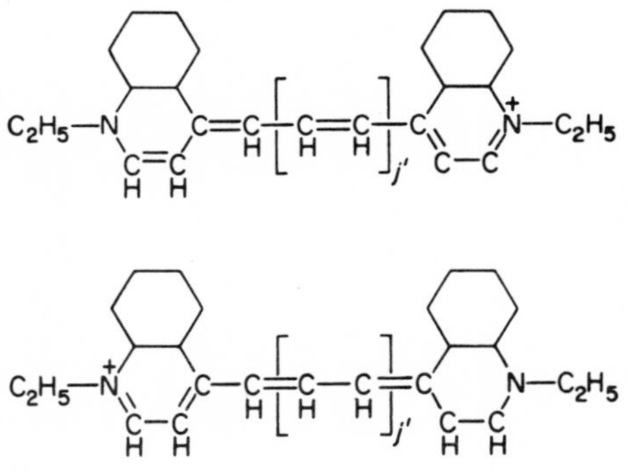

Fig. 14-10

More complicated cases, as where benzene rings are linked to the nitrogens, may often be taken care of by adjusting the value of L.

Kuhn extended the electron gas method to certain nonlinear molecules such as dipyridylviolet, for example (Fig. 14-11). (Branched

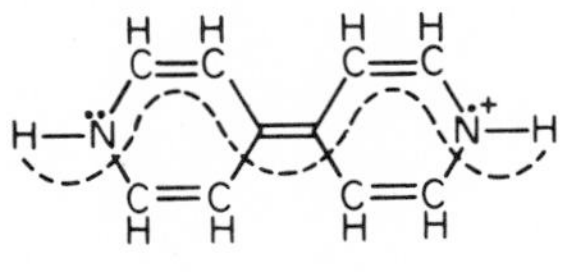

Fig. 14-11

electron gas; see his paper [337].) In his hands the electron gas method became a quantum-mechanical tool quite capable of practical predictions of the color of dye molecules. In a review paper he gave a number of examples covering a variety of compounds [338].

In later papers he examined the relationship between more elaborate quantum-mechanical methods and the electron gas method, providing justification for the latter (see, for example, [339] and [340]).

It is natural to try to improve the electron gas method by assuming, instead of the constant potential, a potential field closer to the actual conditions. Attempts in this direction have been made by Bayliss and Rivière [341, 342] and by Kuhn and his collaborators [343, 344].

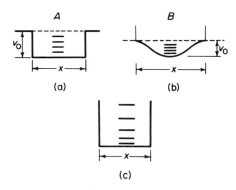

Fig. 14-12

Bayliss and Rivière considered three potential-energy models. They described the first one as the "rectangular potential well" [Fig. 14-12 (a)]. The potential energy is given the constant value V_0 within a space of length X; outside this space it is taken to be zero. The second model [Fig. 14-12 (b)] is the "cosine potential well." Within a space of length X, the potential energy is expressed as

$$V = 2k \cos^2 \frac{\pi x}{X} - V_0 \qquad (14\text{-}11)$$

where $2k = V_0$ is the depth of the well.

The model shown in Fig. 14-12 (c) is the simple model used previously, where the potential is V_0 inside the space of length X and jumps to infinite at both ends.

The third model takes into account the fact that "the potential energy must be a periodically oscillating function and it must also have the general shape of a well flattening off to a constant value of zero (corresponding to ionization) outside the molecule." This model is shown in Fig. 14-13 for *trans*-butadiene [341].

For an electron distant from the molecule (P) we may assume that it is acted upon by charge $+e$ located at the center of the molecule.

The potential energy is

$$V_P = \frac{-e^2}{R}$$

For an electron inside the molecule (Q) the screening of the nuclei by the other electrons is only partial. Supposing that this can be adequately represented by assigning an effective nuclear charge to each carbon, $Z'e$, and considering the hydrogen nuclei as completely screened, the potential energy at point Q can be written as

$$V_Q = \sum_k \left(\frac{-Z'e^2}{r_k} \right)$$

where r_k is the distance from Q to the kth carbon.

Bayliss and Rivière have solved the Schrödinger equation with these three different potential functions and found good agreement with experimental spectral data.

Kuhn *et al.* [343, 344, 340] considered three stages of refinement for polyenes, for which the simple model did not give satisfactory results. These are: a sine-curve potential model, a one-dimensional wave-shape potential model, and a two-dimensional potential trough model.

For details of all these calculations we refer to the original authors.

We wish to draw the attention of the reader to Simpson's [345] and Rackow's [346, 347] work on porphines and to further free-electron work by Nikitine [348–350].

Free-electron methods have no claim to high accuracy but they have rendered great services in correlating spectra of large categories of compounds. In particular, they have contributed a great deal to our present understanding of the electronic spectra of aromatic and dyestuff molecules.

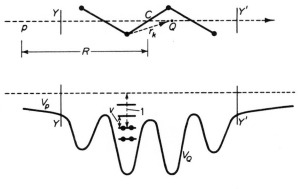

Fig. 14-13

15

A Brief Review of Chemical Spectroscopy

15-1 CHROMOPHORES

Saturated paraffinic hydrocarbons absorb only in the far ultraviolet. All but the smallest have their extinction maximum at about 1700 Å. Ethylene has a broad, strong band system at about 1620 Å and a problematic weak one near 2000 Å. The regions of absorption of longest wavelength lie around 2100 Å for butadiene, 2550 Å for benzene, 3800 Å for anthracene (which is still not colored, though its fluorescence is visible, violet)·, 4750 Å for naphthacene which is orange-yellow, and 6800 Å for azulene which is blue. In general, all organic compounds absorbing in the visible or in the ultraviolet down to 2000 Å are unsaturated compounds. Although sharp lines cannot be drawn, we shall call the region of the spectrum between 7000 and 4000 Å visible, the region from 4000 Å to 3000 Å the near ultraviolet, the one between 3000 Å and 2000 Å the medium ultraviolet, and the waves shorter than 2000 Å the far ultraviolet.

Unsaturated organic molecules contain π electrons. Groups of atoms containing π electrons are often called *chromophores*. Originally the term referred to a group of atoms having electronic energy levels so close to one other that their energy difference determines a photon with a wavelength in the visible part of the spectrum. At present this term is used in a more general sense. We speak of a chromophore in relation to a given band system of the spectrum; it is that part of a molecule, or class of molecules, which is indispensable for giving rise to the band system under consideration. In this sense π electronic systems are chromophores for visible and ultraviolet spectra, σ electrons for far ultraviolet spectra, although, naturally, the situation is not quite so simple. Thus, groups containing π electrons have their higher transitions in the far ultraviolet, and there are transitions in which σ electrons become π electrons. The correct use of the word *chromophore* is not crucial, however.

Auxochromes (certain substituents) are groups of atoms which, added to chromophores, make their energy levels move closer to each other. Thus, for example, the benzene ring is a chromophore, and an OH group substituted for one of its hydrogens is an auxochrome. In the steroid molecule, oestriol, the chromophore is still the benzene ring and its spectrum is actually *about* the same as the spectrum of benzene.

Ions and free radicals usually have spectra that are shifted toward longer waves with respect to the related neutral and undissociated molecules. In general, a shift toward longer waves (lower frequencies) is referred to as a red shift and a shift toward shorter waves (higher frequencies) is called a blue shift, regardless of the part of the spectrum in which the given band is located. Quite often ions and radicals are colored while the corresponding neutral (undissociated) molecules are not.

To summarize, under normal circumstances the visible and near ultraviolet absorption of organic compounds is due to electrons in π orbitals. There are also numerous inorganic compounds which absorb in the visible and in the near ultraviolet. This is due to transitions of electrons in partly filled d, f, or g shells. This is the case of the positive ions of the metals of the iron group, Ti, V, Cr, Mn, Fe, Ni, Co, and Cu, and of the ions of the rare earths. For example, the hydrated ions of these metals are colored in solution while ions with rare gas configurations are colorless. These ions are, of course, chromophores too.

An important fact of chemical spectroscopy is linked to the chromophoric properties of groups that contain π electrons. It is sometimes called the *insulation of chromophores*. Ramart-Lucas [351], on the basis of a great number of measurements, stated that if A and B are π electron-containing chromophores, then:

1. If A and B are directly linked together then the spectrum of molecule A—B will usually be very different from the spectrum of either A or B. A—B is then a new chromophore.

2. If A and B are linked to the same CH_2 group then they take back their individuality almost completely, and in the spectrum we find side by side the more or less modified spectra of A and B.
3. If A and B are separated by two or more CH_2 groups then the spectrum is practically the sum of those of A and B.

All this is easy to understand. If A and B are linked directly together, the π electrons form a new, more extended π-electronic system. For this new system the energy levels will be, in general, different from those of A or B. Thus the spectrum of stilbene is not the sum of the spectra of the two benzene rings and of ethylene, but it is a new spectrum. (Longest-wavelength bands: benzene, 2550 Å, stilbene, 3200 Å.)

In A—CH_2—B the methylene carbon atom is tetrahedrally hybridized and breaks the π electronic system into two. A modest degree of interaction between A and B is possible because of hyperconjugation. Mulliken, Rieke, and Brown [352] have shown the possibility of forming group orbitals from the three or two hydrogen 1s orbitals of the CH_3 or CH_2 groups having a nodal plane like the π orbitals. Then the carbon and the H_3 or H_2 group may be regarded in a certain measure as contributing π electrons to the system. This idea has been challenged by Dewar and Schmeising [353], who have shown that the experimental proofs offered in favor of the existence of this effect become invalidated when new, improved data are used. Whatever the right way of describing the behavior of a CH_3 or CH_2 group attached to conjugated systems, there is enough evidence to say that a CH_2 group "transmits" conjugation slightly. With more than one CH_2 group, the mutual insulation of chromophores A and B becomes practically complete.

The insulation of chromophores by saturated groups is one of the elementary facts of the electronic spectroscopy of organic molecules, which is applied every day by the chemical spectroscopist.

Chromophores may be separated from each other by groups other than—CH_2—groups. These groups invariably contain lone pairs of electrons, and the degree of insulation provided by them depends on steric conditions. It can be said, however, that the ether linkage, —O—, usually acts rather as an insulator, but the —NH— group transmits conjugation to an appreciable extent.

15-2 SOME GENERAL REMARKS

A recent review by Mason [354] covers much the same ground as this chapter; therefore it will be kept short and will be limited to fundamental facts. The reader who is interested in the electronic spectra of given organic compounds may consult C. N. R. Rao's book

[355] which provides nearly complete coverage. Another excellent survey was given by Pestemer and Brück [356].[1]

Concerning diatomic molecules, the classic is Herzberg's *Spectra of Diatomic Molecules.*

The word "Chemical" in the title of this chapter describes a practical aspect and there is nothing rigorous about it. There are no physical or chemical spectra, only spectra. What we mean by chemical spectroscopy is the study of the spectra of larger molecules, usually measured in solutions. Then the information obtainable from the rotational structure of the electronic-vibrational bands and, often, that obtainable from the vibrational structure of electronic band systems, has to be sacrificed, but, on the other hand, chemical knowledge and comparisons between parent molecules often help with the interpretation of the spectra.

The following categories of spectra are of great interest.

$\pi \to \pi^*$ *band systems.* These are due to transitions in which an electron jumps from one π orbital to another. In general, using the language of molecular orbital theory, the jump takes place from a (mainly) bonding to an (mainly) antibonding orbital (the latter indicated by an asterisk). These band systems account for many spectra in the visible and in the near and medium ultraviolet.

$n \to \pi^*$ *band systems.* These are due to transitions from the orbitals of lone pairs of electrons localized around a heteroatom to an excited molecular π orbital. They cause weak bands in the visible or the near or medium ultraviolet.

$\sigma \to \sigma^*$ *band systems.* These are linked to transitions of electrons in σ orbitals and appear in the far ultraviolet.

$n \to \sigma^*$ *band systems.* An electron in a lone-pair orbital may jump to a σ^* orbital. These band systems are located in the medium or far ultraviolet.

Charge-transfer spectra. The electronic charge distribution changes in every transition, and in many cases the dipole moment of the excited state is different from that of the ground state. Following the more recent use of the term we shall designate as charge-transfer spectra only those related to electronic transitions resulting in an intermolecular or interionic transfer of electronic charge. Organic and inorganic compounds both provide interesting cases of charge-transfer band systems.

Ligand-field spectra. In complex molecules having a central ion with incompletely filled d or f shells the field of the ligands may

---

[1] To see how very much was done in spectroscopy in the twenties and thirties it is still interesting to have a look at Förster's review, *Z. Elektrochem.*, **45**, 548 (1939).

Since this book was written an extensive work appeared on the spectra of larger molecules: "Theory and Applications of Ultraviolet Spectroscopy." by H.H. Jaffé and M. Orchin. (New York: John Wiley and Sons, Inc., 1962.)

partly or entirely lift degeneracy of the $(5)d$ or $(7)f$ orbitals, creating energy differences and thus the possibility of transitions between them. Such band systems are responsible for the visible and near ultraviolet spectra of many inorganic complex ions.

Some of these various types of spectra will now be treated in more detail.

15-3 $\pi \to \pi^*$ TRANSITIONS

Ethylene has a strong and broad band with its maximum at about 1620 Å in the gas phase and between 1700 and 1800 Å in solution, which is easily assigned to an allowed singlet-singlet transition of an electron from the $^1A_{1g}$ ground state to a $^1B_{1u}$ excited state where the electron is in an antibonding orbital. The band has a shoulder around 2000 Å, which for a long time was believed to be a separate electronic band system (see Sec. 9-4). Potts' low-temperature work has shown, however, that this is not so. The first singlet-triplet transition of ethylene gives rise to an extremely weak band at about 3000 Å (ϵ_{max} about 0.0001) [357, 358].

There is an extensive literature relating to the spectrum of ethylene, which has been reviewed up to 1944 by Klevens and Platt [359]. Among later contributions we mention those of Walsh [360], Gary and Pickett [361], and Wilkinson and Mulliken [362]. The molecule is not coplanar in its B_{1u} excited state [363, 360].

In the series of conjugated polyenes the first band system shifts gradually to longer wavelengths and becomes stronger with an increasing number of double bonds (see [130, p. 208]).

Ethylene	1620 Å	or	61,500 cm^{-1}
Butadiene	2170		46,080
Hexatriene	2510		39,750
Octatetraene	3040		32,900

This is one of those phenomena which even the most approximate methods of quantum chemistry are able to interpret. We have encountered it on various occasions.

Dienes absord between 2170 and 2300^2 Å, but for cyclic dienes great bathochromic effects are observed. Thus, for cyclopentadiene, the maximum of the first band system is at 2385 Å; for cyclohexadiene, at 2565 Å; and for cycloheptadiene, at 2480 Å [391, 392, 393].[2]

Much less is known about the higher transitions of polyenes.

Triple-bonded and cumulative systems can be thought of in terms of digonal hybridization with one π_z and one π_y electron from each carbon or nitrogen if the bond lies in the x direction. Acetylene

---

[2] Regular shifts are observed upon alkyl substitution. (R. B. Woodward, *J. Am. Chem. Soc.* **63**, 1123 (1941); **64**, 72, 76 (1942).

$$H—C \equiv C—H$$

is a linear molecule which has fourteen electrons. The ground-state configuration is (see Chapter 6)

$$KK(\sigma_g[HC])^2(\sigma_g[CH])^2(\sigma_g[CC])^2(\pi_u[CC])^4$$

The lowest excited states are produced from the configuration... $(\pi_u)^3(\pi_g)$. These are the singlet and triplet Σ_u^+, Σ_u^-, and Δ_u states, the latter being doubly degenerate. The three first band systems of acetylene are at about 2200 Å (weak), 1820 Å (medium), and 1520 Å (strong). They have been shown to correspond to transitions from the $^1\Sigma_g^+({}^1A_{1g})$ ground state to $^1\Sigma_u^-({}^1A_{2u})$, $^1\Delta_u({}^1E_{2u})$, and $^1\Sigma_u^+({}^1A_{1u})$ states, respectively [364, 365, 366]. Only the last one would be allowed if the molecule remained linear in the excited states. It is known, however, that it is bent [367]. Spectra of polyacetylenes show the expected shift toward longer wavelengths. A thorough theoretical treatment of acetylene, using antisymmetrized molecular orbitals with configuration interaction and taking into account π-σ interaction, is due to Ross [364].[3]

The spectra of aromatic hydrocarbons exhibit a number of now well-known regularities. These were first emphasized by Clar [368] and were very successfully used by Klevens and Platt to reach a general understanding of these spectra (see Chapters 8 and 14).

In the spectrum of benzene the three first band systems are at about 2550 Å (39,200 cm^{-1}), 2050 Å (48,800), and 1830 Å (54,600). They correspond to transitions $^1L_b \leftarrow {}^1A$, $^1L_a \leftarrow {}^1A$, and $^1B \leftarrow {}^1A$, respectively, in Platt's free-electron scheme. Clar calls these bands α, p, and β in the same order. The first two are forbidden under D_{6h} symmetry and appear only in combination with nontotally symmetrical vibrations (cf. Chapters 8 and 9) with a low intensity.

The first three band systems of the acenes exhibit a certain analogy with the three benzene band systems. In naphthalene the α band is of lowest frequency (about 3080 Å or 32,470 cm^{-1}) and it is polarized in the molecular plane according to the long axis. It is weak although not forbidden, as extensive studies of McClure and Craig et al. [369, 370] have shown. The second band (Clar's p band) is short-axis polarized, also in the molecular plane, and it is stronger. The third, the β band, is very strong, and like the first band it is long-axis polarized.

The p band, under the influence of linear annellation in the series naphthalene-anthracene-naphthacene-pentacene, shifts more rapidly toward longer wavelengths than the α and β bands. Thus, for anthracene and naphthacene the weak and slowly moving α band is covered

[3] See also J. Serre and G. Berthier, J. chim. phys. 50, 447 (1953).

by the p band, which now becomes the first band. In the spectrum of pentacene the α band appears at the short-wavelength side of the p band. The third band shifts at about the same rate as the first one.

In aromatic hydrocarbons with angular annellation, such as phenanthrene or benzo[a]anthracene the p band shifts more slowly. As a consequence the change of place of the α and p bands, which for the linear acenes occurs between naphthalene and anthracene, does not occur here. For this reason the spectrum of phenanthrene resembles the spectrum of naphthalene rather than that of anthracene.

In the spectra of the larger molecules there is still another strong band (β') at the short-wavelength side of the β band before 2000 Å. (The two bands correspond to Platt's ^1B_a and ^1B_b states.)

The first singlet-triplet transition of aromatic hydrocarbons produces a very weak band in the visible or sometimes in the near infrared [371-374]. This metastable triplet state has been identified by Lewis and Kasha [375] as the phosphorescent state of conjugated molecules, while fluorescence almost always takes place from the first excited singlet level.[4] If higher levels are excited they usually lose their excitation energies by radiationless transition through the cascade of vibrational levels until the lowest excited singlet level is reached. Then, if the excitation energy is not used up in collisions, by chemical reaction, or by other mechanisms during the lifetime of the excited state, emission will take place (fluorescence) or radiationless transition will transfer the molecule into the lowest triplet state from which emission (phosphorescence) can take place. The triplet state cannot be populated by direct absorption because of the extremely low intensity of the single-triplet transition, but it can be populated from above by the excited singlet states. This mechanism involving two excited states has been proposed by Jablonski [376]. Fluorescence and phosphorescence are better studied in rigid glasses where the possibility of intermolecular energy transfer is greatly reduced.

The extinction coefficients and oscillator strengths of the α, p, β, and t (singlet-triplet) band systems are in the following orders of magnitude:

	ϵ_{max}	f
α	10^2	10^{-3}
p	10^4	10^{-1}
β	10^5	1
t	0.1 or less	10^{-5} or less

Many successful theoretical treatments were carried out on these

[4] A confirmed case of fluorescence from the second excited singlet level is that of azulene. (M. Beer and H. C. Longuet-Higgins, $J. Chem. Phys.$ **23**: 1390 (1955)).

molecules. In addition to the references given above we mention Moffitt's improved free-electron calculations [377], the improved molecular orbital treatment of Dewar and Longuet-Higgins [378], the semiempirical self-consistent field approach of Pople [379]. The closest match of experimental results was achieved by Pariser [380] who used the Pariser and Parr semiempirical method.

Nonalternant hydrocarbons also have three band systems which resemble the α, p, and β band systems of the alternant ones except that the whole spectrum lies at considerably longer wavelengths. The latter fact can be correctly interpreted by both the molecular orbital and the free-electron methods. For example, in the spectrum of fulvene—an isomer of benzene—the first band system has its maximum at 3730 Å and the second one at 2420 Å [381]; in the spectrum of azulene—an isomer of naphthalene—the first one is at 6540 Å, the second at 3470 Å, and the third at 2700 Å [382]. Acenaphthylene has a spectrum somewhat similar to 1-vinyl-naphthalene with a lesser shift toward longer waves (3380, 3240, 2650 Å) [383].

Aza-aromatic molecules such as pyridine, quinoleine, and acridine, for example, have spectra similar to the related hydrocarbon [384–389]. The effect of the heteroatom can be treated as a perturbation (see p. 220). However, outside of the $\pi \to \pi^*$ transitions these molecules also have $n \to \pi^*$ transitions which will be discussed in Section 15-4.

Methyl-substitution on ethylene, conjugated polyenes, and aromatic compounds exerts a slight bathochromic effect on the spectrum. In the case of nonalternant hydrocarbons, however, methyl-substitution causes either bathochromic or hypsochromic shifts depending upon the place of substitution. For azulene (Fig. 15-1) methyl-substitution in 5 or 1 causes a bathochromic shift ($1 > 5$) but in 4, 6, or 2 it causes a hypsochromic shift ($2 > 4 > 6$). Pullman, Mayot, and Berthier [390] successfully interpreted these facts by the simple molecular orbital method.

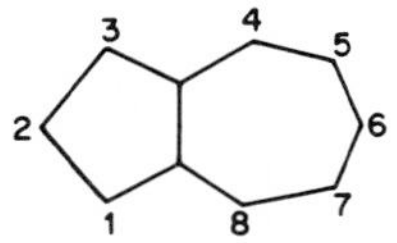

Fig. 15-1

Substitution by auxochrome (basic) groups like OH or NH_2 causes larger shifts (about 200 to 400 Å). This case was discussed in Chapter 10. Further theoretical work was done by Murrell and Longuet-Higgins [265] [267] (inductive and mesomeric (resonance) effects).

In 1951 Platt made an attempt to systemize the spectra of organic compounds [397]. He calls two coplanar, conjugated molecules "iso-conjugate" or "iso-π-electronic" if they have the same number of π electrons, which are equally tightly bound in a similar molecular skeleton. The π-electronic spectra of two such molecules are very similar. For example, aniline and styrene are isoconjugate. Platt defines "variconjugate" sequences as a series of molecules in which the localization of certain π electrons decreases gradually. This is paralleled by the decrease of the corresponding frequencies. An example of such a variconjugate sequence is: benzene, fluorobenzene, phenol, aniline, styrene. Then, it can be shown that the electronic spectrum of any organic molecule with a closed-shell ground state lies on a variconjugate sequence between the spectra of two conjugated hydro-carbons. Thus, we have a whole network of spectra in which every organic molecule has its place.

Many of the fundamental facts concerning the effect of substitution were established by Jones [395, 396] in the early forties.

The interaction between two π orbitals is greatest when their axes are parallel and decreases fairly quickly with the increasing torsion of these axes with respect to each other. Coplanarity can be rendered impossible in certain cases for steric reasons, because the atoms have finite sizes and space requirements.

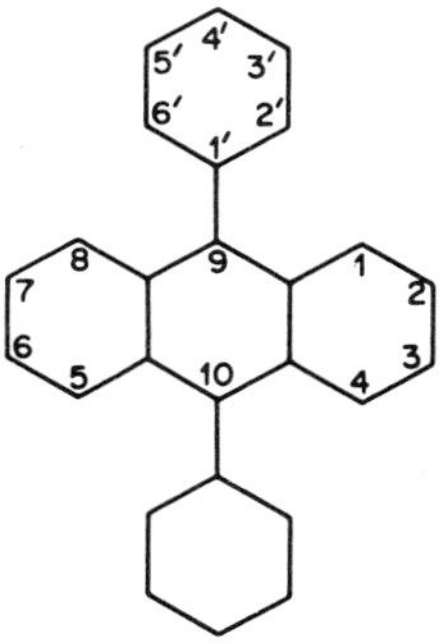

Fig. 15-2

A good example is 9,10-diphenylanthracene, one of the typical cases of steric hindrance given by Jones [395] (Fig. 15-2). The two phenyl groups are only weakly conjugated with the anthracene ring to about the same extent as the methyl groups in 9,10-dimethylanthracene. The absorption spectra of the diphenyl and the dimethyl compound are very similar. Clearly the repulsion between the hydrogen atoms in 8 and 6', and the other three similar pairs, forces the phenyl rings to turn out of the plane of the anthracene molecule. The spectrum

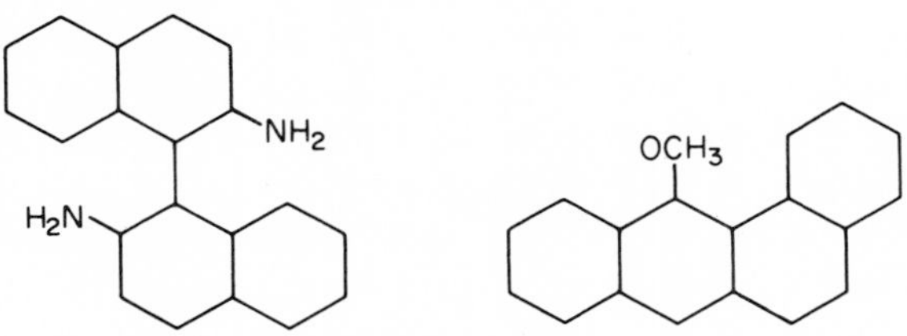

Fig. 15-3

of 2, 2'-diamino-1, 1'-dinaphthyl (Fig. 15-3) is practically the same as the spectrum of β-naphthylamine because of steric hindrance between the NH$_2$ groups and the hydrogens on the α carbon atoms. The spectrum of α,α'-dinaphthyl is about the same as that of naphthalene with twice the intensity, for similar reasons. Another interesting case is the one of 9,10-dinaphthylanthracene. The two naphthyl groups cannot accommodate themselves in the plane of the anthracene ring and so the spectrum will be composed additively of anthracene and naphthalene bands. Since, in the near ultraviolet, naphthalene has a maximum absorption where anthracene has a minimum, this is easy to observe.

Other typical examples are found among *ortho*-substituted benzene derivatives. Klevens and Platt [399] studied the case of *ortho*-X-dimethylaniline, with X = F, Cl, Br, CH$_3$, di-*o*-*o'*-CH$_3$. The bulkier is X, the greater will be the angle between the axis of the $2p_z$ orbital of nitrogen and the axes of the carbon π orbitals. The oscillator strength diminishes approximately with the square of the cosine of this angle.

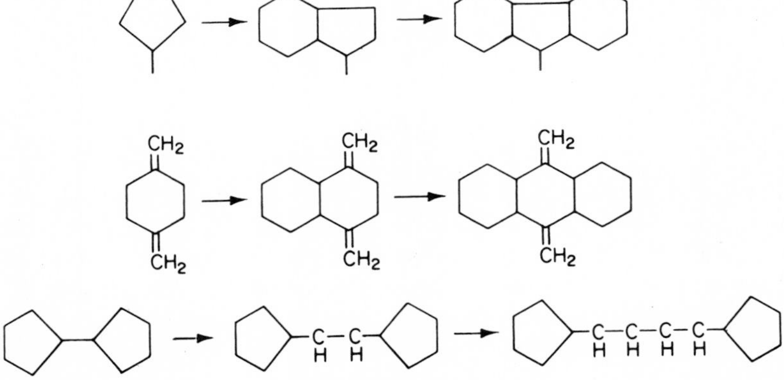

Fig. 15-4

It is often assumed that an increase of the size of the conjugated system is necessarily accompanied by a shift of the spectrum toward longer wavelengths. Thus, we give examples where the contrary is the case, as in the three lines of Fig. 15-4 [398]. Other examples are given in Fig. 15-5 [397]. When the two dimensions of the molecules become more comparable, the p (and sometimes the α) bands undergo a hypsochromic shift.[5]

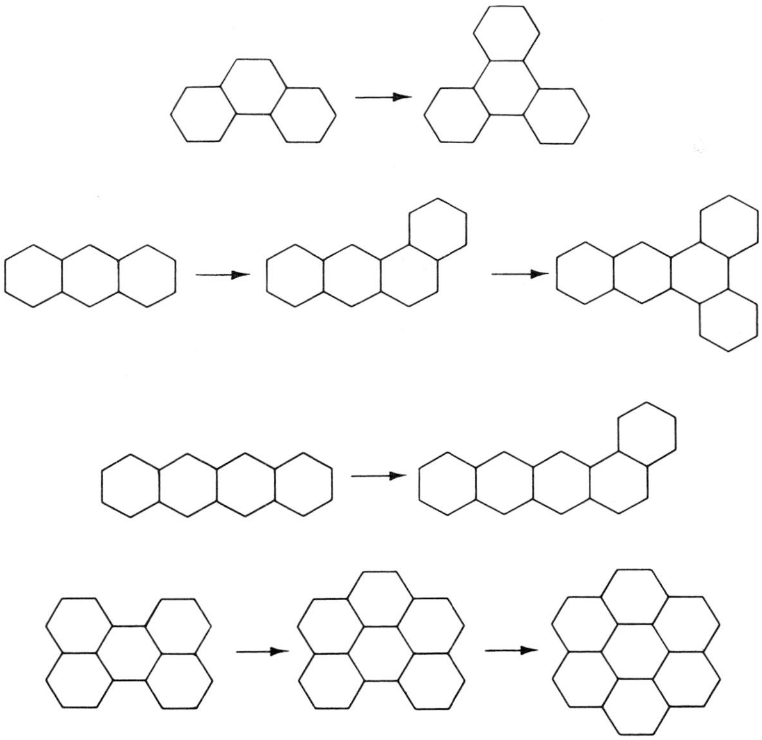

Fig. 15-5

Empirical rules should be applied with caution. What is good for one type of molecule does not necessarily apply to another.

15-4 $n \rightarrow \pi^*$ TRANSITIONS

An excellent review on $n \rightarrow \pi^*$ transitions was published in 1958 by Sidman [400]. "According to the simple LCAO MO description of

[5] Double bonds were omitted on the figures.

an $n \rightarrow \pi^*$ transition, an electron is excited from a nonbonding orbital (n orbital), which to a great extent is localized on one atom in the molecule, into an antibonding orbital, which is antisymmetric to reflection in the molecular plane (π^* orbital), and which extends over more than one atom in the molecule."

Such transitions occur in certain types of heteroatomic molecules like aza-aromatic compounds and compounds containing nitro, nitroso-, azo-, carbonyl, thiocarbonyl, and similar groups. As early as 1930 Burawoy [401] observed that band systems, due to the presence of such groups, behave differently from $\pi \rightarrow \pi^*$ band systems, in particular toward solvent effects. He called the former R bands and the latter K bands. The $n \rightarrow \pi^*$ designation was introduced by Kasha [402], who contributed a great deal of the progress made in this field.

The understanding of the nature of these transitions is due to Mulliken [273] and McMurry [274, 403], who were concerned with carbonyl compounds, and it was Kasha [402] who recognized the generality of their occurrence.

In pure conjugated hydrocarbons there are, of course, no lone pairs of electrons. In substituted compounds such as aniline, for example, there is a lone pair of electrons (on the nitrogen atom) but these are in $2p_z$ orbitals whose axes are parallel to those of the π electrons of the carbon atoms and form an integral part of the π-electronic system of the molecule. There is no $n \rightarrow \pi^*$ transition for aniline.

The case of pyridine is different. We may assume trigonal hybridization for the nitrogen atom in both aniline and pyridine. The nitrogen atom, being outside of the ring in aniline, will have three σ bonds forming single bonds with one carbon and two hydrogen atoms. The remaining two electrons will occupy the $2p_z$ orbital. In pyridine the nitrogen atom forms part of the ring. Two σ orbitals will form single bonds with the two contiguous carbon atoms. One electron will be in the $2p_z$ orbital, and there remain two more electrons for the third σ orbital, an sp^2 hybrid whose axis *is* in the plane of the molecule. Now the $n \rightarrow \pi^*$ transition is obtained when one of these electrons forming the lone pair jumps to an excited molecular π^* orbital.[6]

A transition of this type is expected to be weak because the two wave functions under the transition moment integral overlap very little. The one is to a large extent localized around the heteroatom, the other is an extended molecular orbital. If the lone pair is in a pure p_x or p_y orbital, it can be seen that the various contributions to the

---

[6] This is an approximate language. The energy of the π states is dependent upon the number of electrons in the lone pair orbital.

integral cancel. This would be a forbidden $n \to \pi^*$ transition and the corresponding band system will be very weak (f is of the order of 10^{-3} or 10^{-4}). If, however, the lone-pair orbital is an sp hybrid the transition will be allowed, thanks to the s component, and f will have values of the order of 10^{-2}. In Platt's nomenclature [404] the allowed $n \to \pi^*$ bands are designated by $^1W \to {}^1A$ and the forbidden ones by $^1U \leftarrow {}^1A$. The $n \to \pi^*$ transitions are polarized perpendicular to the plane of the ring.

Pyridinelike molecules have allowed $n \to \pi^*$ transitions. In pyridine itself it is between 3000 and 2700 Å and it is overlapped from the short-wavelength side by the stronger $\pi \to \pi^*$ band (about 2700 to 2450 Å). If we put more than one nitrogen atom in the ring, the $n \to \pi^*$ spectrum undergoes a large shift toward longer wavelengths (pyridazine: 3400 Å; pyrimidine: 2980 Å; pyrazine: 3280 Å; sym-tetrazine: 5420 Å), while the position of the $(\pi \to \pi^*)$ α band changes only slightly. The reasons for this large shift are not as simple as one might imagine at first sight. It is linked to changes in the energies of both the ground and excited states. The shift is the largest, however, if the two nitrogen atoms are in *ortho* positions, probably because then the two n orbitals interact strongly, giving rise to two levels ($n_1 + n_2$ and $n_1 - n_2$) with the possibility of a transition of low excitation energy.

The $n \to \pi^*$ bands lie close to the first $\pi \to \pi^*$ band system and they become hidden under the latter for systems as large as naphthalene, since the $\pi \to \pi^*$ bands shift faster (from pyridine to quinoline, for example) than the $n \to \pi^*$ bands, the n level remaining about the same. However, with two nitrogen atoms the $n \to \pi^*$ bands again become clearly distinguishable.

For more knowledge about these molecules we refer to Halverson and Hirt [385, 386], Ito, Shimada, Kuraishi, and Mizushima [405], and Sponer and Rush [406]. Many other references are given in Sidman's and Mason's reviews (400, 389].

Carbonyl compounds also have well-known $n \to \pi^*$ bands. These are closer to the $^1U \leftarrow {}^1A$ type. In acetone it is near 2900 Å, in simple conjugated ketones it moves to 3100–3300 Å. In acetone the next band is an $n \to \sigma^*$ band at 1800 Å; the first $\pi \to \pi^*$ transition is near 1570 Å (in $>C{=}0$ the π electrons are more tightly bound than in $C{=}C$). Again in the presence of two $>C{=}O$ groups, as in quinones, longer-wavelength absorption may be obtained.

Singlet-triplet $n \to \pi^*$ transitions are extremely weak ($\epsilon \sim 10^{-3}$). In the case of acetone it is near 4000 Å. However, the singlet-triplet separation is somewhat less than for $\pi \to \pi^*$ levels [407]. This is connected to the fact that there is generally no fluorescence from $n \rightarrow \pi^*$ levels. There exists an easy way of radiationless deactivation through the close-lying triplet level.

We are not going into the discussion of other types of hetero-molecules but two important properties of $n \rightarrow \pi^*$ band systems will be mentioned.

First, they generally consist of very sharp bands in the vapor phase, but of broad, diffuse bands in solution owing to the highly associable character of the lone-pair electrons.

Secondly, if we vary the solvent in order of increasing polarity (for example, hexane $\rightarrow$ alcohol $\rightarrow$ water $\rightarrow$ dilute hydrochloric acid) the $n \rightarrow \pi^*$ bands undergo a gradual, hypsochromic (blue) shift whereas $\pi \rightarrow \pi^*$ bands (except for a few weak bands) undergo bathochromic (red) shift. The plausible explanation is that since the wave functions of the ground and excited states are very different for $n \rightarrow \pi^*$ (and some weak $\pi \rightarrow \pi^*$) band systems, the solvent "cage" around the solute molecules, which is adapted to the ground state and lowers its energy appreciably, will affect the excited state much less. The extent to which hydrogen bonding is involved in these solute-solvent interactions has been argued by McConnell [408], Brealey and Kasha [409], and Pimentel [410].

In acid solutions $n \rightarrow \pi^*$ transitions "disappear" completely (i. e., shift to much higher frequencies) since the lone-pair electrons are then tied down by a proton and their energies become much lower. Salt formation also has a profound effect on the spectra of amines such as aniline since then the π electrons contributed by the hetero-atom are withdrawn from the system. Thus in acid solution the spectrum of aniline reverts to an approximate benzene spectrum. This important phenomenon was first described by Jones [396].[7] The difference is that for pyridine, for example, protonation of the nitrogen would make the $n \rightarrow \pi^*$ bands disappear but would affect only slightly the $\pi \rightarrow \pi^*$ spectrum, whereas for aniline it is the $\pi \rightarrow \pi^*$ spectrum which is strongly perturbed.

The extinction coefficients of the types of band systems which have been discussed in this chapter are of the following orders of magnitude:

[7] The acid concentration at which this occurs depends on the electronic charge on the nitrogen atom, which in turn varies from one electronic state to the other. Förster gave a striking demonstration of this by measuring the absorption and fluorescence spectra of a number of aromatic amines at a series of pH. The change from the aniline-type spectrum to the benzene-type spectrum occurs at widely different acid concentrations in the two. [See *Z. Elektrochem.*, **54**, 42 (1950); **54**, 531 (1950); **59**, 976 (1955)].

forbidden $n \rightarrow \pi^*$ transitions: 10 to 100;

allowed $n \rightarrow \pi^*$ transitions: 100 to 1000;

forbidden or otherwise weak $\pi \rightarrow \pi^*$ transitions: 200 to 1000;

allowed $\pi \rightarrow \pi^*$ transitions: 1000 to 100,000.

Thus, if a strong band shows the red solvent shift, it is $\pi \rightarrow \pi^*$. A very weak, blue-shift band must be $n \rightarrow \pi^*$. For intermediate cases the distinction is not always easy to make.

15-5 CHARGE-TRANSFER SPECTRA

Ordinary salt molecules like sodium chloride may absorb a photon $h\nu$ of the appropriate frequency and dissociate into two neutral atoms as a result of the absorption.

$$Na^+Cl^- \xrightarrow{h\nu} Na + Cl$$

This fact was first recognized for alkali halide crystals by Przibram in 1923 [411] and for alkali halide molecules in the gas phase by Franck and his collaborators, Kondratjew [412] and Kuhn and Rollefson [413], in 1926; and much progress was made by Hilsch and Pohl [414]. As a consequence of the absorption an electron has been transferred from the negative Cl^- ion to the positive Na^+ ion. Figure 15-6 taken from Franck, Kuhn, and Rollefson [413] shows the absorption curves of gaseous NaCl, NaBr, and NaI. The latter have

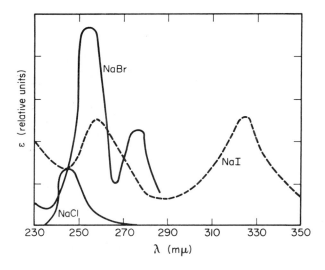

Fig. 15-6

two peaks separated by 3300 cm^{-1} for NaBr and 7200 cm^{-1} for NaI. These correspond in each case to the energy difference between the two components of the ^2P ground state of the halogens, namely

$$^2P_{3/2} \quad \text{and} \quad ^2P_{1/2}$$

The transition may lead to the one or to the other. This observation strongly supports the interpretation of these spectra as electron-transfer spectra. (The respective components for NaCl are too close to each other to be separated under low resolution.) In certain cases the transition leads to excited atoms.

Such electron-transfer transitions are extremely common among inorganic salts in both the gaseous and crystalline phases.

In solutions electron transfer often occurs between solute and solvent. Examples are, for hydrated ions,

$$Cl^-(H_2O)_n \rightarrow Cl(H_2O)_n^-, \quad Fe^{2+}(H_2O)_n \rightarrow Fe^{3+}(H_2O)_n^-$$

Both anions and cations exhibit this phenomenon. In particular the strong bands found in the solution spectra of most anions between 2500 and 2000 Å are charge-transfer bands. Among cations the alkali metal ions and the alkaline earth metal ions absorb only in the far ultraviolet. A number of other ions were studied by Fromherz and his collaborators [415]. These included ions having rare-gas configuration and also transition-metal ions [416, 417]. Their charge-transfer bands are again between about 2500 and 2000 Å. The electron may be transferred from the ion to a solvent molecule forming its cage or from a molecule of the cage to the ion[418].

In general charge-transfer bands are one of the most characteristic features of the spectra of inorganic molecules.

Organic systems also exhibit charge-transfer spectra and in recent years there has been a considerable evolution in this field.

Such systems are most often of the donor-acceptor type, where the donor molecule has a low ionization potential and the acceptor molecule has a high electron affinity. Systems of this type often form stable, solid complexes although the intermolecular bonding energy is usually rather small ($\frac{1}{2}$ to 4 kcal/mole, i.e., less than the energy of most hydrogen bonds) and they may dissociate in solution. In other cases the complexes cannot be isolated, but color changes in their solutions reveal the occurrence of complex formation. They have absorption bands which neither the donor nor the acceptor has, and often these bands lie in the visible, yielding intensely colored solutions.

For example, benzene and iodine, I_2, form a 1:1 complex which has a strong absorption band near 2900 Å where neither benzene nor I_2 possesses bands. Another example is the complex formed between chloranil and hexamethylbenzene. The former is yellow in solution, the latter is colorless. Yet if we mix their solutions together a red solution is obtained with an absorption band near 5000 Å. The intensity of the band is proportional to the product of the concentrations of the two components, showing that again we have a 1 : 1 complex. Nakamoto [419] has shown that in such complexes the transition moment of the new bands is polarized in a direction perpendicular to the planes of the aromatic rings, in contrast to the transitions taking place in the aromatic molecules themselves. This can be taken as an indication of electron transfer between the two parts.

Andrews in a review paper [420] compiled a long list of molecules which may act as donors or acceptors. The following are a few examples:

Acceptor	Donor
Maleic anhydride	Benzene, stilbene, styrene, anthracene
Oxalyl chloride	Benzene
Chloroform	Benzene, toluene, xylenes
Carbon tetrachloride	Benzene
Hydrogen chloride	Benzene, chlorobenzene, nitrobenzene
Silver ion	Phenol, aromatic amines, cresols
Ferric chloride	Perylene, *cis-* and *trans*-stilbenes
S-trinitrobenzene	Aromatic ketones, aromatic amines
Picric acid	Alkyl and hydroxy derivatives of aromatic hydrocarbons
Benzoquinone	Hydroquinone

The phenomenon is astonishingly general.

According to Mulliken's theory [421, 422] the ground-state wave function of these donor-acceptor complexes is essentially a no-bond wave function,

$$\psi_0 = \psi(D, A) + \lambda\psi(D^+A^-)$$

where λ is small compared to unity. The wave function of the excited state is, to the contrary, essentially a wave function corresponding to a polar bonded state,

$$\psi_1 = \psi(D^+A^-) + \mu\psi(D, A)$$

where μ is again small compared to unity. Thus, the transition $\psi_0 \rightarrow \psi_1$ is essentially a transition from a no-bond ground state to a charge-transfer excited state. This is contrary to the case for alkali halides. Mulliken's theory has been very successful in interpreting a large number of phenomena related to charge-transfer complexes.

Cases of *intra*molecular charge-transfer absorption are also known [426] (Fig. 15-7).

The field of charge-transfer spectra is one of the best reviewed

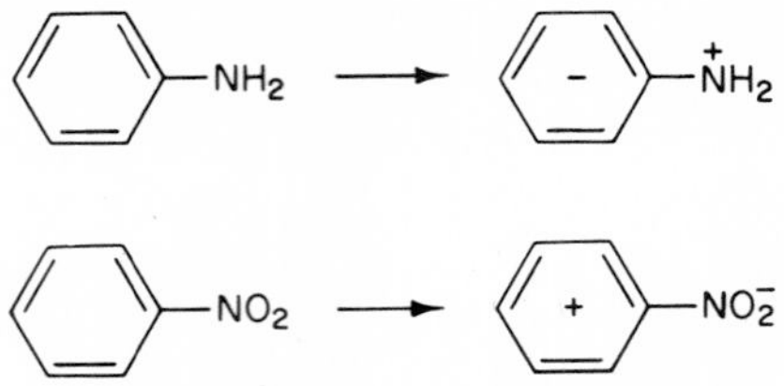

Fig. 15-7

fields in molecular spectroscopy. An excellent review related mainly to inorganic compounds was given by Rabinowitch in 1942 [423]. More recently Andrews [420], Orgel [424], McGlynn [425], and Murrell [426] offered general reviews which treat the problems related to molecular complexes from a variety of points of view.

15-6 LIGAND FIELD SPECTRA

The spectra of transition metal complexes distinguish themselves by rather conspicuous features. Their spectra, in addition to the charge-transfer bands,[8] contain absorption bands in the visible showing that they possess close-lying electronic levels. In these molecules the central metal ion is surrounded by a certain number of "ligands" which are generally either negative ions as in

$$K_3^+ [Fe(CN)_6]^{-3}$$

or dipolar molecules whose negative end is oriented toward the metal ion as in

$$[Co(NH_3)_6]^{3+} Cl_3^-$$

or in the hydrated ion

$$[Ti(H_2O)_6]^{3+} Cl_3^-$$

The central ions are ions of transition metal atoms varying from scandium to copper (Sc, Ti, V, Cr, Mn, Fe, Co, Ni, Cu). They all possess an incomplete $3d$ shell. The connection between this fact and the visible absorption of the related complexes has been established empirically by a long series of works by experimental spectroscopists, of which we should like to mention those of Kiss and his collaborators [427–429]. An extensive list of references was given in a review article by Jorgensen [430].

These spectra were not understood, however, until 1951 when Ilse and Hartmann [275] had the idea of applying crystal field theory,

---

[8] See [424] and [442], p. 99. Bands due to both internal and solute-solvent charge transfer are possible in this case.

due to Bethe [431], Van Vleck [432], and others [433, 434] to the case of the spectrum of the $[Ti(H_2O)_6]^{3+}$ ion. This was followed by a rapid development of "ligand field theory" due mainly to Orgel [435], Hartmann and his collaborators (for references see [436]), Jorgensen [437], and Griffith [438, 439].

This field, too, is one of the best reviewed ones of molecular spectroscopy. One review was written by Schlafer [440], another by Griffith and Orgel [441]; then Orgel published a book on this subject [442], and there is a shorter review in the second edition of Coulson's *Valence* [11].

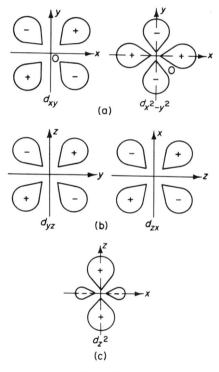

Fig. 15-8

For a discussion of problems in this field the mutual orientation of the five $3d$ orbitals has to be kept in mind. They are drawn in Fig. 15-8, taken from Griffith and Orgel. Among them $d_{x^2-y^2}$ and d_{z^2} have their greatest amplitude along two of the coordinate axes but d_{xy}, d_{yz}, and d_{zx} along lines forming angles of $45°$ with two of the coordinate axes. The d orbitals are five-fold degenerate, i.e., they all have the same energy—but only in the absence of an external field. Such a field is always present in transition metal complexes because of the presence of the ligands, and it is due mainly to the electrons in orbitals facing the metal ion.

The continuation of the argument depends on the geometrical arrangement of the ligands around the central ion, and a good idea of the conditions may be obtained by simple electrostatic consider-ations. A very frequently occuring, highly symmetrical arrangement is the octahedral one. Let us place the six ligands one each on the positive and negative sides of the three coordinate axes at equal distances from the center. It is immediately seen that they will not affect the five d orbitals in the same way. The energies of the electrons in the d_{z^2} and $d_{x^2-y^2}$ orbitals will be substantially raised because of the repulsion from the negative fields of the ligands which they face directly, but d_{xy}, d_{yz}, and d_{zx} will be less affected. A closer look at Fig. 15–8 shows that for reasons of symmetry the two former will be affected to the same extent and also the three latter. Thus, we have obtained a triply degenerate lower state and a doubly degenerate upper state. Under octahedral symmetry (O_h) these correspond to irreducible representations T_{2g} and E_g, respectively, as may be verified by the use of the character table (see p. 176). Then an electronic transition becomes possible between these two states. It will be weak since it is forbidden by symmetry and by the Laporte rule.

If the complex is a square planar one, the situation is different. We may place the four ligands on the $\pm x$ and $\pm y$ axes (as in $[Ni(CN)_4]^{--}$). Then it is seen that $d_{x^2-y^2}$ will be very much affected since all four lobes face the ligands directly, it will have a high energy. d_{xy} will be less affected, d_{yz} and d_{yx} are affected equally, but less than d_{xy}. d_{z^2} will also be influenced, but the order of the latter is uncertain.[9] Thus, four states result, three of them non-degenerate, one of them doubly degenerate. Figure 15–9, taken from Coulson, gives a pictorial representation of the conditions related to tetrahedral, octahedral, tetragonal, or square prism and square planar complexes.

This general scheme of the energy levels does not depend on what the ligands are—it is determined by symmetry—but the actual split-ting does, since it depends on the strength of the ligand field. It also depends on the choice of the central atom, but for a given central atom the splitting increases in the following series:

I^-, Br^-, Cl^-, F^-, C_2H_5OH, H_2O, NH_3, $NH_2CH_2CH_2NH_2$, NO_2^-, CN^-

This series was established by Tsuchida [443] long before ligand field

[9] Either d_{z^2} or d_{yz} and d_{zx} may have the lower energy according to cases.

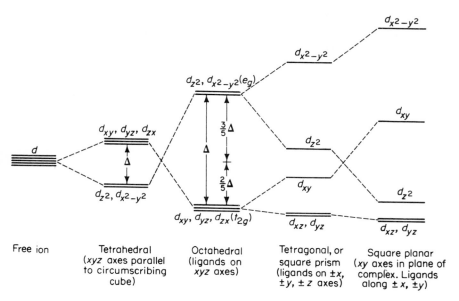

Fig. 15-9

theory was born. That it applies to any central atom was an important experimental result, and making this understandable is one of the successes of the present theory.

The next question is, how will the d electrons fill the available orbitals? This depends, first of all, on their number. Let us take the octahedral case. If there is only one d electron as in $Ti(H_2O)_6^{3+}$ it will, of course, occupy the T_{2g} orbital in the ground state. A transition is then possible to E_g. It is at $20,400 \text{ cm}^{-1}$ (4900 Å) and $\epsilon_{max} \cong 10$. If there is more than one d electron, two tendencies have to be considered. First, the electrons will tend to occupy the lowest-energy orbitals. Second, they will tend to occupy different orbitals with the same spin, since thereby their mutual repulsion will be less and their exchange interaction will be greatest (Hund's rule). The actual energy of a state will depend on both factors. If there are only two or three d electrons they still can all go to T_{2g} with parallel spins. If we have four to seven electrons, however, we have to choose between putting as many electrons as possible into the T_{2g} orbital or placing them so as to give the same spin to as many of them as possible. In a strong ligand field the splitting is large; consequently the lower energy is obtained if we put as many electrons as possible into T_{2g}, giving them antiparallel spins if necessary. In a weak ligand field the splitting is moderate and it will be more important for the stability of the ground state to keep as many spins as possible parallel, even if because of this we have to place some of the electrons into E_g. Thus, strong and weak fields will correspond to low and high spin, respectively. Intermediate cases are possible. With eight or nine d electrons we no longer have a choice. Table 15-1 [11, 441] makes these conditions easy to understand. $[Co(NH_3)_6]^{3+}$ (six d electrons) is an example of the strong-field case; examples for the weak-field case are $[Mn(H_2O)_6]^{2+}$ or $[Fe(H_2O)_6]^{3+}$ (five d electrons). The $[FeF_6]^{3-}$ ion is a weak-field case, the $E_g \leftarrow T_{2g}$ excitation energy being about 10,000 cm^{-1}. The $[Fe(CN)_6]^{3-}$ ion is a strong-field case; the excitation energy is about 30,000 cm^{-1}. Measurements of magnetic susceptibility can also distinguish between the two cases.

Complexes other than octahedral may be treated similarly.

TABLE 15-1 Spins in octahedral complexes

No. of d electrons	Arrangement in weak-field high-spin case t_{2g}			e_g		Resultant spin	Arrangement in strong-field low-spin case t_{2g}			e_g		Resultant spin
1	↑					$\frac{1}{2}$	↑					$\frac{1}{2}$
2	↑	↑				1	↑	↑				1
3	↑	↑	↑			$1\frac{1}{2}$	↑	↑	↑			$1\frac{1}{2}$
4	↑	↑	↑	↑		2	↑↓	↑	↑			1
5	↑	↑	↑	↑	↑	$2\frac{1}{2}$	↑↓	↑↓	↑			$\frac{1}{2}$
6	↑↓	↑	↑	↑	↑	2	↑↓	↑↓	↑↓			0
7	↑↓	↑↓	↑	↑	↑	$1\frac{1}{2}$	↑↓	↑↓	↑↓	↑		$\frac{1}{2}$
8	↑↓	↑↓	↑↓	↑	↑	1	↑↓	↑↓	↑↓	↑	↑	1
9	↑↓	↑↓	↑↓	↑↓	↑	$\frac{1}{2}$	↑↓	↑↓	↑↓	↑↓	↑	$\frac{1}{2}$
10	↑↓	↑↓	↑↓	↑↓	↑↓	0	↑↓	↑↓	↑↓	↑↓	↑↓	0

The obvious shortcoming of the electrostatic approach is that it does not allow for the formation of covalent bonds between the ligand orbitals and the orbitals of the central ion; and often such bonds are formed. A molecular orbital treatment can make this allowance. Group orbitals have to be formed from the ligand orbitals, which are of the right symmetry to form molecular orbitals with the $3d$, $4s$, and $4p$ orbitals of the central ion. This procedure would lead to the same qualitative picture as the one obtained by the simple electrostatic theory and leads to further results. The references given at the beginning of this section may be consulted for more information on this subject.

The spectra of transition metal complexes are usually considerably more complicated than it might appear at first sight from the above discussion. In order to understand this the reader has to recall the way atomic spectra are treated. (see Chapter 6). All we have obtained so far are the configurations, that is, the distribution of the electrons among the available orbitals. If there is more than one electron, the electrons interact by electric and magnetic forces yielding states with certain quantized values of the total angular momenta, —states with different angular momenta having different energies. This would be true for the central ion even if there were no ligands. For the complex molecule too, we shall find, that, in general, the bands predicted from the configuration alone will split into a number of components. Furthermore, other configurations (of higher energy) are possible giving still other sets of states. The reader is referred to Chapter 6 of Orgel's book [442] for more detailed information.

15-7 SPECTRA OF IONS AND RADICALS

Broadly speaking, ions and radicals may be obtained from molecules by three methods:

1. by chemical reactions;
2. in the gaseous phase by strong irradiation (flash techniques) or heating to elevated temperatures or discharges;
3. by irradiation in rigid media.

First, we are going to mention some π-electronic organic ions obtained from aromatic hydrocarbons. For example, if anthracene is oxidized by CrO_3 or H_2O_2 in strongly acidic media [444] the positive ion of anthracene is obtained, which is capable of forming salts with acids:

$$(C_{14}H_{10})^+ ClO_4^-$$

The latter compound is readily dissolved in acetone; the solution has a deep brown color and it can be electrolyzed. Volmer [445] has shown that the positive ion of anthracene can also be obtained by ultraviolet irradiation if the wavelength is sufficiently short to separate an electron from the molecule (about 1900 Å). The color comes from this positive ion. Michaelis, Schubert, and Granick [446] obtained other ions of this type by chemical methods, Lewis and Lipkin [447, 448] by irradiation.

Lewis and his collaborators used an exceedingly important technique—that of the measurement of spectra in rigid glasses at low temperature.[10] This procedure was used as long ago as 1896 by Schmidt

[10] More recently Shpolski and his collaborators used matrices of crystalline paraffin hydrocarbons. If the dimensions of the molecule forming the matrix are about the same as those of the solute, spectra are obtained with highly resolved vibrational fine structure containing lines which are often no wider than 2 or 3 cm⁻¹. For a review see E.V. Shpolski, Usp. Fiz. Nauk **71**, 215 (1960) translated into English in Soviet Physics Uspekhi **3**, 372 (1960). (Published by the American Institute of Physics.)

[449] and in 1926 by Vavilov [450] but its potentialities were put to full advantage only when Lewis took up his work in 1941. Subsequently the method was greatly developed by several authors, in particular by Potts [451, 452]. The rigid glasses usable at liquid nitrogen temperature ($77°K$) are usually mixtures of highly purified hydrocarbons; for example, a 6:1 mixture of isopentane and 3-methyl pentane, or various mixtures of isopentane and methylcyclohexane. A mixture of ethanol, isopentane, and ether (2:5:5), often abbreviated as EPA, was used in Lewis and Lipkin's work, as were mixtures of higher alcohols, syrupy phosphoric acid [453], and many others. In such rigid media translational motion is at a standstill, and with the concentrations used by Lewis and Lipkin (10^{-4} M or less) the average distance between two solute molecules or ions was of the order of 100 angstroms. Under these circumstances the unstable species formed by irradiation may often be kept for hours or days. The irradiated molecule may split into two uncharged free radicals, or into a positive and a negative ion, or it may simply lose an electron. The latter process is very often encountered; it was called *photooxidation* by Lewis and Lipkin. These illuminated rigid solutions are generally highly colored. Triphenylamine gives a blue ion, $(C_6H_5)_3N^+$ (6560 Å), by loss of an electron. Würster's blue and the similar molecule in Fig. 15-10 also give deeply colored ions as do many other aromatic amines and hydroxy derivatives. The illumination of tetraphenylhydrazine yields a green radical, $(C_6H_5)_2N^·$ and $(C_6H_5)_2N^+$ and $(C_6H_5)_2NN(C_6H_5)_2^+$. Hexaphenylethylene gives triphenylmethyl radicals. An extensive study of the spectra of a number of triarylmethyl radicals was carried out by Chu and Weissman [454]. Further studies of photooxidation of organic molecules in rigid media were made by Linschitz, Berry, and Schweitzer [455] (recombination luminescence).

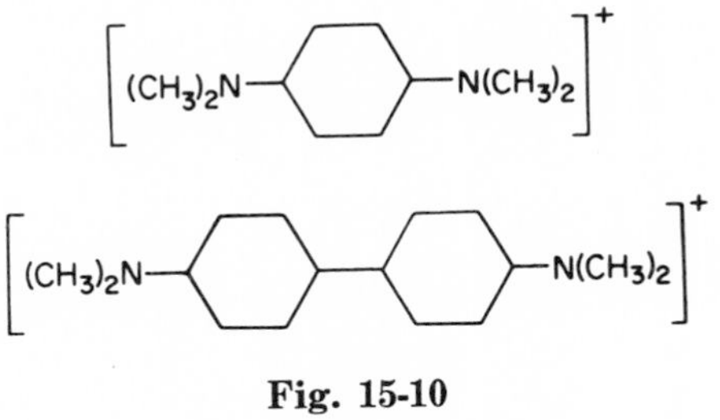

Fig. 15-10

The explanation for the closeness of the first two energy levels in such ions and radicals is linked to the possibility of transitions into and out of the singly occupied level. Longuet-Higgins [456] and Longuet-Higgins and Pople [457] carried out both Hückel molecular orbital and self-consistent field molecular orbital calculations on free radicals derived from alternant hydrocarbons, including the cations and anions that may be formed from the radicals. They found that the cation and anion of a given radical should have very similar spectra, a fact confirmed by experiment.

Negative ions of aromatic hydrocarbons can be obtained through the reaction of metallic sodium (or other alkali metals) with aromatic hydrocarbons in tetrahydrofuran solution. For example, with naphthalene,

$$Na + C_{10}H_8 \rightarrow Na^+ + (C_{10}H_8)^-$$

Paul, Lipkin, and Weissman [458] prepared a number of these and determined their spectra. They are all deeply colored. These highly interesting ions serve as initiators for the preparation of Szwarc's "living polymers," a rather sizable application [459].

Flash illumination in most cases leads to small molecular fragments. Ramsay recently reviewed this and other more physical methods for obtaining free radicals [460].

Keys to the Literature for Related Subjects

The vibrational fine structure of electronic band systems

G. Herzberg and E. Teller, *Z. physik. Chem.*, **B21,** 410 (1933) (the fundamental paper).

For a brief summary of the selection rules:

F. M. Garforth, C. K. Ingold, and H. G. Poole, *J. Chem. Soc.*, 407 (1948).

Benzene: C. K. Ingold *et al.*, *J. Chem. Soc.*, 407–517 (1948). Naphthalene: D. S. McClure, *J. Chem. Phys.*, **22,** 1668 (1954); D. P. Craig et al., *Proc. Chem. Soc.*, 361, 389 (1959). Anthracene: J. Sidman, *J. Chem. Phys.*, **25,** 115 (1956); D. P. Craig and P. C. Hobbins, *J. Chem. Soc.*, 2309 (1955).

Dependence of the fine structure on intramolecular factors:

G. N. Lewis and M. Calvin, *Chem. Rev.*, **25,** 273 (1939); R. N Jones, *J. Am. Chem. Soc.*, **67,** 2127 (1945); G. Kortüm and G. Dreesen, *Chem. Ber.*, **84,** 182 (1951).

Environmental (solvent) effects

For vibrational spectra (one electronic state involved only):

A. D. Buckingham, *Trans. Faraday Soc.*, **56,** 753 (1960); N. Q. Chako, *J. Chem. Phys.*, **2,** 644 (1934); S. R. Polo and M. K. Wilson, *J. Chem. Phys.*, **23,** 2376 (1955).

For electronic spectra (two electronic states involved):

Y. Ooshika, *J. Phys. Soc. Japan*, **9,** 594 (1954); N. S. Bayliss and E. G. McRae, *J. Phys. Chem.*, **58,** 1002, 1006 (1954); E. G. McRae, *Spectrochim. Acta*, **12,** 192 (1958); H. C. Longuet-Higgins and J. A. Pople, *J. Chem. Phys.*, **27,** 192 (1957).

Solvent effects on merocyanine dyes:

L. G. S. Brooker *et al.*, *J. Am. Chem. Soc.*, **73,** 5332 (1951).

The Jahn-Teller effect

H. A. Jahn and E. Teller, *Proc. Roy. Soc. London*, **A 161,** 220 (1937); N. S. Ham, *Spectrochim. Acta* **18,** 775 (1962).

Far ultraviolet spectra

W. C. Price, *Advances in Spectroscopy*, vol. I (New York: Interscience Publishers Inc., 1959), p. 56; W. I. Kaye, *Applied Spectroscopy*, **15,** 130 (1961).

Electronic spectra of crystals

A. S. Davydov, *Theory of Molecular Excitations*, trans. M. Kasha (New York: McGraw-Hill Book Company Inc., 1962).

Color centers

M. C. R. Symons and W. T. Doyle, *Quart. Rev.*, **14,** 62 (1960).

Bibliography

[1] P. A. M. Dirac, *Proc. Roy. Soc. London*, **A114,** 243 (1927)
P. A. M. Dirac. *Quantum Mechanics*, 2nd ed. (New York: Oxford University Press Inc., 1935), Chap. 11.

[2] E. Fermi, *Rev. Mod. Phys.*, **4,** 87 (1932).

[3] H. E. White, *Introduction to Atomic Spectra* (New York: McGraw-Hill Book Company Inc., 1934), Chap. 21.

[4] C. J. Davisson and L. H. Germer, *Phys. Rev.*, **30,** 707 (1927).

[5] M. Born, *Z. Physik*, **37,** 863; **38,** 803 (1926).

[6] See, for example, J. C. Slater and N. H. Frank, *Introduction to Theoretical Physics* (New York: McGraw-Hill Book Company Inc., 1933), p. 217.

[7] K. S. Pitzer, *Quantum Chemistry* (Englewood Cliffs, N. J.: Prentice-Hall Inc., 1953).

[8] W. Kauzmann, *Quantum Chemistry* (New York: Academic Press, Inc., 1957).

[9] L. Pauling and E. B. Wilson, *Introduction to Quantum Mechanics* (New York: McGraw-Hill Book Company Inc., 1935).

[10] P. A. M. Dirac, *Proc. Roy. Soc. London*, **A117,** 610 (1928).

[11] C. A Coulson, *Valence*, 2nd ed. (New York: Oxford University Press Inc., 1961).

[12] H. M. James and A. S. Coolidge, *J. Chem. Phys.*, **1,** 825 (1933).

[13] E. A. Hylleraas, *Z. Physik*, **48,** 469 (1928); **54,** 347 (1929); **65,** 209 (1930)

[14] L. Pauling, *Proc. Nat. Acad. Sci.*, **14,** 359 (1928).

[15] J. C. Slater, *Phys. Rev.*, **37,** 481 (1931); **38,** 325, 1109 (1931).

[16] R. S. Mulliken, *Phys. Rev.*, **41,** 67 (1932).

[17] L. Pauling, *J. Am. Chem. Soc.*, **53,** 1367 (1931).

[18] E. Hückel, *Z. Physik*, **70,** 204 (1931).

[19] See R. Daudel, R. Lefebvre, and C. Moser, *Quantum Chemistry* (New York: Interscience Publishers Inc., 1959), app. 1.

[20] C. A. Coulson and G. S. Rushbrooke, *Proc. Camb. Phil. Soc.*, **36,** 193 (1940); H. C. Longuet-Higgins and C. A. Coulson, *Trans. Faraday Soc.* **43,** 87 (1947)

[21] C. A. Coulson, *Proc. Roy. Soc. London,* **A161,** 413 (1939); C. A. Coulson and H. C. Longuet-Higgins, *Proc. Roy. Soc. London,* **A191,** 39 (1947).

[22] See R. Daudel, *Bull. Soc. chim. France,* **15,** 340 (1948).

[23] W. Moffitt, *Trans. Faraday Soc.,* **45,** 373 (1949).

[24] C. A. Coulson and H. C. Longuet-Higgins, *La Revue Scientifique,* **85,** 929 (1947).

[25] C. A. Coulson and H. C. Longuet-Higgins, *Proc. Roy. Soc. London,* **A192,** 16 (1948).

[26] G. W. Wheland *J. Am. Chem. Soc.,* **64,** 900 (1942).

[27] P. Yvan, *J. chim. phys.,* **49,** 457 (1952).

[28] A. and B. Pullman, *Les théories électroniques de la chimie organique,* (Paris: Masson, 1952).

[29] C. A. Coulson and R. Daudel, *Dictionary of Values of Molecular Constants* (Mathematical Institute, Oxford; Centre de Mecanique Ondulatoire Appliquée, Paris).

[30] G. W. Wheland, *J. Am. Chem. Soc.,* **63,** 2025 (1941).

[31] C. A. Coulson, *Proc. Roy. Soc. London,* **A201,** 196 (1950).

[32] L. Pauling, The Nature of the Chemical Bond, 3rd ed. (Ithaca: Cornell University Press, 1960), Chap. 3; *J. Am. Chem. Soc.,* **54,** 3570 (1932).

[33] M, Haïssinsky, *J. phys. radium,* **7,** 5 (1946).

[34] J. Bellugue and R. Daudel, *La Revue Scientifique,* **84,** 541 (1946).

[35] R. S. Mulliken, in *La liaison chimique* Paris: Publications du Centre National de la Recherche Scientifique, (1948), p. 197; *J. Chim. Phys.,* **46,** 497, 675 (1949)

[36] W. Heitler and F. London, *Z. Physik* **44,** 455 (1927).

[37] W. T. Simpson, *Theories of Electrons in Molecules* (Englewood Cliffs, N. J.: Prentice-Hall Inc., 1962), p. 138.

[38] W. Pauli, *Z. Physik,* **31,** 765 (1925).

[39] J. C. Slater, *Phys. Rev.,* **34,** 1293 (1929); **38,** 1109 (1931).

[40] H. Eyring, J. Walter, and G. E. Kimball, *Quantum Chemistry* (John Wiley & Sons, Inc., 1944).

[41] C. Vroelant and R. Daudel, *Bull. Soc. chim. France,* **16,** 36, 217 (1949).

[42] J. C. Slater, *Rev. Mod. Phys.,* **25,** 199 (1953).

[43] L. Pauling, L. O. Brockway, and J. Y. Beach, *J. Am. Chem. Soc.,* **57,** 2075 (1935).

[44] See [40], p. 234.

[45] G. Rumer, *Nachr. Ges. Wiss. Göttingen, Math-physik. Kl.,* 337 (1932).

[46] L. Pauling, *J. Chem. Phys.,* **1,** 280 (1933).

[47] G. Rumer, E. Teller, and H. Weyl, *Nachr. Ges. Wiss. Göttingen, Math.-Physik. Kl.,* 499 (1932).

[48] L. Pauling and J. Sherman, *J. Chem. Phys.,* **1,** 679 (1933).

[49] G. W. Wheland, *J. Chem. Phys.,* **3,** 356 (1935).

[50] R. Daudel and A. Pullman, *Comt. rend.*, **220,** 888 (1945); *J. phys. radium*, **1,** 59 (1946).

[51] N. Svartholm, *Arkiv. f. Kemi Min. Geol.* **A15;** 13 (1941).

[52] R. Daudel, M. Jean, R. Jacques, C. Sandorfy, and C. Vroelant, *J. chim. phys.*, **46,** 187, 249 (1949).

[53] C. Sandorfy, *Compt. rend.*, **226,** 1611 (1948).

[54] W. G. Penney, *Proc. Roy. Soc. London*, **A158,** 306 (1937).

[55] H. Eyring and G. E. Kimball, *J. Chem. Phys.*, **1,** 239, 626 (1933).

[56] L. Pauling, *J. Chem. Phys.*, **1,** 280 (1933).

[57] H. Eyring and H. Gershinowitz, *J. Chem. Phys.*, **3,** 224 (1935).

[58] G. W. Wheland, *J. Chem. Phys.*, **3,** 230 (1935).

[59] H. Eyring, A. A. Frost, and J. Turkevich, *J. Chem. Phys.*, **1,** 777 (1933)

[60] E. U. Condon and G. H. Shortley, *The Theory of Atomic Spectra.* (New York: Cambridge University Press, 1957), p. 80.

[61] R. S. Mulliken, *J. Chem. Phys.*, **7,** 14 (1939).

[62] See [8], pp. 576, 651.

[63] See [8], p. 651–653.

[64] R. S Mulliken, *J. Chem. Phys.*, **3,** 375, 564 (1935).

[65] R. S. Mulliken and C. A. Rieke, *Reports on Progress in Physics,* **8,** 231 (1941).

[66] J. Bielicki and V. Henri, *Physik. Z.*, **14,** 576 (1913).

[67] W. Kuhn and E. Braun, *Z. Phys. Chem.*, **B8,** 281 (1930); **B9,** 428 (1930).

[68] T. M. Lowry and H. Hudson, *Phil. Trans. Roy. Soc.* **A232,** 117 (1933).

[69] A. Mead, *Trans. Faraday Soc.*, **30,** 1052 (1934).

[70] R. N. Jones and C. Sandorfy, "The Application of Infrared and Raman Spectrometry to the Elucidation of Molecular Structure," in *Technique of Organic Chemistry*, vol. 9 (New York: Interscience Publishers Inc., 1956), p. 280.

[71] K. S. Seshadri and R. N. Jones, *Spectrochim. Acta*, **19,** 1013 (1963).

[72] G. Herzberg, *Atomic Spectra and Atomic Structure* (New York: Dover Publications, Inc., 1944).

[73] F. Hund, *Linien Spektren und Periodisches System der Elemente* (Berlin: Springer, 1927).

[74] E. Wigner and E. E. Witmer, *Z. Physik*, **51,** 859 (1928).

[75] H. E. White, *Introduction to Atomic Spectra* (New York: McGraw-Hill Book Company Inc., 1934).

[76] G. Herzberg, *Molecular Spectra and Molecular Structure. I. Spectra of Diatomic Molecules,* 2nd ed. (D. Van Nostrand Co., Inc., 1950).

[77] G. Herzberg, *Molecular Spectra and Molecular Structure. II. Infrared and Raman Spectra of Polyatomic Molecules* (D. Van Nostrand Co., Inc., 1945).

[78] See [73], p. 124.

[79] E. U. Condon and G. H. Shortley, *The Theory of Atomic Spectra* (New York: Cambridge University Press, 1935).

[80] See [74].

[81] See [76].

[82] R. S. Mulliken, *Rev. Mod. Phys.*, **4,** 1 (1932).

[83] R. S. Mulliken, *J. Chem. Phys.*, **7**, 14 (1939).

[84] R. S. Mulliken, *J. Chem. phys.*, **7**, 20 (1939).

[85] C. R. Bailey and R. R. Gordon, *Trans. Faraday Soc.*, **34**, 1133 (1938).

[86] W. G. Penney and G. B. B. M. Sutherland, J. Chem. Phys. **2**, 492 (1934)
L. R. Zumwalt and P. A. Giguère, *J. Chem. Phys.*, **9**, 458 (1941).

[87] J. M. Robertson, *Organic Crystals and Molecules* (Ithaca: Cornell University Press, 1953).

[88] P. J. Wheatley, *The Determination of Molecular Structure* (New York: Oxford University Press, Inc., 1960).

[89] H. Margenau and G. M. Murphy, *The Mathematics of Physics and Chemistry* (D. Van Nostrand Co., Inc., 1943).

[90] C. Reid. *Excited States in Chemistry and Biology* (Toronto: Butterworth & Co., Ltd., 1957).

[91] E. B. Wilson, J. C. Decius, and P. C. Cross, *Molecular Vibrations* (New York: McGraw-Hill Book Company Inc., 1955).

[92] R. S. Mulliken, *J. Chem. Phys.*, **7**, 121 (1939).

[93] R. McWeeny, *J. Chem. Phys.*, **19**, 1614 (1951).

[94] G. Payette and C. Sandorfy, *J. Chem. Phys.*, **30**, 168 (1959).

[95] B. H. Chirgwin and C. A. Coulson, *Proc. Roy. Soc. London*, **A201**, 1961 (1950).

[96] P. O. Löwdin, *J. Chem. Phys.*, **18**, 365 (1950).

[97] J. E. Lennard-Jones, *Proc. Roy. Soc. London*, **A158**, 280 (1931).

[98] A. Smakula. *Angew. Chem.*, **47**, 657 (1934).

[99] R. S. Mulliken, *J. Chem Phys.*, **7**, 121 (1939).

[100] W. C. Price and A. D. Walsh, *Proc. Roy. Soc. London*, **A174**, 220 (1940)

[101] J. E. Lennard-Jones, *Proc. Roy. Soc. London*, **A158**, 280 (1937).

[102] K. W. Hausser, R. Kuhn, A. Smakula, and K. H. Kreuchen, *Z. techn. Physik*, **15**, 1 (1934).

[103] The same authors, *Z. Phys. Chem.*, **B29**, 363–454 (1935).

[104] W. C. Price and A. D. Walsh, *Proc. Roy. Soc. London*, **A185**, 182 (1946).

[105] G. F. Woods and L. H. Schwartzmann, *J. Am. Chem. Soc.*, **71**, 1396 (1949).

[106] E. Hückel, *Z. Elektrochem.*, **43**, 752 (1937).

[107] A. and B. Pullman, *J. chim. phys.*, **46**, 212 (1949).

[108] C. A. Coulson and H. C. Longuet-Higgins, *Proc. Roy. Soc. London*, **A193**, 447 (1948).

[109] L. Zechmeister, A. L. Le Rosen, W. A. Schroeder, A. Polgar, and L. Pauling, *J. Am. Chem. Soc.*, **65**, 1940 (1943).

[110] J. H. Pinckard, B. Wille, and L. Zechmeister, *J. Am. Chem. Soc.*, **70**, 1938 (1948).

[111] C. A. Coulson, *Proc. Roy. Soc. London*, **A169**, 413 (1939).

[112] W. Moffitt and C. A. Coulson, *Trans. Faraday Soc.*, **44**, 81 (1948).

[113] E. Wigner, *Group Theory and its Application to the Quantum Mechanics of Atomic Spectra* (New York: Academic Press, Inc., 1959).

[114] M. Tinkham, *Advanced Quantum Mechanics of Atoms, Molecules, and Solids* (Department of Physics, University of California, 1958).

[115] R. S. Mulliken, *J. Chem Phys.*, **7**, 339 (1939).

[116] A. L. Sklar, *J. Chem. Phys.*, **5**, 669 (1937).

[117] A. C. Albrecht and W. T. Simpson, *J. Chem. Phys.*, **23**, 1480 (1955).

[118] C. A. Coulson, *Proc. Phys. Soc.*, **60**, 257 (1948).

[119] A. S. Davydov, *J. Exp, Theor. Phys. USSR*, **17**, 1106 (1947).

[120] See [29], pt. II.

[121] H. B. Klevens and J. R. Platt, *J. Chem. Phys.*, **17**, 470 (1949).

[122] E. Hückel, *Z. Physik*, **72**, 310 (1931),

[123] G. W. Wheland and L. Pauling, *J. Am. Chem. Soc.*, **57**, 2086 (1935),

[124] H. C. Longuet-Higgins and C. A. Coulson, *Trans. Faraday Soc.*, **43**, 87 (1947).

[125] R. S. Mulliken, *J. Chem. Phys.*, **2**, 782 (1934).

[126] R. S. Mulliken, *J. Chem. Phys.*, **3**, 573 (1935).

[127] L. Pauling, *J. Am. Chem. Soc.*, **54**, 3570 (1932), and ref. [32]

[128] W. Gordy and W. Thomas, *J. Chem. Phys.*, **24**, 439 (1956).

[129] A. Laforgue, *J. chim. phys.*, **46**, 568 (1949).

[130] A. Streitwieser, *Molecular Orbital Theory for Organic Chemists* (John Wiley & Sons, Inc., 1961).

[131] H. Pritchard and H. Skinner, *Chem. Rev.*, **55**, 745 (1955).

[132] L. E. Orgel, T. L. Cottrell, W. Dick and L. E. Sutton, *Trans. Faraday Soc.*, **47**, 113 (1951).

[133] M. J. S. Dewar. *J. Chem. Soc.*, 463 (1949); 2329 (1950).

[134] C. Sandorfy, *Bull. Soc. chim. France.* **16**, 615 (1949).

[135] C. Sandorfy, *Can. J. Chem.*, **36**, 1739 (1958).

[136] J. P. Cartier and C. Sandorfy, *Can. J. Chem.*, **41**, 2759 (1963).

[137] G. W. Wheland, *J. Am. Chem. Soc.*, **63**, 2025 (1941).

[138] C. Sandorfy and R. Daudel, *Compt rend.*, **238**, 93 (1954).

[139] C. Sandorfy, *Can. J. Chem.*, **33**, 1337 (1955).

[140] H. Yoshizumi, *Trans, Faraday Soc.*, **53**, 125 (1957).

[141] K. Fukui, H. Kato, and T. Yonezawa, *Bull. Chem. Soc. Japan*, **33**, 1197 (1960).

[142] *Ibid.*, **33**, 1199 (1960).

[143] *Ibid.*, **34**, 442 (1961).

[144] *Ibid.*, **34**, 1111 (1961).

[145] *Ibid.*, **35**, 38 (1962).

[146] G. Del Re, *J. Chem. Soc.*, 4031 (1958).

[147] C. A. Coulson, *Proc. Phys. Soc.* **A65**, 933 (1952).

[148] H. C. Longuet-Higgins and C. A. Coulson, *J. Chem. Soc.*, 971 (1949).

[149] M. J. S. Dewar, *J. Chem. Soc.*, 329 (1950); 3532, 3534 (1952).

[150] M. J. S. Dewer and H. C. Longuet-Higgins, *Proc. Roy. Soc. London*, **A214**, 482 (1952).

[151] F. A. Matsen, *J. Am. Chem. Soc.*, **72**, 5243 (1950).

[152] F. A. Matsen, W. W. Robertson, and R. L. Chuoke, *Chem, Rev.*, **41**, 273 (1947).

[153] W. W. Robertson and F. A. Matsen, *J. Am. Chem. Soc.*, **72**, 5252 (1950)

[154] D. P. Craig, *Proc. Roy. Soc. London*, **A200**, 390 (1950).

[155] D. P. Craig and A. Maccoll, *J. Chem. Soc.*, 1949, 964.

[156] M. Kovner, *Acta Physiochim. USSR*, **19**, 385 (1944).

[157] G. Herzberg and E. Teller, *Z. physik. Chem.*, **B21**, 410 (1933).

[158] A. C. Albrecht and W. T. Simpson, *J. Chem. Phys.*, **23**, 1480 (1955)

[159] See S. F. Mason, *Quart. Rev.*, **15**, 287 (1961).

[160] D. P. Craig, J. M. Hollas, and G. W. King, *J. Chem. Phys.*, **29**, 974 (1958).

[161] D. P. Craig, *Proc. Roy. Soc. London*, **A200**, 272 (1950).

[162] G. B. Kistiakowsky, J. R. Ruhoff, H. A. Smith, and W. E. Vaughan, *J. Am. Chem. Soc.*, **58**, 146 (1936).

[163] M. Simonetta, *J. chim. phys.*, **49**, 68 (1952).

[164] G. Frobenius, *Sitzungsber. Preuss. Acad. Wiss.*, 516 (1900); 303 (1901).

[165] V. German, *Doklady Acad. Nauk.*, USSR, **41**, 197 (1943).

[166] V. German, *J. Phys. USSR*, **8**, 276 (1944).

[167] L. Pauling and G. W. Wheland, *J. Chem. Phys.*, **1**, 362 (1933).

[168] J. Sherman *J. Chem. Phys.*, **2**, 488 (1934).

[169] L. A. Blumenfeld, *J. Phys. Chem. USSR*, **21**, 529 (1947).

[170] H. Sponer and G. P Nordheim, *Disc. Faraday Soc.*, **9**, 19 (1950],

[171] See D. A. McClure, *J. Chem. Phys.*, **22**, 1668 (1954).

[172] D. P. Craig, *Proc. Roy. Soc.*, London **A200**, 272 (1950).

[173] D. P. Craig, *Proc. Roy. Soc.*, London **A200**, 390 (1950).

[174] D. P. Craig, *Proc. Roy. Soc.*, London **A200**, 401 (1950).

[175] M. Simonetta, *J. chim. phys.*, **49**, 68 (1952).

[176] W. J. Potts, *J. Chem. Phys.*, **23**, 65 (1955).

[177] M. Simonetta and V. Schomaker, *J. Chem. Phys.*, **19**, 649 (1951)

[178] B. Eistert, *Tautomerie und Mesomerie* (Stuttgart: Enke, 1938), p. 173.

[179] C. R. Bury, *J. Am. Chem. Soc.*, **57**, 2115 (1935).

[180] L. Pauling, *Proc. Nat. Acad. Sci.*, **25**, 577 (1939).

[181] Th. Förster, *Z. physik. Chem.*, **B47**, 245 (1940).

[182] Th. Förster, *Z. physik. Chem.*, **B48**, 12 (1940).

[183] K. T. Herzfeld and A. L. Sklar, *Rev. Mod. Phys.*, **14**, 294 (1942),

[184] R. Wizinger, *Organische Farbstoffe* (Bonn: Dümmler, 1933).

[185] Th. Förster, *Z. Elektrochem.*, **45**, 548 (1939).

[186] N. I. Fisher and F. M. Hamer. *Proc. Roy. Soc. London*, **A154**, 707 (1936),

[187] B. Beilenson, N. I. Fisher, and F. M. Hamer, *Proc. Roy. Soc. London*, **A163**, 138 (1937).

[188] L. G. S. Brooker, *Rev. Mod. Phys.*, **14**, 275 (1942).

[189] K. T. Herzfeld, *J. Chem. Phys.*, **10**, 508 (1942).

[190] M. Goeppert-Mayer and A. L. Sklar, *J. Chem. Phys.*, **6**, 645 (1938).

[191] H. Hartmann, *Z. physik. Chem.*, **B53**, 96 (1943).

[192] R. G. Parr and B. L. Crawford, *J. Chem. Phys.*, **16**, 526 (1948),

[193] R. S. Mulliken, *J. chim. phys.*, **46**, 497, 675 (1949).

[194] J. C. Slater, *Phys. Rev.*, **36**, 57 (1930).

[195] V. Guillemin and C. Zener, *Z. Physik*, **61**, 199 (1930).

[196] C. Zener, *Phys. Rev.*, **36**, 51 (1930).

[197] W. E. Moffitt and C. A. Coulson, *Phil. Mag.*, **38**, 634 (1947).

[198] M. P. Barnett and C. A. Coulson, *Phil. Trans. Roy. Soc. London*. **A243**, 221 (1951).

[199] R. Taylor, *Proc. Phys. Soc.*, **A64**, 249 (1951).

[200] R. S. Barker and H. Eyring, *J. Chem. Phys.*, **21**, 912 (1953); **22**, 114 (1954).

[201] I. Shavitt and M. Karplus, *J. Chem. Phys.*, **36**, 550 (1962).

[202] R. S. Mulliken, *J. chim. phys.*, **46**, 497 (1949).

[203] A. L. Sklar, *J. Chem phys.*, **7**, 984 (1939).

[204] R. G. Parr and B. L. Crawford, *J. Chem. Phys.*, **17**, 726 (1949).

[205] C. A. Coulson and I. Fischer, *Phil. Mag.*, ser. 7, **11**, 386 (1949).

[206] C. Sandorfy, *Compt. Rend.*, **232**, 2449 (1950)

[207] R. Daudel and A. Laforgue, *Compt. Rend.*, **233**, 623 (1951).

[208] D. P. Craig, *Proc. Roy. Soc. London*, **A200**, 474 (1950).

[209] O. Chalvet, R. Daudel, M. Roux, C. Sandorfy, and C. Vroelant, *J. chim. phys.*, **49**, 262 (1952).

[210] O. Chalvet and R. Daudel, *J. chim. phys.*, **49**, 629 (1952).

[211] A. London, *J. Chem. Phys.*, **13**, 417 (1945).

[212] R. G. Parr and B. L. Crawford, *J. Chem. Phys.*, **16**, 1049 (1948).

[213] D. P. Craig, *Proc. Roy. Soc. London*, **A200**, 474 (1950).

[214] R. G. Parr, D. P. Craig, and I. G. Ross, *J. Chem. Phys.*, **18**, 1561 (1950).

[215] J. Jacobs, *Proc. Phys. Soc.*, **61**, 710 (1949).

[216] A. Julg and A. Pullman, *J. chim. phys.*, **50**, 459 (1953).

[217] H. C. Longuet-Higgins, *Proc. Phys. Soc.*, **60**, 270 (1948).

[218] A. L. Sklar, *J. Chem. Phys.*, **7**, 984 (1939)

[219] A. L. Sklar, *J. Chem. Phys.*, **10**, 135 (1942).

[220] H. Conrad-Billroth, *Z. physik. Chem.*, **B20**, 227 (1933).

[221] K. Wolf and W. Herold, *Z. physik. Chem.*, **B13**, 201 (1931).

[222] K. L. Wolf and O. Strasser, *Z. physik. Chem.*, **B21**, 389 (1933).

[223] Th. Förster, *Z. Naturforschung*, **2a**, 149 (1947).

[224] H. Conrad-Billroth, *Z. physik. Chem.*, **B29**, 170 (1936).

[225] A. Kiss, J. Molnar, and C. Sandorfy, *Bull. Soc. chim. France*, **16**, 275 (1949).

[226] W. F. Forbes, *Can. J. Chem.*, **36**, 1350 (1958), and subsequent papers.

[227] M. Goeppert-Mayer and K. J. McCallum, *Rev. Mod. Phys.*, **14**, 248 (1942).

[228] C. Sandorfy, *Can. J. Chem.*, **31**, 439 (1953), and ref. [206].

[229] W. E. Moffitt, *Proc. Roy. Soc. London*, **A202**, 534 (1950).

[230] W. E. Moffitt, *Proc. Roy. Soc. London*, **A210**, 224 (1951).

[231] R. Pariser and R. G. Parr, *J. Chem. Phys.*, **21**, 466 (1953),

[232] R. Pariser and R. G. Parr, *J. Chem. Phys.*, **21**, 767 (1953).

[233] R. Pariser, *J. Chem. Phys.*, **21**, 568 (1953).

[234] R. S. Mulliken, *J. Chem. Phys.*, **2**, 782 (1934).

[235] R. Pariser, *J. Chem. Phys.*, **24**, 250 (1956).

[236] E. T. Stewart, *J. Chem. Soc.*, 1959, 70.

[237] G. Wannier, *Phys. Rev.*, **52**, 191 (1937).

[238] P. O. Löwdin, *J. Chem. Phys.*, **18**, 365 (1950).

[239] F. G. Fumi and R. G. Parr, *J. Chem. Phys.*, **21**, 1864 (1953).

[240] G. G. Hall, *Trans. Faraday Soc.*, **50**, 773 (1954).

[241] P. O. Löwdin, *Svensk Kem. Tidskr.*, **67**, 380 (1955).

[242] R. McWeeny, *Proc. Roy. Soc. London*, **A227**, 288 (1955).

[243] F. Peradejordi, *Compt. rend.*, **243**, 276 (1956).

[244] R. Pariser, *J. Chem. Phys.*, **24**, 250 (1956).

[245] R. Pariser and R. G. Parr, *J. Chem. Phys.*, **21**, 767 (1953).

[246] D. R. Hartree, *Calculation of Atomic Structures* (John Wiley & Sons, Inc., 1957).

[247] D. R. Hartree, *Proc. Cambridge Phil. Soc.*, **24**, 89 (1927).

[248] V. Fock, *Z. Physik*, **61**, 126 (1930).

[249] C. C. J. Roothaan, *Rev. Mod. Phys.*, **23**, 69 (1951).

[250] R. G. Parr and R. S. Mulliken, *J. Chem. Phys.*, **18**, 1338 (1950).

[251] J. F. Mulligan, *J. Chem. Phys.*, **19**, 347, 1428 (1951).

[252] R. G. Parr and A. R. Taylor, *J. Chem. Phys.*, **19**, 497 (1951).

[253] G. Berthier, *J. chim. phys.*, **50**, 344 (1953).

[254] A. Julg, *J. chim. phys.*, **52**, 377 (1955).

[255] R. Lefebvre, *Compt. rend.*, **240**, 1094 (1955).

[256] R. McWeeny, *Proc. Roy. Soc. London*, **A235**, 496 (1956).

[257] C. C. J. Roothaan, *Rev. Mod. Phys.*, **32**, 179 (1960).

[258] J. L. Masse, Ph. D. Dissertation, Sorbonne (Paris, 1962).

[259] C. M. Moser and R. Lefebvre, *J. Chem. Phys.*, **23**, 598, 754 (1955).

[260] C. C. J. Roothaan and R. G. Parr, *J. Chem. Phys.*, **17**, 1001 (1949).

[261] J. A. Pople, *Trans. Faraday Soc.*, **49**, 1375 (1953).

[262] J. A. Pople, *J. Phys. Chem.* **61**, 6 (1957).

[263] M. J. S. Dewar and H. C. Longuet-Higgins, *Proc. Phys. Soc.*, **A67**, 795 (1954).

[264] J. A. Pople, *Proc. Phys. Soc.*, **A68**, 81 (1955).

[265] J. N. Murrell and H. C. Longuet-Higgins, *Proc. Phys. Soc.*, **A68**, 329 (1955).

[266] H. C. Longuet-Higgins and J. A. Pople, *Proc. Phys. Soc.*, **A68**, 591 (1955).

[267] J. N. Murrell, *Proc. Phys. Soc.*, **A68**, 969 (1955).

[268] K. L. McEwen and H. C. Longuet-Higgins, *J. Chem. Phys.*, **24**, 771 (1956).

[269] J. N. Murrell and K. L. McEwen, *J. Chem. Phys.*, **25**, 1143 (1956).

[270] H. Brion, R. Lefebvre, and C. M. Moser, *J. Chem. Phys.*, **23**, 1972 (1955).

[271] R. Daudel, *Structure électronique des molécules* (Gauthier-Villars, 1962), p. 210

[272] J. R. Platt, *J. Chem. Phys.*, **17**, 481 (1949); **18**, 1168 (1950).

[273] R. S. Mulliken, *J. Chem. Phys.*, **3**, 534 (1935).

[274] H. L. McMurry and R. S. Mulliken, *Proc. Nat. Acad. Sci.*, **26**, 312 (1940).

[275] F. E. Ilse and H. Hartmann, *Z. physik. Chem.*, **197**, 239, 751 (1951).

[276] R. S. Mulliken, *J. Am. Chem. Soc.*, **74**, 811 (1952).

[277] R. Pariser, *J. Chem. Phys.*, **24**, 250 (1956).

[278] E. Hückel, *Z. Physik*, **70**, 204 (1931); **76**, 628 (1932).

[279] S. L. Altmann, *Proc. Roy. Soc. London*, **A210**, 327. 343 (1951).

[280] I. G. Ross, *Trans. Faraday Soc.*, **48**, 973 (1952).

[281] R. D. Brown, *J. Chem. Soc.*, 2615 (1953).

[282] M. J. S. Dewar and R. Pettit, *J. Chem. Soc.*, 1625 (1954).

[283] J. E. Lennard-Jones and G. G. Hall, *Trans. Faraday Soc.*, **48**, 581 (1952).

[284] J. L. Franklin, *J. Chem. Phys.*, **22**, 1304 (1954).

[285] K. Fukui, H. Kato, and T. Yonezawa, *Bull. Chem. Soc. Japan*, **33**, 1197 (1960).

[286] S. Besnainou and M. Roux, *J. chim. phys.*, **56**, 250 (1959).

[287] A. Julg, *J. chim. phys.*, **53**, 548 (1956).

[288] A. Julg, *J. chim. phys.*, **57**, 19, 434 (1960).

[289] C. C. J. Roothaan, *Reports of the Laboratory of Molecular Structure and Spectra* (Department of Physics, University of Chicago, June 1949 to March 1950), pt. II.

[290] E. T. Stewart, *J. Chem. Soc.*, 1856 (1959).

[291] T. Murai, *Progr. Theoret. Phys. Kyoto.* **7**, 345 (1952).

[292] J. F. Mulligan, *J. Chem. Phys.*, **19**, 347 (1951).

[293] C. W. Scherr, *J. Chem. Phys.*, **23**, 569 (1955).

[294] R. C. Sahni, *J. Chem. Phys.*, **25**, 332 (1956).

[295] H. Hartmann, *Z. Naturforsch.*, **15a**, 993 (1960).

[296] J. Jacobs, *Proc. Phys. Soc.*, **A68**, 72 (1955).

[297] S. F. Boys, *Proc. Roy. Soc. London*, **A200**, 542 (1950).

[298] S. F. Boys, *Proc. Roy. Soc. London*, **A201**, 125 (1950).

[299] S. F. Boys, F. B. Cook, C. M. Reeves, and I. Shavitt, *Nature*, **178**, 1207 (1956).

[300] S. F. Boys, I. Jones, and I. Shavitt, *Calcul des fonctions d'onde moléculaires* (Paris: Centre National de la Recherche Scientifique, 1958), p. 253.

[301] C. Zauli, *J. Chem. Soc.*, 2204 (1960).

[302] A. Mangini and C. Zauli, *J. Chem. Soc.*, 2210 (1960).

[303] E. A. Magnusson and C. Zauli, *Proc. Phys. Soc.*, **78**, 53 (1961).

[304] M. Kotani *et al.*, *J. Phys. Soc. Japan*, **12**, 707. 1355 (1957).

[305] A. B. F. Duncan, *J. Chem. Phys.*, **27**, 423 (1957).

[306] H. Kaplan, *J. Chem. Phys.*, **26**, 1704 (1957).

[307] R. S. Mulliken, *Technical Report, Laboratory of Molecular Structure and Spectra* (Department of Physics, University of Chicago, 1957–1959), pt. II, p. 15.

[308] C. C. J. Roothaan and A. W. Weiss, *Rev. Mod. Phys.*, **32**, 194 (1960).

[309] E. A. Hylleraas, *Z. Physik*, **54**, 347 (1929).

[310] E. A. Hylleraas, *Z. Physik*, **65**, 209 (1930).

[311] E. A. Hylleraas, *Z. Physik*, **66**, 453 (1930); **83**, 739 (1933).

[312] H. M. James and A. S. Coolidge, *J. Chem. Phys.*, **1**, 825 (1933).

[313] H. M. James and A. S. Coolidge, *J. Chem. Phys.*, **3**, 129 (1935).

[314] H. M. James, A. S. Coolidge, and R. D. Present, *J. Chem. Phys.*, **4**, 193 (1936).

[315] W. Kolos and C. C. J. Roothaan, *Rev. Mod. Phys.*, **32**, 205 (1960).

[316] W. Kolos and C. C. J. Roothaan, *Rev. Mod. Phys.*, **32**, 219 (1960).

[317] G. Herzberg and L. L. Howe, *Can. J. Phys.*, **37**, 636 (1959).

[318] L. Pauling, *J. Chem. Phys.*, **4**, 673 (1936).

[319] K. Lonsdale, *Proc. Roy. Soc. London*, **A159**, 149 (1937).

[320] O. Schmidt, *Z. physik. Chem.*, **B47**, 1 (1940).

[321] N. S. Bayliss, *J. Chem. Phys.*, **16**, 287 (1948); **17**, 1353 (1949).

[322] W. T. Simpson, *J. Chem. Phys.*, **16**, 1124 (1948).

[323] H. Kuhn, *J. Chem. Phys.*, **16**, 840 (1948).

[324] J. R. Platt, *J. Chem. Phys.*, **17**, 484 (1949).

[325] H. B. Klevens and J. R. Platt, *J. Chem. Phys.*, **17**, 470 (1949).

[326] M. Kasha, *Chem. Rev.*, **41**, 401 (1947).

[327] W. E. Moffitt, *J. Chem. Phys.*, **22**, 320 (1954).

[328] N. S. Ham and K. Ruedenberg, *J. Chem. Phys.*, **25**, 13 (1956).

[329] A. D. Walsh, *Quart. Rev.*, **2**, 73 (1948).

[330] A. Sommerfeld and H. Bethe, *Handbuch der Physik*, 2nd ed., vol. 24, pt. 2 (Berlin: Springer, 1933).

[331] See O. Schmidt, *Ber. deut. chem. Ges.*, **A73**, 97 (1940).

[332] N. S. Bayliss, *Austr. J. Sci.*, **12**, 12 (1949).

[333] See N. S. Bayliss, *Quart. Rev.*, **6**, 319 (1952).

[334] H. Kuhn, *Helv. Chim. Acta*, **31**, 1441 (1948); **32**, 2243 (1949).

[335] H. Kuhn, *Z. Elektrochem.*, **53**, 165 (1949).

[336] B. Eistert, *Angew. Chem.* **49**, 33 (1936).

[337] H. Kuhn, *J. Chem. Phys.*, **17**, 1198 (1949).

[338] H. Kuhn, *Progress in the Chemistry of Organic Natural Products*. ed. L. Zechmeister (Berlin: Springer, 1958), pp. 169–205.

[339] H. Kuhn, *J. Chem. Phys.*, **25**, 293 (1956).

[340] H. Kuhn, *Angew. Chem.*, **71**, 93 (1959).

[341] N. S. Bayliss and J. C. Rivière, *Austr. J. Sci. Res.*, **A4**, 344 (1951)

[342] N. S. Bayliss, *Austr. J. Sci. Res.*, **A3**, 109 (1950).

[343] H. Kuhn, W. Huber, G. Handsschig. H. Martin, F. Schäfei, and F. Bär, *J. Chem. Phys.*, **32**, 467 (1960).

[344] F. Bär, W. Huber, G. Handsschig, H. Martin, and H. Kuhn, *J. Chem. Phys.*, **32**, 470 (1960).

[345] W. T. Simpson, *J. Chem. Phys.*, **17**, 1218 (1949).

[346] B. Rackow, *Z. Naturforsch.*, **15a**, 129 (1960).

[347] B. Rackow, *Z. Naturforsch.*, **15a**, 134 (1960).

[348] S. Nikitine, *J. chim. phys.*, **47**, 614 (1950).

[349] S. Nikitine, *J. chim. phys.*, **48**, 37, 44 (1951).

[350] S. Nikitine, *J. chim. phys.*, **49**, 175 (1952).

[351] P. Ramart-Lucas, in V. Grignard, *Traité de Chimie Organique*, vol. 2 (Paris: Masson, 1934), pp. 69–74.

[352] R. S. Mulliken, C. A. Rieke, and W. G. Brown, *J. Am. Chem. Soc.*, **63**, 41 (1941).

[353] M. J. S. Dewar and H. N. Schmeising, *Tetrahedron*, **5** 166 (1959); **11**, 96 (1960).

[354] S. F. Mason, *Quart. Rev.*, **15**, 287 (1961).

[355] C. N. R. Rao, *Ultraviolet and Visible Spectroscopy* (Toronto: Butterworth & Co., Ltd., 1961).

[356] M. Pestemer and D. Brück, in Houben-Weyl's *Methoden der Organischen Chemie*, vol. III, pt. 2 (Stuttgart: Georg Thieme Verlag, 1955).

[357] C. Reid, *J. Chem. Phys.*, **18**, 1299 (1950).

[358] D. F. Evans, *J. Chem. Soc.*, 1960, 1735.

[359] H. B. Klevens and J. R. Platt, *Rev. Mod. Phys.*, **16**, 182 (1944).

[360] A. D. Walsh, *J. Chem. Soc.*, 2325 (1953).

[361] J. T. Gary and L. W. Pickett, *J. Chem. Phys.*, **22**, 599 (1954).

[362] P. G. Wilkinson and R. S. Mulliken, *J. Chem. Phys.*, **23**, 1895 (1955).

[363] R. S. Mulliken, *J. Chem. Phys.*, **3**, 517 (1935).

[364] I. G. Ross, *Trans. Faraday Soc.*, **48**, 973 (1952).

[365] C. K. Ingold and G. W. King, *J. Chem. Soc.*, 2702–2745 (1953).

[366] R. S. Mulliken, *Can. J. Chem.*, **36**, 10 (1958).

[367] K. K. Innes, *J. Chem. Phys.*, **22**, 863 (1954).

[368] ꓶ. Clar, *Aromatische Kohlenwasserstoffe* (Berlin: Springer, 1952).

[369] D. P. Craig, J. M. Hollas, M. F. Redies, and S. C. Wait, *Proc. Chem. Soc.*, 361 (1959).

[370] D. P. Craig, L. E. Lyons, S. H. Walmsley, and J. R. Walsh, *Proc. Chem. Soc.*, 389 (1959).

[371] D. S. McClure, *J. Chem. Phys.*, **19**, 670 (1951).

[372] C. Reid, *J. Chem. Phys.*, **20**, 1214 (1952).

[373] G. Porter. *Proc. Roy. Soc. London*, **A200**, 2684 (1950).

[374] W. T. G. Rubb and G. B. Kistiakovsky, *J. Am. Chem. Soc.*, **72**, 419 (1950)

[375] G. N. Lewis and M. Kasha, *J. Am. Chem. Soc.*, **66**, 2100 (1944).

[376] A. Jablonski, *Z. Physik*, **94**, 38 (1935); Nature, **131**, 839, (1933).

[377] E. W. Moffitt, *J. Chem. Phys.*, **22**, 320 (1954).

[378] M. J. S. Dewar and H. C. Longuet-Higgins, *Proc. Phys. Soc.*, **A67,** 795 (1954).

[379] J. A. Pople, *Proc. Phys. Soc.*, **A68**, 81 (1955).

[380] R. Pariser, *J. Chem. Phys.*, **24**, 250 (1956).

[381] J. Thiec and J. Wiemann, *Bull. Soc. chim. France*, 177 (1956); 102 (1957).

[382] Pl. A. Plattner and E. Heilbronner, *Helv. Chim. Acta*, **30**, 910 (1947); **31**, 804 (1948).

[383] L. C. Craig, W. A. Jacobs, and G. I. Lavin, *J. Biol. Chem.*, **139,** 277 (1941).

[384] G. M. Badger, R. S. Pierce, and R. Pettit, *J. Chem. Soc.*, 3199 (1951).

[285] F. Halverson and R. C. Hirt, *J. Chem. Phys.*, **17**, 1165 (1949).

[386] F. Halverson and R. C. Hirt, *J. Chem. Phys.*, **19**, 711 (1951).

[387] R. McWeeny and T. E. Peacock, *Proc. Phys. Soc.*, **A70**, 41 (1957).

[388] J. N. Murrell, *Mol. Physics*, **1**, 384 (1958).

[389] S. F. Mason, *J. Chem. Soc.*, 1247 (1959).

[390] B. Pullman, M. Mayot, and G. Berthier, *J. Chem. Phys.*, **18**, 257 (1950)

[391] G. Scheibe, *Ber.*, **59**, 1333 (1926).

[392] V. Henri and L. W. Pickett, *J. Chem. Phys.*, **7**, 439 (1939).

[393] E. Pesch and S. L. Friess, *J. Am Chem. Soc.*, **72**, 5756 (1950).

[394] R. S. Mulliken, *Tetrahedron*, **5**, 253 (1959).

[395] R. N. Jones, *J. Am. Chem. Soc.*, **67**, 2127 (1945).

[396] R. N. Jones, *Chem. Rev.*, **41**, 353 (1947); **32**, 1 (1943).

[397] H. C. Longuet-Higgins, C. W. Rector and J. R. Platt, *J. Chem. Phys.*, **18**, 1174 (1950).

[398] B. Pullman and G. Berthier, *Compt. rend.*, **229**, 717 (1949).

[399] H. B. Klevens and J. R. Platt, *J. Am. Chem. Soc.*, **71**, 1714 (1949).

[400] J. W. Sidman, *Chem. Rev.*, **58**, 689 (1958).

[401] A. Burawoy, *Ber.*, **63**, 3155 (1930); *J. Chem. Soc.*, 1177 (1939).

[402] M. Kasha, *Disc. Faraday Soc.*, **9**, 15 (1950).

[403] H. L. McMurry, *J. Chem. Phys.*, **9**, 231, 241 (1941).

[404] J. R. Platt, *J. Opt. Soc. Am.*, **43**, 252 (1953).

[405] M. Ito, R. Shimada, T. Kuraishi, and W. Mizushima, *J. Chem. Phys.*, **26**, 1508 (1957).

[406] H. Sponer and J. H. Rush, *J. Chem. Phys.*, **17**, 556 (1949).

[407] L. Goodman and R. W. Harrell, *J. Chem. Phys.*, **30**, 1131 (1959).

[408] H. McConnell, *J. Chem. Phys.*, **20**, 700 (1952).

[409] G. J. Brealey and M. Kasha, *J. Am. Chem. Soc.*, **77**, 4462 (1955).

[410] G. C. Pimentel, *J. Am. Chem. Soc.*, **79**, 3323 (1957).

[411] K. Przibram, *Z. Physik*, **20**, 196 (1923).

[412] V. Kondratjew, *Z. Physik*, **39**, 191 (1938).

[413] J. Franck, H. Kuhn, and G. Rollefson, *Z. Physik*, **43**, 155 (1927).

[414] R. Hilsch and R. W. Pohl, *Z. Physik*, **57**, 145 (1929); **59**, 812 (1930); **64**, 606 (1930).

[415] H. Fromherz and W. Menschik, *Z. Physik Chem.*, **B3**, 1 (1929); **B7**, 439 (1930).

[416] H. Diamond and H. Fromherz, *Z. Physik. Chem.*, **B9**, 289 (1930).

[417] H. Fromherz and K. H. Lih, *Z. Physik. Chem.*, **A153**, 321 (1931); **A167**, 103 (1933).

[418] E. Doehlemann and H. Fromherz, *Z. Physik. Chem.*, **A171**, 353 (1934).

[419] K. Nakamoto, *J. Am. Chem. Soc.*, **74**, 1739 (1952).

[420] L. J. Andrews, *Chem. Rev.*, **54**, 713 (1954).

[421] R. S. Mulliken, *J. Am. Chem., Soc.*, **74**, 811 (1952).

[422] R. S. Mulliken, *J. Phys. Chem.*, **56**, 801 (1952).

[423] E. Rabinovitsch, *Rev. Mod. Phys.*, **14**, 112 (1942).

[424] L. E. Orgel, *Quart. Rev.*, **8**, 422 (1954).

[425] S. P. McGlynn, *Chem. Rev.*, **58**, 1113 (1958).

[426] J. N. Murrell, *Quart. Rev.*, **15**, 191 (1961).

[427] A. Kiss and D. Czegledy, *Z. anorg. allgem. Chem.*, **239**, 27 (1938).

[428] A. Kiss, J. Abraham, and I. Hegedüs, *Z. anorg. allgem. Chem.*, **244**, 98 (1940).

[429] A. Kiss, G. Auer, and E. Major, *Z. anorg. allgem. Chem.*, **246**, 28 (1941).

[430] C. K. Jorgensen, *Mol. Phys.*, **2**, 309 (1959).

[431] H. Bethe, *Ann. Physik*, **3**, 133 (1929).

[432] J. H. Van Vleck, *Phys. Rev.*, **41**, 208 (1932).

[433] R. Schlapp and W. G. Penney, *Phys. Rev.*, **42**, 666 (1932).

[434] J. B. Howard, *J. Chem. Phys.*, **3**, 813 (1935).

[435] L. E. Orgel, *J. Chem. Phys.*, **23**, 1004, 1819 (1955).

[436] H. Hartmann, *Z. Elektrochem.*, **61**, 908 (1957).

[437] C. K. Jorgensen, *Proceedings, Tenth Solvay Congress in Chemistry* (Brussels, 1956).

[438] J. S. Griffith, *J. Inorg. Nuclear Chem.*, **2**, 1, 229 (1956).

[439] J. S. Griffith, *Disc. Faraday Soc.*, **26**, 81 (1958).

[440] H. L. Schläfer, *Z. Physik. Chem.*, **3**, 222, 263 (1955).

[441] J. S. Griffith and L. E. Orgel, *Quart. Rev.*, **11**, 381 (1957).

[442] L. E. Orgel, *An Introduction to Transition Metal Chemistry* (London: Methuen & Co., Ltd. and New York: John Wiley & Sons, Inc., 1960).

[443] R. Tsuchida, *Bull. Chem. Soc. Japan*, **13**, 388, 436, 471 (1938),

[444] J. Weiss, *Nature*, **147**, 512 (1941).

[445] M. Volmer and K. Riggert, *Z. Physik. Chem.*, **100**, 502 (1922).

[446] L. Michaelis, M. P. Schubert, and S. Granick, *J. Am. Chem. Soc.*, **61**,

1981 (1939).

[447] G. N. Lewis and D. Lipkin, *J. Am. Chem. Soc.*, **64,** 2801 (1942).

[448] G. N. Lewis, D. Lipkin, and T. T. Magel, *J. Am. Chem. Soc.*, 63, 3005 (1941).

[449] G. C. Schmidt, *Ann. Physik. Chemie*, **58,** 103 (1896).

[450] C. J. Vavilov and W. L. Levshin, *Z. Physik*, **35,** 920 (1926).

[451] W. J. Potts, *J. Chem. Phys.*, **20,** 809 (1952).

[452] W. J. Potts, *J. Chem. Phys.*, **21,** 191 (1953).

[453] M. Kasha, *Chem. Rev.*, **41,** 401 (1947).

[454] T. L. Chu and S. I. Weissman, *J. Chem. Phys.*, **22,** 21, (1954).

[455] H. Linschitz, M. G. Berry, and D. Schweitzer, *J. Am. Chem. Soc.*, **76,** 5833, 5839 (1954).

[456] H. C. Longuet-Higgins, *J. Chem., Phys.*, **18,** 265 (1950).

[457] H. C. Longuet-Higgins and J. A. Pople, *Proc. Phys. Soc.*, **68A,** 591 (1955).

[458] D. E. Paul, D. Lipkin, and S. I. Weissman, *J. Am. Chem. Soc.*, **78,** 116 (1956).

[459] M. Szwarc, *J. Am. Chem. Soc.*, **78,** 2656 (1956) ; *Nature*, **178,** 1168 (1956).

[460] D. A. Ramsay, *Advances in Spectroscopy*, vol. 1 (New York: Interscience Publishers Inc., 1959), p. 1.

General References

Doing research work in quantum chemistry with interest in the electronic spectra of molecules requires books of roughly three kinds: general books on quantum mechanics, books on atomic and molecular spectroscopy, and books on quantum chemistry.

The following list has no claim to completeness nor does it pretend to offer the best possible selections. It simply lists those books which the writer found most helpful in his work.

QUANTUM MECHANICS

Pauling L. and E. B. Wilson, *Introduction to Quantum Mechanics*, McGraw-Hill Book Co., Inc., New York, 1935.

Rojansky, V., *Introductory Quantum Mechanics*, Prentice-Hall, Inc., Englewood Cliffs, N. J., 1938.

Bohm, D., *Quantum Theory*, Prentice-Hall, Inc., Englewood Cliffs, N. J., 1951.

Sherwin, C. W., *Introduction to Quantum Mechanics*, Holt, Rinehart and Winston, Inc., New York, 1960.

Heitler, W., *Elementary Wave Mechanics*, Second Edition, Oxford University Press, Inc., New York, 1956.

SPECTROSCOPY

Atomic spectra

Condon, E. U. and G. H. Shortley, *The Theory of Atomic Spectra*, Cambridge University Press, New York, 1957.

White, H. E., *Introduction to Atomic Spectra*, McGraw-Hill Book Co., Inc., New York, 1934.

Herzberg, G., *Atomic Spectra and Atomic Structure*, Dover Publications, Inc., New York, 1944.

Molecular spectra

Herzberg, G., *Molecular Spectra and Molecular Structure. I. Spectra of Diatomic Molecules. II. Infrared and Raman Spectra of Polyatomic Molecules*, D. Van Nostrand Co., Inc., Princeton, N. J., 1950.

Barrow, G. M., *Introduction to Molecular Spectroscopy*, McGraw-Hill Book Co., Inc., New York, 1962.

Bauman, R. P., *Absorption Spectroscopy*, John Wiley & Sons, Inc., New York, 1962.

West, W., *Chemical Applications of Spectroscopy*, Chapters I and VI. In Weissberger's *Technique of Organic Chemistry*, Vol. 9, Interscience Publishers, Inc., New York, 1956.

Reid, C., *Excited States in Chemistry and Biology*, Butterworth & Co. [Publishers], Ltd., London, 1957.

Pringsheim, P., *Fluorescence and Phosphorescence*, Interscience Publishers, Inc., New York, 1949.

Förster, Th., *Fluorescence Organischer Verbindungen*, Vandenhoeck and Ruprecht, Göttingen, 1951.

QUANTUM CHEMISTRY

Eyring, H., J. Walter, and G. E. Kimball, *Quantum Chemistry*, John Wiley & Sons, Inc., New York, 1944.

Pitzer, K. S., *Quantum Chemistry*, Prentice-Hall, Inc., Englewood Cliffs, N. J., 1953.

Kauzmann, W., *Quantum Chemistry*, Academic Press, Inc., New York, 1957.

Daudel, R., R. Lefebvre, and C. M. Moser, *Quantum Chemistry, Methods and Applications*, Interscience Publishers, Inc., New York, 1959.

Hartmann, H., *Theorie der Chemischen Bindung auf Quanten-Theoretischer Grundlage*, Springer-Verlag, Berlin, 1954.

Coulson, C. A., *Valence*, Second edition. Oxford University Press, Inc., New York, 1961.

Pullman, A. and B., *Les Théories électroniques de la chimie organique*, Masson, Paris, 1952.

Streitwieser, A., *Molecular Orbital Theory for Organic Chemists*, John Wiley & Sons, Inc., New York, 1961.

Simpson, W. T., *Theories of Electrons in Molecules*, Prentice-Hall, Inc., Englewood Cliffs, N. J., 1962.

Linnett, J. W., *Wave Mechanics and Valency*, Methuen & Co., Ltd., London, 1960.

This book offers probably the easiest way for the beginner to introduce himself into quantum mechanical thinking.

We should like to add a few books treating more practical aspects.

Descriptive works on spectra of larger molecules

Brode, W. R., *Chemical Spectroscopy*, John Wiley & Sons, Inc., New York, 1939.

Gillam, A. E. and E. S. Stern, *An Introduction to Electronic Absorption Spectroscopy in Organic Chemistry*. Arnold [Edward] [Publishers], Ltd., London, 1954.

Rao, C. N. R., *Ultraviolet and Visible Spectroscopy*, Butterworth & Co., [Publishers], Ltd., London, 1961.

Pestemer, M. and D. Brück, *Absorptions Spektroskopie im Sichtbaren und Ultraviolett. In Houben-Weyl's Methoden der Organischen Chemie. Band III, part 2*, Georg Thieme, Berlin, 1955.

OPTICAL AND ANALYTICAL ASPECTS

Jenkins, F. A. and H. E. White, *Fundamentals of Optics*, Third edition. McGraw-Hill Book Co., Inc., New York, 1957.

Nachtrieb, N. H., *Principles and Practice of Spectrochemical Analysis*, McGraw-Hill Book Co., Inc., New York, 1950.

Mellon, M. G., *Analytical Absorption Spectroscopy*, John Wiley & Sons, Inc., New York, 1950.

Harrison, G. R., R. C. Lord, and J. R. Loofbourow, *Practical Spectroscopy*, Prentice-Hall, Inc., Englewood Cliffs, N. J., 1948.

Collections of spectra

Friedel, R. A. and M. Orchin, *Ultraviolet Spectra of Aromatic Compounds*, John Wiley & Sons, Inc., New York, 1951.

Lang, L., *Absorption Spectra in the Ultraviolet and Visible Region*, Hungarian Academy of Sciences, Vol. I, 1959. Vol. II, 1961. Vol. III, 1962. Vol. IV, 1963.

Hershenson, H. M., *Ultraviolet and Visible Absorption Spectra*, Index for 1930–1956, Academic Press, Inc., New York, 1956.

American Petroleum Institute Research Project 44. Carnegie Institute of Technology, Pittsburgh, 1957.

Manufacturing Chemists Association Research Project. Carnegie Institute of Technology, Pittsburgh, 1957.

A good book on theoretical physics is necessary. The writer likes:

Slater, J. C. and N. H. Frank, *Introduction to Theoretical Physics*, McGraw-Hill Book Co., Inc., New York, 1933.

A relatively simple book on mathematical means

Margenau, H. and G. M. Murphy, *The Mathematics of Physics and Chemistry*, D. Van Nostrand Co., Inc., Princeton, N. J., 1943.

Index

Bands (Cont.):
  transitions associated with, 341–359
"Basis function generating machine",
  199–200
Beer—Lambert—Bouguer law, 101, 102
Benzene:
  LCAO MO method, 196
  valence-bond method, 228
  configuration interaction, 291
  free electron method, 325
  spectrum, 235, 342
  vibrational fine structure, 235
Blue shift, 338
Bohr formula, 2, 6
Bohr magneton, 113
Bond orbitals, method of, 315
Bond order:
  in MO method, 40–42
  in valence-bond method, 79–80
Bonding, Pauli principle and, 55, 65
Bonding energy, total, 41
Butadiene:
  LCAO MO method, 35, 182
  valence-bond method, 60, 223, 241
  self-consistent field method, 304
  spectrum, 341

Canonical structures, 77–80, 223–225,
  238, 314
  number of, 79
Carbon atoms:
  AO's of, 26–31
  cores of, 54
Cata-condensed hydrocarbons, 320, 321
Characters, 161–163
  defined, 161
  tables of, 169–180
Charge densities, electronic:
  in MO method, 40–42, 189
  in valence-bond method, 79–80
Charge-transfer spectra, 351–354
"Chemical" spectra, 340
Chromophores, 337–339
Classes, in group theory, 149–150, 153
Color:
  and bands, 109, 184, 194, 257
  of dyes, 25, 258
Configuration interaction, 281–295
  rules for computation of matrix com-
    ponents in, 284–290

Conjugate elements, 149–150, 153
Conjugated molecules, 345
  Schmidt model for, 331
  spectra of, 5, 337
Core potential function of Goeppert-
  Mayer and Sklar, 270
Cores:
  of carbon atoms, 54
  of molecules, 33, 48, 128, 246, 266
Correlation energy, defined, 317
Correlation function, 318–319
Coupling of angular momenta, 117–119
Cross links, 77
Curve analysis, 105
Cycle (in symmetric group), 238
Cycle method of counting Slater func-
  tions common to two wave functions,
  81

De Broglie's formula, 2, 9–11
Degeneracy of energy levels, 69
  induced emission coefficients and, 98
  quantum numbers and, 111
  representation of molecule's group and,
    165, 167
Dematerialization and gamma rays, 3
Dewar-type structures, 77
Diatomic molecules, see Molecules, di-
  atomic
Digital computers, computation of inte-
  grals by, 317
Dimension of representation, 152, 165
Dipole radiation, 140
Dipole strength, 92
  Einstein's coefficients and, 98–100
  experimental band intensity and, 103
Dissociation energy, 318–319
Dyes:
  color of, 25, 258
  valence-bond method and, 255–261
  free electron methods and, 331–336

Eigenfunctions, properties of, 12–14
Einstein absorption and emission coef-
  ficients, 90–92
Electronegativity, 44, 213
Electron-pair method, *see* Valence-bond
  method

37039